a Paradoxical Existence

by

Paul René Albert

&

The
CLF

a.k.a. the Timeless Mystics of Infinite Zero
a.k.a. the Ancient Mystics of Infinite Zero
a.k.a. the Magical Mystics of Infinite Zero
a.k.a. the Mythical Mystics of Infinite Zero
a.k.a. the Boundless Seers of Infinite Zero
a.k.a. the Enigmatic Ancients of Infinite Zero

(it seems whatever they are known as Infinite Zero is their leitmotiv)
(except they are also known as the Timeless and Boundless Avatars of Causal Causality)

Copyright © Paul René Albert 2025

MH Publications, 1st edition

All rights reserved

No part of this book may be used or reproduced in any manner without the author's written permission, except for the use of brief quotations.

ISBN 979-8-336-51853-5

die Ewigkeit ist bloß ein Augenblick, gerade lange genug für einen Spaß

– Herman Hesse –

Part 1

Chapter 1 **The most burning questions everybody asks (but nobody really wants answered)**

And so it was that a large crowd gathered around the Ancient Mystics of Infinite Zero. A gentle breeze swept over the curvy landscape like a whisper in a girl's ear. As far as the eye could see, there was nothing but long, green grass stirred in patterns which revealed many secrets if only one could read them.

The Ancient Mystics of Infinite Zero found themselves seated on an age-old Tumulus (some were standing, too). On the lower grounds they appeared surrounded by a bunch of weird looking people, odd people, funny people and, on occasion, even some normal people. Actually, there were a lot of normal people. Or at least they considered themselves as much: normal, yet special too, and at the same time 'not good enough', or 'lost', 'in doubt', while still eager to meet any challenge if only it would present itself in the right way – all pretty peculiar things that identify them as humans for sure.

It didn't take long for the crowd to go quiet. The Ancient Mystics of Infinite Zero remained as such, too: absolutely quiet.

Respectfully, the quietness was preserved for some time. Until it was no longer bearable, and one person in the crowd dared to raise a question:

"Why do you remain quiet while we are waiting?"

"What are you waiting for?" countered One.

"I don't know," the daring questioner replied, a bit taken aback by that response. He first looked left and right for backup before he dared to continue. "I guess for you to tell us the Truth, of course, aren't we?"

"Oh, hang on there," answered One. "If we may set one thing straight from the very beginning, pretty please: do not see us as prophets, teachers or guides, for we are nothing of the sort. We merely are the Ancient Mystics of Infinite Zero. We sell nothing, we preach no laws, we teach no methods, and we don't give directions – unless you're looking for the nearest post office. All we do is meet any question asked with nothing but the Truth."

"Oh," reacted the daring questioner with a taunting tone, "it's a Q&A! Why didn't you say so from the beginning?"

This prompted a girl to raise her hand. She clearly did not raise it to be picked for the next question. It was more like a declaration of her authority as she immediately spoke out: "I want to know why we are here."

"I have no idea why you are here," shrugged One (which, by the way, wasn't the same One as the One before). "You have to be more specific than that."

"Well, you know," she tried again, "like, who are we? Why do we exist?"

"Or is there a God?" asked someone else. "Is there life after death?"

"What's the sense of this all?" asked another, immediately followed by yet another: "What is the true nature of our reality?"

"Can a decent bloke get a decent beer around here?" In his head, the crowd burst into laughter. In reality they did not.

"Do we have free will?" asked a person who clearly lacked exactly that (his wife had been poking him in the kidney for the last 30 seconds to ask that question).

"Or are we living in a computer simulation?" squeaked the archetype of nerdiness.

One started: "Well…"

But then One interrupted One immediately: "Oh, come on! Don't bother answering any of these questions. Each and every one of them has already made up their mind about all this. They only want to hear a confirmation of what they believe…"

"… and want …"

"… and need …"

"… the answers to be. They don't want to hear the Truth as we have come to know and experience it in full."

"Still," One said, "we do have promised to answer each question with the

Truth. And so, we will."

"Even though they are looking from completely the wrong place?" asked One. "You do realize Truth can't be found from their current point of view?"

"Let's not get overly judgemental," hushed One. "We will discover soon enough if they are capable of switching their perspective."

Now, I'm not sure if any of you readers already noticed how the Ancient Mystics of Infinite Zero all wore hooded cloaks. There was something peculiar about their faces, too. They were hidden behind a white mask depicting cheerful eyes and a wide, pleasant smile. It's a bit hard to discern though whether their cloaks were all in the same colour or each was wearing a different one. I guess that's at the readers' own discretion to decide.

"Look," said One, "we could tell you the answer to all these questions. In fact, it would only take a few words."

"A single sentence at most."

"But One is right. At this point, none of you truly are interested in the Truth."

"Even more so," continued One (another One!), "and forgive me if this sounds patronizing, you wouldn't be able to understand It to begin with. Not in this state, anyways."

"Perhaps," suggested One, "you could all first tell us what you currently believe in?" – "Hey, that's a good idea," nodded One (this was the same One, pretending to be another One just to emphasize her idea).

"Well, I believe in God, of course," proclaimed an older man. "How else would all of existence have come to pass!"

"I believe in Allah," stated a younger man, causing another in the crowd to shout: "That's the same Dude as God, dude!" – "But clearly Christ and Mohammed are two different persons," responded the younger man, followed by the dude saying "Tomayto tomahto, dude. Spaghetti sauce or ketchup, all the same thing in a different form." – "Ketchup and spaghetti sauce aren't the-"

"I guess there must be Something," someone else tried in a pacifying attempt. "I mean, I'm sure there is. There must be! I'm not saying this means 'all' those stories we believe are true. Still hey, look, everything being created out of nothing is pretty mindboggling, too. It's downright absurd if you ask me. Must be some Reason for all this. Must be Some-Thing responsible for it."

"I believe we all go to heaven after we die", someone most honestly declared.

"What?" bantered a middle-aged man, "And have rice pudding with my mother-in-law for all eternity?" This time, the crowd did chuckle for a brief moment. But then their faces retook that serious frown of attention as they all shared similar thoughts about a boring ever after.

"I think we reincarnate and come back in another life," someone whispered hesitantly. "I think we reincarnate," the lady repeated a bit louder when all went like 'what?' "until we have fulfilled our final destiny and can return to The Light."

"Solution to FOMO, man," jested another, "all the time, uh, lives in the world."

"I say, the idea of reincarnation is insane," objected a man. "First of all, I'd have to go to school over and over again. And secondly, what's the point? All this trouble, life after life, and in the end, you disappear in some light or whatever. I mean, what's the point of being eternally in some light where you aren't even you anymore? Sounds like a hell of a lot of procrastination about coming to terms with our temporary existence."

"That's right," agreed a man in a suit (not that a man in a suit is the stereotype for people of his opinion). "We live, and then we die. Simple. Make the best of it while you're here; that's what I say."

"YOLO, man," acknowledged the FOMO-jester.

"Listen, people, you got it all wrong," declared a tall man standing out in the crowd as tall men happen to do. "When we die, our disembodied spirit lingers on earth for three days. You sit at the head of your body and need to chant the-"

"Ah, come on," interjected an old man with a long beard. He could have been God in disguise, although in that case, his disguise was pretty lame if you think about it. "We simply can't know all that for sure, now can we? In fact, I am sure we simply can't figure that out like ever. We simply are inadequate and incapable of providing any rational grounds whatsoever to prove the existence – or non-existence for that matter – of God and the afterlife." Then he had a coughing fit (that's what you get when your sentences are too long).

At this point, a small child walked up the hillslope where the Ancient Mystics of Infinite Zero had dozed off. She tapped one on the shoulder, and they all woke simultaneously.

"Right," said One. "You see our problem here? Each of you is pulling in way too different directions. So your question for Truth is actually about who's right and who's wrong. For example, let's just pretend we'd say that the Christian God is the only true God, and all stories about him are true. That would get us into trouble with those believing in a multitude of other gods… or no god at all, now wouldn't it?"

"Yeh," scoffed One. "Even with that story, you'd still be in trouble. Some claim you go to heaven straight away, while others say you first go to some in between until… Well, until a bloody long time – unless they decide to nuke the planet or something."

"Exactly," added One. "Even while making that group the happy, cheery, righteous ones, you'll unavoidably meet division once again. Soon enough, you will also need to explain how Truth relates to abortion, climate change, gender equality or whether or not we should enforce democracy on bee hives and hold elections to choose their queen."

"Thing is," sighed One, "whichever way we'd let this ball roll, we'd always create a worldwide, great division between those who had it all wrong and those who were right."

"Luckily for us," declared One, "all of you are wrong."

A buzz of disagreement sparked left and right in the crowd.

"What?" shrieked a man in the audience. "All of us? Wait! Damn it, I can't recall all that's been said. What were all the wrongs so far? Shoot, I should have taken notes."

"Just re-read this chapter," hinted One. "Anyway, the bottom line remains, all of you are wrong. Every single one of you." That last sentence he emphasized with a clap of his hands on every word (except for the word 'of', there was no clap there – just try it yourself, it makes sense).

For a minute, the buzzing in the crowd rose to the level of a hornet's nest, sounding right next to one's ear.

"Look," spoke One loud. "At this point, I think we can agree that we all tend to disagree on this topic. The thing is, we are not discussing who likes apples and who likes cherries. Neither are we discussing if one should cross the street when the light is red while no one is coming from the other direction. We are dealing here with the most profound and most paramount questions mankind can have."

"Perhaps," hinted One, "the first real question might be: why are you all asking these questions which we collectively deem so important? Is it boredom? Is it lack of meaning or purpose? Or is it a bit of each of your very own unique mixture of fear and despair, wonder and hope?"

"A means to clear doubts about lovers and jobs?" rambled One. "Decide about have children and a house? Which path to take, which choice to make? Perhaps you are looking for a way to deal with sickness and pain, with dying and death? Or may-be, it rather is an inner longing for peace and happiness, physical comfort and mental consolation? Really, I mean, your questioning can just as well come forth from all the little things which seem to bother you on a daily basis…"

"… or from the biggies," added One, "when you dare to contemplate your lives in a more distant future, even beyond your life now?" Behind his mask, his eyes turned up and left, wondering if he himself understood what he just said.

"So you see," continued One. "At this point, we may, in all fairness, attest you are not really looking for Truth. You are simply looking for some kind of fulfilment. For something that meets your personal needs and standards in your daily existence here and now."

"Deep down as well, " said One, "you are continuously looking for means to correct or improve yourselves in this life and even the one beyond. However, you all are mostly unaware of how much this personal endeavour is actually shaped by a view of reality you created for yourselves, without having the faintest idea whether or not this view is fundamentally in alignment with reality as it truly is."

"Wow," gasped the YOLO-jester. "That's deep man."

Ignoring that, One continued: "For that matter, Truth is a rather frightening concept to all of you. Each and every one of you has already huddled yourselves in your own little comfort zone where you have formed an opinion that suits you best at that moment. Why would you leave that cosy spot unless a little spark of doubt or discomfort pushes you out once more? Either the spark gets extinguished straight away. Or, it becomes a fire driving you into yet another direction."

"But which direction to take?" pondered One out loud.

Yes indeed, which direction to take?

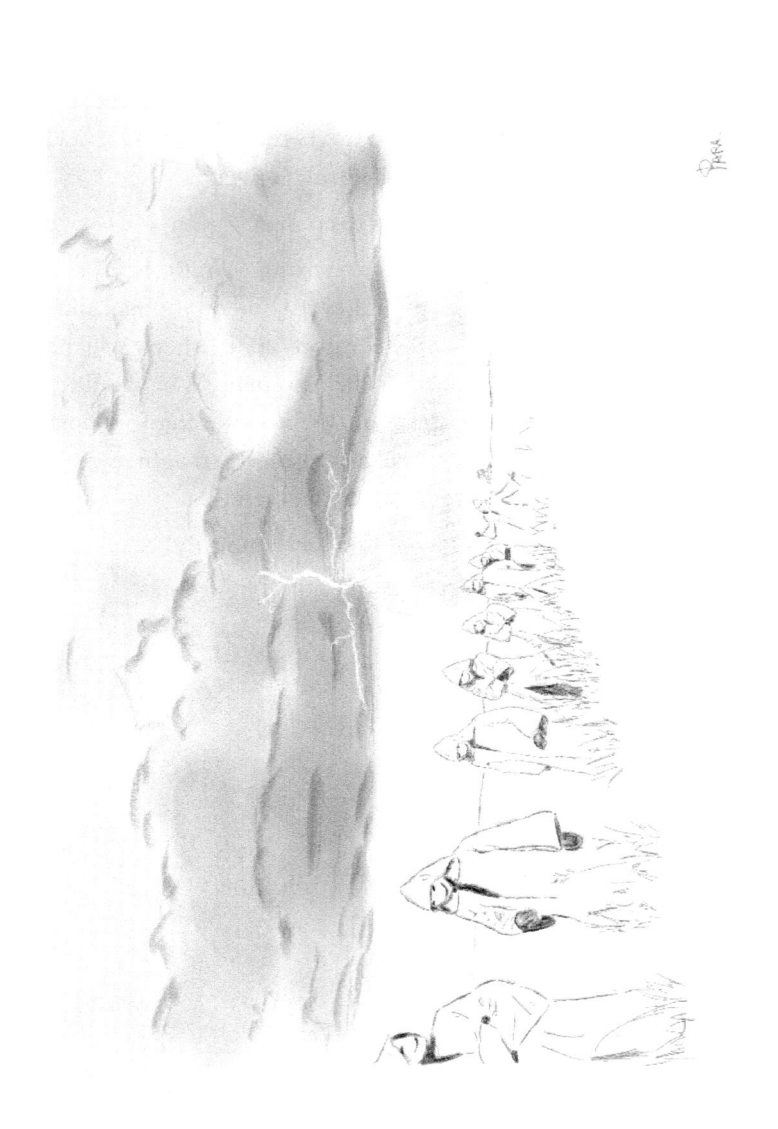

Chapter 2   Which path to take, when all of them seem to contradict one another?

Thunder rumbled in the distance like an old crone calling her nearly dead husband to take out the trash. While swiping the dust from their robes, the Timeless Mystics of Infinite Zero all rose at precisely the same time. In single file, they strode off in no particular direction (although, by some coincidence, it seemed to be opposite from where the thunder was coming from).

Many in the crowd stood up as well and followed without hesitation. Others took a brief moment to see which way the wind would blow. Since the wind seemed very indecisive about this, they decided to follow all the same. Some chose not to follow. But when the thunderclouds started to swell ominously overhead, they also quickly tagged along.

The One in front realized he turned out to be the First One. With a quick movement, he stepped sideways and backwards, squeezing himself between the fourth and fifth positions (actually, fourth and fifth became third and fifth from the moment he switched positions). With a little push, he urged the One before him to the first position: "You be the First One this time." And so, the Second One became second once more while the Third never realized what just happened. The Fourth, the One who was first, remained fourth. At the same time, the Fifth One never stopped being fifth (mathematicians on the distant planet Pu are still working hard to solve this particular mystery).

After a while, the Timeless Mystics of Infinite Zero slowed their firm pace to a gentle stroll. A mild sunshine met them on their path. Their body language indicated they were open to questions once again.

"Please," begged a young woman who had become a true believer for no reason at all (at this point, there most certainly was no reason at all to become a true believer, especially when the ones she believed in declared to be no prophets or gurus of any kind). "Please," he pleaded once more. "Can you tell us what path to follow to find the True answers to our questions?" (By the way, did you notice 'she' became a 'he' in a single paragraph's time? I hope you are paying attention and not looking at your smartphone all the time. Remember Feynman!)

"I can't help but wonder if this young lady, er, man, realises how privileged he is to ask this question," spoke the Fourth One. "I mean, here we have humanity in a constant struggle to pay the bills, nourish their children, worry about war, mow their lawns or suffer from accidents caused by texting while driving. I'm just saying, they hardly have any time left to wonder about such stuff, no?"

"Indeed," confirmed the Second One, "being involved in life itself to the fullest, or being dragged into its many challenges and the suffering that comes with it, it all tends to render any questions about life's origin and purpose superfluous. Yes, this quest surely is no endeavour for all, to say the least."

"But - but that's the the thing," stammered the young man. "I have hardly any of that, and still, I ám suffering somehow. I can't explain it. I can't say I even understand it myself, but somehow, somewhere deep down, I am suffering. I mean, there must be something more, right? Something more profound than commodities and achievements, something more than brief instants of consumed joy and happiness. We have endless things to buy and a zillion choices to make. We chase identity in comfort and wealth, and still, still our lives, my life, fails to be fulfilling when I add it all up."

"Me too," shared an older woman. "I have lost loved ones. And believe me, I cannot count the challenges I've met on my way. And that's exactly why I want to understand all that. I need to understand all that. To me, it's certainly not some occasional musing like, 'Oh, what would Truth be like?' No, it's the distress caused by life itself which stresses me to find answers."

"Er," one boy said, "to be honest, I'm here because I'm exactly like 'Oh, what would Truth be like?' or something."

"Never mind that," another woman insisted. "I can't explain it myself either, except as an inner urgency to find Truth. But which path to take? I have tried so many already. There are countless truths out there, countless religions, countless spiritual and esoteric directions."

"Same here," raised an older man. "Some of them touched my heart. Some touched my mind. But none of them managed to touch me in my totality. None of them succeeded in erasing all doubts."

"How could we be?" spoke a younger girl who seemed pretty bright for her age. "Be without doubts, I mean. It's always the same. Teachers, books, magazines… Sometimes they agree and vaguely point towards the same path. And then there are others pointing in completely the opposite direction. It is so frustratingly confusing."

"Yes, I agree," nodded the other woman. "It's always the same. It starts with this vague promise. They nicely paint out all our problems. – More often than not, these are not even my problems, but I have come to believe they are anyway. – And then they offer their solution. At first, they make it sound so easy. And then it turns out it can only be obtained through great effort, patience or sacrifice. And more training. And more lectures."

"And more money!" added the younger girl in recognition.

"I must admit," confessed a man, "most of my looking into particular spiritual or esoteric paths happened because I haphazardly came across them. And each time, I truly believed this particular book, or person, or organisation, came on my path because I was guided by Some-Thing. Like it was Meant to be for me. Only later did I realise that I was that silly frog in a well, thinking this was 'It', while in reality, there was ever more. I couldn't figure out which path to take after that. It makes me feel so helpless, you know, because despite all that, I still believe 'It' must be out there."

"Same here," nodded the woman. "You think there's this One Special Path, and then you realize there's like countless others, all pointing to a different 'Truth'. It's like this great shopping mall of enlightenment, with different heavens sold on the same shelf. It's all happy smiles, happy colours, shiny methods and steps and stuff, all gift-wrapped to our appeal by words like 'scientific' …"

"… 'ancient' …"

"… 'newly discovered' …"

"… 'revealed again' …"

"And all those sweet pearls of wisdom like 'accept yourself', 'it is no coincidence', 'you are enough'. Really. It all sounds beautiful, but it's mostly a sham! All these masters and gurus we are feeding our money, devotion and attention; I mean, how did we come to that?"

The Timeless Mystics of Infinite Zero came to a dead stop.

"Quite amazing," remarked the Third One.

"Indeed, indeed," agreed the First One. "This lot has already come to a far end."

"Look," started the Second One. "It's not that we don't want to answer your questions and tell you the Truth. And truth be told, you have come a long way already. Still, it is good to realize it is absolutely vital to recognize the undeniable fact that it is simply impossible not to be biased about what Truth should be."

Most faces went like 'What?'.

"One means you folks have already ventured a lot into this realm where there is no real scientific consensus about things, like a grey zone, where evidence and proof ever seem to be this frustratingly short inch out of reach. Ergo, since the great reveal is not likely to appear on the six o'clock news any time soon, and uncertainty gives no ground for stability, you all have come to a personal opinion, a satisfying conclusion, which henceforward doesn't allow any opposition."

Then some faces went like 'Oh' (a lot of faces remained stuck in 'What?').

"The question, in all honesty is: did you come to your current view on things simply because it resonates with your present state of being? Because it simply feels right for you and the folks around you? And more importantly, what if your view on things changes? What if you change?"

"What we mean is this. How many of you have come to abandon a truth you were willing to defend with your life before, even at the cost of family and friends? None of them could persuade you to be wrong until you yourself found something else to believe in."

There was still a lot of 'What?' on faces left and right. One shrugged in a way indicating not to worry about all that and come to the point. "Basically, we are trying to warn you to not make these same mistakes once again. We wouldn't want you to agree with our words because we're the new batch to follow. Even more, we simply wouldn't want you to blindly believe anything we may tell you at all."

"On the contrary, only the opposite would be true," the Fifth One emphasized. "We ask you no less than to be wary, to question and to doubt."

The Fifth One paused and looked around.

"What is it?" asked the First One. And the Fifth One replied: "Oh, nothing. Felt like it was a moment for a brief pause."

The Seventh One shrugged. "Look, we know that many of you have some sort of preconception of what Truth should be. You have been talked into heavens and incarnation-cycles. Our ancestors supposedly came from another planet, and we will all transgress into another dimension. And there we will reach a significantly raised vibration or a higher level of consciousness."

"You make it sound ridiculous," a young woman said, "but in fact, I must confess, you are pretty much right. It is a bit ridiculous. Sometimes, I simply can't believe how I used to absorb all that stuff. Especially because I have never been given actual proof. I always had to 'trust', you know. And yes, in the moment, in my despair and longing, I wanted to believe all those stories to be true. As long as they transcended the mundane and I felt surrounded by like-minded people, one could aaaalways count me in. But in the end, I only found my trust to be abused, over and over again."

Many nodded or looked away.

The Timeless Mystics of Infinite Zero all faced each other. Then, it seemed they silently came to some mutual agreement. "Look," said One while turning back to the crowd. "Here's a challenge. You all know many groups, sects, cults, and orders exist. Each and all of them uphold their own particular bubble of Truth. They filter everything out which doesn't meet their pre-set standards. They are convinced of being absolutely right, while those believing the exact opposite are equally convinced of being right."

"So here's the thing," launched One. "Knowing these so-called Truths cannot all be actually true, how will you be able to recognise Truth when you come across it? How will you validate it? I mean, let's be honest, it's not like a beaming ray of light will start to light up your face when you see Truth, is it?"

"It's not?" sighed a younger man with a disappointed expression.

"We can only urge you not to simply believe anything we say. But believe this-"

"Really?" One huffed.

"Believe this," One continued determined, "the silliest thing to believe in the first place is to think that you need a guide pointing you towards the Truth, to think you need to follow some experienced somebody who has walked the path and now can show you the way. You do not need any of that. You really don't."

"We don't? But how can we find the Truth without a guide?"

"Because each and every one of you is perfectly capable of finding the Truth by yourselves," exclaimed One. "That's why. That's the big thing you need to know above all else. Even if you were the last person on earth, even if all books of knowledge were lost, still, you yourself, by yourself, would be able to discover the Truth, to recognize it and experience it to the fullest. The only path to follow is your own."

"Well, that's clear!" concluded a tall, muscled man. With a firm stride, he turned his back on the group and walked away. About twenty paces further, he came to a stop and turned around. "Wait, that's not clear at all!"

"Perhaps you could at least share a few suggestions on how to find our own path?" tried a woman. "I mean, I myself certainly am not the typical prodigy who finds this stuff out by herself."

"Yes, please," pleaded another man. "We need some guidance here. Or could you give us at least a clue?"

"Well," imparted One to the others. "The odds of them finding their own path aren't that great, now are they?"

"Chances are they wander off and start worshipping or idolizing saints or statues again…"

"…or build bonfires and dance naked around them. Can you imagine the amount of carbon dioxide this would release!"

"Fair enough," chuckled One. "Well, I guess you could follow us just a little longer if you feel like that."

"Anyway," vowed One, "you will learn soon enough that you could have figured it all out by yourselves."

And so, the crowd decided to follow the Timeless Mystics of Infinite Zero just a little longer. They had absolutely no clue how deep the rabbit hole was about to go.

Chapter 4   In search of a means to find and realize Truth (if any such means would exist at all)

After a long, quiet walk, the motley group wandered into the heart of an ancient forest, where they found a clearing with an impressive megalithic structure. According to Google, these were Les Menhirs de Monteneuf.

A mysterious woman in a white, sleeveless gown and long brown hair was meandering between the stones, admiring them one at a time. She did not heed the newcomers whatsoever (if you google the stones, you will see her).

The Enigmatic Ancients of Infinite Zero modestly entered what looked like the centre of the structure. Each sat down near one of the tall, standing stones. The crowd respectfully sat down near the outer line.

It was quiet, as it often tends to be amongst the Enigmatic Ancients of Infinite Zero. Even more so, it was extremely quiet. Not even their breaths were making an audible sound, nor did the leaves on the trees. The stones were silent, too.

If God did exist, He must have figured quietness to be the most tedious aspect of creation. After all, He did start things with The Word according to the scriptures. And so, quite unexpectedly, a group of lost wanderers emerged loudly from a barely discernible path winding through low brush.

When they noticed the Enigmatic Ancients of Infinite Zero, the group turned quiet. It was a silence hastily broken by what seemed to be their leader.

"Excuse us," he started, "but we seem to be lost."

"Of course you are," One replied. "After all, aren't we all?"

"Be seated amongst us, friends," called a man in the crowd from across the circle. "These fine… err, people here are leading us the way towards the Truth."

"The Truth?" exclaimed their leader. "I'm afraid you misunderstood. We are in no need of Truth. We are actually lost-lost. And we're a little desperate, too, since it is nearing dinner time. You wouldn't happen to know which way we need to go to reach that famous tavern in these woods?"

"Oh, that's easy," said One. "It's that way!"

The leader of the group looked in the direction that One was pointing. Relief fell over his face as well as over the faces of all the others in his group.

"Thank you so much," he said. And off they went.

"Is it really that way?" One asked One when the group disappeared out of sight.

"I haven't got the slightest clue," replied One. "But did you see the look on their faces? At least I got rid of their silly despair, didn't I?"

Right.

"Will you teach us some breathing techniques today," shouted a clearly impatient man from the more distant part of the crowd.

"We will do no such thing," answered One determined. Then he hesitated. "Well, actually, we do have breathing techniques. And they do assist in experiencing the Truth on a certain level, sure." Then, he became determined again. "But such methods alone will never get you to cross the bridge like many CSDCs promise you."

(CSDCs??? You best sit this one out for just a wee little while.)

"In fact," chuckled One, "when we come across such 'breatharians', we always have a hard time not to burst out into laughter. Stuff people do with their breath, hoping they somehow will reach enlightenment like it all is just a matter of mechanics, it really is mind-boggling." All were shaking their masked heads.

"But surely Yoga is-" protested the man.

"Yoga is the biggest scam ever!" interrupted One firmly.

"What?" interjected a tanned woman in loose, colourful clothing and dreadlocks draping over her shoulders (not saying she is the archetype for that lot, of course). "That's utter nonsense! Yoga is-"

"It's a scam," repeated One. "No greater army has been formed in the past decades as the army of those idiots. I mean, really, here you have a bunch of people being trained in parroting about ida-pingala stuff and the many great benefits of all that. And for some reason, these Yoga teachers all think they've become expert psychologists after 200 hours of brainwashing, all ready to help out people with whatever inner problems they have. No issue which can't be solved with an Asana or doing something funny with your nose, right?"

"There there," hushed One. "We know, we know, they do tend to preach some remarkable claims which are farfetched, to say the least. But Yoga can also be a beneficial form of relaxation, now can it not?"

"Remarkable claims? Farfetched?" ranted One on. "It's really a quixotic-hoping-to-accomplish-wish-list going viral like those chain letters we had in the past. Here, you have one beatific parrot being trained by another and the one before that, all drivelling about the cosmic implications of poses and gestures. They repeat the most ludicrous memes and facts full of pseudoscientific fakery; it's painful to see. Apart from some genuine inner peace and revitalization that keeps them hooked, they never achieve the promised longevity-levitation-clairvoyant-mindreading-intuition-magic-healing-stuff."

"Deep breaths," offered One to the ranting One. "Inhale – Exhale. You really should do some Yoga, you know."

"My apologies," excused the ranting One himself while he calmed down. "Got a bit carried away there."

The tanned woman dared to raise her hand. "So all Yoga is-"

"Well, I wouldn't say all," answered One. "I mean, the physical postures, stretching, and all that stuff surely offer some beneficial exercise for the body and mind, certainly when it is combined with proper breathing."

"Yeh," scoffed the ranting One, "but when they go kundalini on you, you better run as fast as you can. Once you are sucked into the stuff of Yogi Sing-Along or people who claim they can activate your kundalini by playing ludicrously loud music, Mr and Mrs Reality have vacated the building. Best parrots of the whole lot! Can you imagine your doctor, the person you're supposed to trust, advising you to do some Yoga, and then you end up in these cults?"

"There there, let's not start again, shall we," One hushed One once again. Then she started pondering. "Makes one wonder how we all can become these colourful birds so easily in the first place, no?"

"Could be the schooling system?" offered One to the raised question. "Then again, we always blame the schooling system."

"Still," said the poking wife who didn't know how to poke the following out of her husband: "We are a bit conditioned to take in information and take it for granted. So when a guru shows up with an elaborate method, we rather take it straight in and carry it straight out instead of tossing it around for a bit first."

"Fair enough," added the husband. "We could use a lesson or two about having a constructive debate or examining facts and stuff. Fake politicians with fake news, confirmation bias, the filter bubble, empathy abuse and all that. It's all the result of taking information for granted."

"Good point," confirmed One. "Besides, Yoga is far from the only culprit in this line of Truth-business. There are countless CSDCs roaming around with countless promises and techniques and methods."

(CSDCs??? If you are really anxious to find out, you might wanna spell it out loud. That will give you a clue.)

"Indeed, I can't stress this enough," appealed One. "Truth is pure and ever available, regardless of human existence and their many creative fabrications to dissect an essence which simply is beyond dissecting."

"Any system," continued One, "any arcane wisdom, any ancient or newly shared method, each outclassing the other by complexity in design or an overdisplay of humble devotion, it all is merely a distraction leading nowhere but away from the Truth."

"As we said already, the path of Truth is one of simplicity and purity, not one of rising above the rest of humanity. It's not about refuting the ordinary in favour of the extraordinary or the miraculous."

"And surely it is not about dividing us into those having accomplished or attained something profound and those who have not."

"Yes indeed," concluded One. "Simply trust yourself capable of finding Truth by yourself. Unveiling Truth is not about creativity, intelligence or wit. So please abandon all ideas of paths, steps, gates, visions or initiations. Look in the here and now, not in fantasized dimensions of those deluding themselves and pulling you in along the way."

"But how?" pressed one woman in the crowd. "Could you please, please pretty please tell us how?"

"Yes, please," pleaded another. "There must be a how. There always is."

"Well," said One, "frankly speaking, there needn't be a 'how'. For some, it's as natural as going to the loo. But truth be told, a pinch of 'how' still might help a little to get you going."

One stood up and started pacing up and down. Then, he came to a stop and looked at the crowd. "Let us ask you lot," he challenged, "if we didn't happen to be around, how would you go about that?"

"Find a good book?" suggested a younger fellow in his early twenties. His suggestion was followed by the sound of someone slapping herself on the forehead.

"I happen to have the latest monthly issue of Happy Cheerfulness with me", started a thirty-year-old lady with a thick Australian accent. "In it, there's an article about exactly this topic. Imagine the coincidence!" – The same sound followed.

"Nah," interrupted a more sturdy-looking woman of about the same age. Her forehead seemed to have a bit of a reddish colour. "Can't be as simple as a book or an article. What we need is some form of initiation. I'm sure you will soon come to tap us on our third eye so we can instantaneously realize the Truth as you do."

"Tapping with a hammer might just do the trick," grinned One silently against One. "I mean, really? Tapping on the third eye?"

"Truth is not realized intellectually!" objected the women who had overheard the words of One.

"Fair enough," answered One, "though our intellectual capacities do prevent us from stepping into great folly, don't they?"

"Come on," insisted One. "You lot can do better than that, can you?"

"Ley Lines? – Consult the Akashic Records? – Angelic channelling? – The Bible? – Merkaba? – Manifesting? – A Vipassana retreat? – A transmission ritual? – Tantra? (which colour?) – Become a psychic medium? – The Koran? – Make contact with the spaceships of the Elohim? – I heard the Elohim are in conflict with the Galactic Confederacy! – Nonsense, that's fake news! – Reiki? – Speak in tongues? – Buddhism? (which one? The one that believes in reincarnation or the one that doesn't?) – Spiritual epigenetics? – The Veda's? – Pranic healing? – Regression? – I Ching? – Shake like crazy for hours? – Nondual therapy? – Unconditional love? – Quantum spirituality? – Open your Chakra's – YouTube? – …'

The Enigmatic Ancients of Infinite Zero kept shaking their heads in response to each new suggestion fired by the crowd.

"Are these all really methods to find Truth?" gasped the youngest in the crowd. – "That's just the tip of the iceberg, my friend," someone else remarked matter-of-factly.

Then, a younger woman, her face adorned with a captivating array of freckles, timidly raised her arm. "I think I know how."

And thus this chapter ends with a pretty mean cliffhanger. Most probably, you are too tired to start a new one. And tomorrow's probably an important day at work, right? Yet still, one more? Why not?

PS: Did you notice that the previous chapter is missing? You really need to focus. Before you know it, you'll miss out on the Truth, which is about to be revealed in the coming chapters.

Chapter 5 How the advice of knowing yourself is the greatest folly of all

The woman in the white, sleeveless gown hovered placidly from stone to stone. She touched each and every one of them like an amazon would touch her mighty steed. Occasionally, she would lay her ear to rest against the ancient rocks, listening to stories long forgotten. She had the looks of a Wisdom, One to be consulted for problems no TikTok can solve. Yet looks can be deceiving. This particular lady was only following the instructions of the crew doing a photoshoot. Then again, this can be deceiving as well. She still could be a Wisdom, couldn't she?

"Well, please! Enlighten us," urged an older man in a wheelchair rather rudely. He clearly didn't have the slightest interest in ladies wandering between old stones. "This is supposed to be a new chapter in me life! And I'm not sure how many I still have to go before me book reaches its last page." He threw a concerned look at his nurse behind him. She examined his IV and nodded he'd still be alright for at least one more chapter.

"There…" started the freckled lass from our previous chapter. She blushed, and when she realized this cursed affliction hit her once again, her cheeks turned an even deeper shade of red. Collecting all her courage, she softly shared her secret. "There is this saying 'Know Thyself'. Isn't that-"

"Yes, yes, indeed", threw another woman in quicker than she realized. With all gazes now upon her, she continued: "Gnothi Seauton, that's the correct phrase, isn't it?" Pride could be read all over her face.

The Enigmatic Ancients of Infinite Zero looked at each other as if they doubted whether to affirm or reject this last proposition. "What do you think?" asked One to the Others. " 'Know Thyself?' "

"Pretty tricky if you ask me," answered One.

"Pret-ty tricky?" scoffed One. "That proposition is like trying to cross a rope over a canyon on a motorbike. That's how tricky it is! 99.9% of all those who try this will fall to their deaths for sure."

Now, here I can add that One was pretty optimistic about the 0.1% success rate. You just try riding a motorbike over a rope yourself. Even if the rope were lying flat on the ground, it'd still be as challenging as hell. Surely, when it's dangling over a canyon, not even the best rider would be able to succeed at this unless it were James or Ethan. John, too, although he'd fall first, get tons of injuries, and then still pull it off.

"It's less tricky if we give them a little help," suggested One calmly.

"Right, okay, fair enough," began One. " 'Know thyself'. Hmmm, it is surely is the most concise advice straight to Truth. However-"

"However, indeed," continued One. "Its brevity is of such a deeply confusing nature that it puts nearly all seekers on the wrong track for sure."

"How's that?" queried a blind spectator.

"It's simply futile," sighed One. "I mean, honestly, 'Know yourself? If you take it from the wrong angle, you are bound to get lost in endless reflections."

"Should I know my personality?" suggested One.

"Should I discover where my feelings are coming from?" added One.

"Should I figure out what I truly want, as opposed to the wants that were imposed on me?" speculated One.

"Or is it my subconscious I need to understand," probed One.

"Might as well be that I need to unravel why I'm always craving for chocolate in the middle of the night?" pondered One.

"Oh, do you?" asked One surprised. – "Errr, no, no, no, of course not," dismissed One. "I'm just making up examples, that's all."

The pace of speculation increased in such a way that there was no longer any point in saying which One was speaking now.

"Maybe we should unravel our id?" – "Or, we should identify what our soul is?" – "It's simple, that what drives me defines me, no?" – "Perhaps a questionnaire could help? You know like an MBTI and stuff." – "Or an Enneagram! I heard that stuff is really powerful!" – "I rather consult my astrologer. Let the stars decide." — "Nonsense! You're supposed to remember your previous lives so you not only understand this one but also the next. That's when you make a leap!" — "You are all taking it too far. You need to find your authentic self. Your true nature. There's nothing more to it than that." — "Getting to know your vices and your virtues, cultivating one and restraining the other, that's what knowing yourself is about."

"There, there," hushed One. "I think you all have made your point." Then One directed herself back to the crowd. "You see, trying to know yourself puts you in a very difficult position."

"A difficult position?" quipped One. "Trying to know yourself is nothing less than finding the exit in a maze where the walls constantly move around. It's impossible to solve! It changes constantly. Just the mere effort of trying to know yourself already changes it."

"Indeed," added One. "To know yourself is impossible in the now. It is always some image which existed in the past, while ever shaping our present… "

"… with a ceaseless aspiration to be different yet again in the future."

"Both scientists and mystics have cracked their heads on this one for ages," spoke One.

"And their tendency to dissect and categorize everything into bits and pieces makes it even harder," chided One. " 'Your ego', 'your soul', 'your id', 'your psyche', 'your subconscious', 'your recent brain', 'your older brain', 'your tummy-brain', 'your inner guide', 'your heart', 'your feelings', 'your emotions', 'your masks and personalities'. I mean, no wonder we all need to consult a psychiatrist every week. We've all collectively been talked into a multiple personality disorder, to say the least."

"True true true," nodded One. "If you step into it this way, you are bound to wander around for years, always thinking you are very well on track and making progress, while in reality, you are just chasing your own tail."

"And ever when you grow weary and want to stop with this nonsense, there's always our enemy lurking around the corner."

"Oh yes, when the CSDCs turn up, you're back on the merry-go-round in no time. They will always have another technique up their sleeves to sell."

"Or another path!" – "Seven or nine steps to your True Self and freedom." – " 'Did you know you actually have eleven bodies?' " – "No, no, it's eight." – "No, five." – " 'You are a vibration of love. But I see you're not in tune with…' "

One rested his elbow in his hand while holding his finger on his smile. "The main theme is always that there is something wrong with you. Something you recognize and can identify with."

"And then they tell you 'you are good enough' as you are."

"And then they teach you how to improve yourself anyways."

Like a true magician, a man suddenly appeared from behind one of the tall standing stones. He wasn't the most handsome man. Yet he had this feel about him that made you want to trust him immediately.

"Hello," he chuckled most kindly and modestly. "My name is Mow Jee. Hi. You all look a bit troubled, am I right?"

"This can't be happening," grunted One silently while slapping himself against the mask.

"I understand where you are coming from," continued the man with the sweetest voice, filled with love beyond compare. "I've been there myself. I know how it feels. Trust me, as bad as it seems, there is a way out. If I did it, surely you can too."

"Really?" muttered a young man in his twenties. Merely the possibility of being liberated from all his troubles spontaneously caused tears to swell in his eyes.

"Truly," answered the man. "It's not even difficult. It's easy. If you like, I will tell you all about it. I have a beautiful place not far from here. It's a place of peace and tranquillity. And there's joy, too. And singing! If you would just join me."

Without further ado the man turned around and walked away at a slow pace. After some hesitation Ella rose from her seat and followed him outside the clearing. Javier rose as well, just like Sylvia. Tom followed, and so did Adika, 梦, Martha, Hee-Young, Frodo, Inessa, Willem, Mischa and Haruno (for clarity, it needs to be said their names have been changed to protect the innocent. For example: Bill is now called Dan, and Dan is now Friday).

"Well, there's that," said One. "Perhaps now we can-"

"Grreetings," said another man popping up from behind another stone.

"Seriously?" snorted One. "How many are there?"

"People call me the Sad Guru," introduced the man himself. While clearly being from a very large, foreign country, his English was surprisingly eloquent. "I have no idea why," he laughed, and many in the crowd laughed as well. "In reality, I am really quite a happy guy. I merely came to tell you, you all can be happy as well. In my country, sages of long ago developed a potent process rooted in their timeless wisdom. It helps you get in touch with the source of existence. Unlock your potential! You will be able to shape your life according to your own wishes and vision. It really is an ancient science, offering you the keys to good health, fulfilling relationships, abundance and happiness. Just allow yourself a practice of 14 and a half minutes every day, and you will experience the immeasurable, transformative power this world so desperately needs. I have a large hall. It's not far. If you just follow me."

The tall man with cheeks as radiant as the sun turned around and slowly walked away. Patrick immediately decided to follow, as did Bjorn, Tegan, István, Roger, Phillipa, Jamie and Marsali. Even Hans – he just got back because he got lost following Mow Jee – immediately decided to follow the Sad Guru (again, for the sake of clarity, here the actual names are used as this group silently agreed, thus revealing that Willem's actual name is Hans).

The Ones sighed deeply. No one could discern whether it was a sigh of frustration or one of regret.

"I'm sure we haven't seen the last of them," shrugged the tallest.

"That's the thing with trying to know yourself," addressed another One to the crowd directly. "As you all just witnessed, plenty of CSDCs lurk behind every corner to lure us into their stories and traps."

"As we already said, it is futile to know the self. The CSDCs will nonetheless convince you that it is not only possible, but along the way, they will also offer you countless ways to improve yourself."

"The tragedy is, if it's not the CSDCs dragging us into their traps, it's we ourselves who collectively set and spring them for and by ourselves."

"We trap ourselves?" asked a confused boy, even more confused. "How can we collectively trap ourselves?"

"It's practically built into our system," replied One. "We all share the same elements, which can be a source of strength or protection…"

"… yet also can lead us astray."

"Like how? What?"

"Hope?" tried One as if he was one of the crowd.

The other Ones joined the game:

"Fear?" – "Grief?" – "Despair and suffering?" – "Innocent ignorance?" – "Cultural bias and prejudice?" – "The unbearableness of insecurity?" – "Language?"

"We are going too fast," hushed One. "Language, words, imagination or emotions, they each have their vices and virtues. The thing is, mostly when we try to unravel something – even when it comes to the Truth – we tend to take the intellectual approach. Now, intellectual probing works pretty well on intellectual things, but it has its shortcomings, too. When people start dissecting the self, which they have done for hundreds and thousands of years, a certain terminology comes into existence. And looking into our psyche, or simply or personhood, does tend to generate quite a vocabulary."

"The point is," elaborated One, "even the simplest words turn out to be the most difficult or confusing of them all. Just take words like 'ego' or 'soul'. They have become opinionated to such an extent that their meaning is decided by each and every individual in their own way."

"And the gravity of seductive beliefs and ideas does the rest", continued One. "It often starts with just one or a few. Then, like attracts like. The world is filled with little bubbles of people sharing similar views."

"Even the most profound spiritual concepts get polluted over time," grunted One. "People become biased. Or worse, they deliberately rewrite knowledge of the past to fit their own agenda. Stories and allegories that once genuinely helped to reveal Truth, mutate into a narrative to support the success of a leader or an organization."

"Bottom line," concluded One, "what we are trying to say is that we, right here and right now, once and for all, should not invest too much time in these confusing misconceptions."

"I can only agree with my masked and hooded fellow here," spoke One solemnly. "It is understandable that we want to explore such attractive avenues, but at a certain point, we should realize how they never seem to fully satisfy us."

One deemed it was time for a conclusion: "So instead, now that we know that many introspective or 'spiritual' paths simply make us walk in circles, we propose to point you directly to the Truth. Not through yet again a new path, but here and now, where you are."

Silence.

Then, suddenly... Still silence.

Chapter 6   **How the advice of not knowing yourself is the greatest wisdom of all (success guaranteed for sure)**

"Well?" badgered the old man from Scotland in the wheelchair (it's the old man who's in the wheelchair, not Scotland – just saying). "Get on with it! It's getting late, and so far, we wouldn't be able to fill a rat's arse with your Truth."

"So knowing yourself is not the way to go?" queried a man from Holland. Just by his facial features anyone could clearly discern him to be from Holland. It's an ability we all have to think ourselves capable of recognizing one's nationality simply by one's face. Well, at least if we know the nationality upfront, we can. 'Of course,' we say, 'a typical Italian woman!' Or: 'Clearly an American male!' But we wouldn't stand a chance when we'd need to identify a nationality in a lineup of random people. Unless it's an Eskimo. Everybody recognizes Eskimos. It's their big furry coats and hoods that give'm away. Then again, if you'd ask in what country Eskimos live, the answer is likely to be 'Somewhere up north, where they chase penguins, no?'

"Yes," said a pregnant woman from Brazil. She didn't really look like someone from Brazil, but by this time, people were getting acquainted enough to know each other's nationalities. – Right, let's wind back a little. This nationality business is consuming too much of our forests.

"Yes," pressed a pregnant woman from Brazil. "if we're not supposed to dig into our psyche to know ourselves, if we're not to recognize our soul, if we're not to expose our hidden fears, or reveal our best qualities, then what do you propose?"

"We are not saying all that stuff is futile," replied One.

"Of course not," concurred One. "All that is pretty meaningful for your daily lives and all. But we are talking about discovering the Truth. And knowing yourself actually does happen to do the trick. You only need to take it from the right angle."

"But what is that angle?" asked a Nigerian man.

"Simple," answered One. "The angle is to not know yourself."

"You lost us there."

"Okay," suggested One, "let us play a small game. It'll clarify it all in no time."

The crowd eagerly agreed.

"Very well then," started One. "Please, sit back and relax."

"We are already sitting and we are relaxed," said a guy from France, sitting serenely and erectly in a meditation pose that involved his legs looking like a pretzel. Fact of the matter is, he had lost all feeling in his legs more than an hour ago.

"Good," said One. "Let's take this slow. Take a good look at your hands. They are your hands, right?"

Everybody in the crowd awkwardly nodded their heads in agreement.

"But are they you?" asked One. "Obviously, they are not you, correct?"

"Now look at your legs. You can conclude the same thing. They are yours; they are part of you, but, they are not you. Not in your essence."

At this point, the French guy could only wonder - he wasn't even sure his legs were still there at all.

"Close your eyes, please," instructed One. "Scan your body for anything you feel. A discomfort. Pain. A little itch in need of scratching."

At this point, a lot of people simultaneously started to scratch every itch that was waiting to start itching.

"You can conclude once again, that annoying little itch is definitely part of you, but it's not you-you."

"Good," continued One. "Now let's up the ante a bit. Take a moment to observe your memories. Anything that pops up."

The Enigmatic Ancients of Infinite Zero went quiet for a few minutes, allowing everyone to dig deep inside.

"When you look at your memories, you basically can come to the same conclusion, yes? They are part of you, but are they you?

You can do the same with your feelings. Or your thoughts. In the end, all of that ends up in the 'My'-category. 'My' hands. 'My' legs. 'My' memories. 'My' this, 'My' that."

Again, there was room for silence and contemplation.

"The question is," mused One after some time, "amidst all the stuff you can look at and say it's yours, but not really you, when exactly, if at all, do you get to that thingy which can no longer be referred to as 'mine', but simply as 'you'?"

"Errrr??" tried a young man from Sweden. "I guess it's the brain, no?"

"No, you dummy," said his neighbour from Finland (hey, that's a coincidence!), "you can still say 'my brain', right?"

"Soul?" tried a German woman, extending the word's vowels across multiple seconds. "Dah", she then banged herself on the forehead. " 'My' soul."

"It's a trick," said an Irish bloke. "Must be. Somewhere between all these 'mines' there's 'me'." Even as he spoke, his face didn't know which way to go, torn between the pride of saying something that seemed incredibly smart and the nagging doubt that it might just as well be plain stupid.

"Hang on a bit," spoke One calmly and gently. "Let's take a step back, shall we?"

"Indeed," One pointed out, "let's certainly not underestimate the importance of this exercise. It may seem funny or even stupid, but it is truly one of the first steps to Truth."

"So let's give it another chance," soothed One.

"Okay, okay," grumbled the Scotsman in the wheelchair (that's less ambiguous, isn't it?). "Carry on."

"Try it this way," began One. "Close your eyes for just a brief moment more. Allow a string of aspects to rise, which all seem to be part of you… or even define you. It can be your body, a part of your body, – a memory, a feeling, a longing, – something that worries you, something you accomplished, – the name of your mother, your children, – something that makes you proud, something you are ashamed of, – something you are known for, anything."

"Now, while you do that," continued One still slowly and with a gentle voice, "mentally write each down on a coloured sticky note, or simply imagine it to land on such a note."

"A yellow one or a green one?" someone in the crowd asked.

"Any colour will do," answered One patiently. Then, after a few moments, she went on. "Okay, good; now visualize your body floating in the air in front of you. Let all the sticky notes land anywhere on it. Remember, your body is just a sticky note as well. Perhaps you can imagine it to be a sticky note in the shape of your body."

The crowd fell into a profound silence, submerged as they were in their little visualization exercise. When One imagined all the floating bodies above the clearing, each filled with multi-coloured sticky notes, she had to bite her lip not to burst into laughter. 'Would make a nice cartoon,' she thought.

"Very good," said One. "now you can try the following: confront each and every single sticky note with a simple question: is it you? Or is it only some part of you, stuck on that billboard you constantly put up for others as well as yourself."

"If it's not you," added One, "gently remove the note and let it fly in the wind. Then look at the next one and do the same."

And so, a whole bunch of sticky-note-bodies were hovering above the standing stones of Monteneuf, each filled with a whole bunch of sticky notes in as much as three or more layers on top of each other. Then, the sticky notes began to fly in the wind as if it were Autumn already. It gently started with just a few here and there. Mere seconds later, it seemed the mental wind grew stronger. Soon enough, the air was filled with sticky notes swirling down and down, a little bit up again, and down, right until…

…there was nothing left but the blue sky.

There was nothing left to know. It was the most peaceful moment for each and every one of them. Still, for it to be a peaceful moment, there had to be 'some-thing' which remained to experience that.

"I wonder what that might be?" mused One in silence.

Chapter 7   From knowing yourself and not knowing yourself back to knowing your self

When they snapped out of the exercise, all looked up. It seemed as if a million starlings had decided to fly right above them in the most awe-inspiring murmurations. In mere seconds, at the backdrop of an orange-going-into-indigo sky, they danced themselves into all possible and impossible shapes. A whale turned into a baby with an umbilical cord still attached. A tea can turned into a vesica piscis. A lemniscate became a receiving hand and then a face with a knight's visor. A dolphin, a giant bird, a sealion with a ball on its nose, an Ancient Mystic of Infinite Zero, a spaceship and a toothbrush. Clearly, they must have rehearsed this intensely to pull of such a tour de force, no?

Mesmerized as they were, all kept staring at the sky until the birds grew tired and decided to land. Oh, then they flew up again and continued their performance for another ten minutes as an encore. Finally (well, they did another five-minute extra-encore first), they all huddled together in a single little bush. While it was clearly impossible for the bush to hold all these birds, none of them could even be spotted in it. Not a single one! It was like they either had opened another dimension or – and this is more plausible – the Tardis got rebuilt from a phonebooth to a bush.

"Would it be like that?" Yvonne from Canada asked. "If you'd take the birds away, one by one, then after the last bird, there'd be nothing left, right?"

"Left? Right?" repeated One in a high pitch. "What kind of a question is that?"

One ignored One and inquired One. "What do you think? Nothing left?"

"Well, right – I mean, wait!" vacillated One. "That's going a bit fast, don't you think?"

"Very well," said One and directed herself to Yvonne. "No."

Yvonne's face took on a weird shape that cannot be described. "Noo-o?"

she said with an extremely distrustful tone. "The way you guys were behaving, I couldn't suppress the feeling there most certainly was a 'yes' coming."

"Well, Yvonne," the thing is, you can't climb a ladder without using all of its rungs.

"Actually," protested One, "one could skip a few every here and there."

"True," said One, "but you can't skip all of them at once. Well, unless you're heading down instead of up. Then again, that wouldn't be the most sane thing to do."

"Yeh, Yvonne," proposed One. "Let's go along with a 'No' for now."

"Indeed, let's take a step back and stick to the sticky notes," chuckled One.

"So," queried One. "What remains when you remove all the sticky notes one by one?"

"Just my body?" tried Ann. (Not sure what country she was from. Must check this later in the list of participants.)

One shook his head. "No, no, as we already said, the body is just a sticky note like everything else."

"So what remains?" tried One again.

"Errrr." It was that guy from Sweden again, Sven (as you might have already guessed, since all guys from Sweden are called Sven, except for the occasional Anders). "A transparent thingy?"

One looked at the other, at the other and at the other. Then, they all spontaneously huddled together with their backs towards the crowd. As such, they formed an impenetrable wall of cloaks and hoods.

There was whispering and hushing. There was a lot of nodding as well. Finally, they fanned out again to their original positions.

"A transparent thingy?" repeated One. Everybody could hear the gulping sound of Sven's throat when he swallowed in fear of what was coming.

"We like that," continued One, pleased. "We actually like that a lot." Sven sighed in relief and allowed himself to relax again.

"You see," began One, "up until now, our focus was on everything that seems to define us. We deliberately chose this approach because that is simply what we instinctively do: we tend to see ourselves as the sum of a bunch of things, both visible from the outside as well as invisible on the inside."

"But this approach comes with an unavoidable pitfall," divulged One, as if revealing a big secret. "Sooner than later, all these things come to appear like a giant puzzle which we think we need to solve or fix. Tweak a little here, remove something there, change the order, turn things around, dress them up…"

"That's the thing," added One. "Looking at yourself from yourself, nothing but stirs yourself. Before you know it, you'll find yourself collecting special spoons to stir things to perfection."

Many in the crowd looked a bit puzzled after that one. In their heads they were trying to make sense of what self was doing what, to which other self, if any. Others were thinking about soup for no apparent reason. Only a few stayed focused and knew exactly what One was trying to explain. (If you're not amongst the latter, you might wanna rewind a page or two.)

"Perhaps," suggested One, "we can simplify our terminology a bit. You know, so we can clearly distinguish the difference between the swirling sticky notes and 'that' which remains. Let us agree. We name everything we call personhood, psyche, identity, ego, emotions, memories, and all that stuff as simply our identity-self."

"Or even shorter, our self?" tried One while drawing an s in the sky and underlying it.

"Seems like a good idea," nodded One. "Don't forget to add body, brain, thinking, soul, higher-self and all thát stuff to it as well, to be clear."

"And now we can reveal the magician's trick!" announced One.

"Could call it the elephant in the room," added One.

"Time to let the Geni out of the bottle," sang One.

"Indeed," continued One. "You see, we asked you to look at all aspects of yourselves as a way to know yourself. But for each and every aspect you came up with, you could conclude it's not you. Not you in your essence, I mean. At best, a part of you, a mere sticky note, nothing more."

"And all the time, you ignored one little thing," revealed One. "That which is doing the looking!"

"That which is doing the looking?" repeated Charles from London (we'll not name the kingdom as this book might last longer than the name it currently carries). His question came with a pitch that elevated with each syllable as if it was climbing a mounting and then suddenly came back down again at the '-ing' part. "What you mean: that which is doing the looking?" With the last sentence, he was clearly back at ground level.

"That essential you," answered One. "You see, all this time, you were so focused on what seems to define you, but you all forgot the most obvious: you – you in your most naked essence."

"No sticky note," added One, "but 'that' what is putting them up and then discarding them again."

"Well, that's not entirely correct," objected One, "but then again, it is a complicated thingy to talk about. Hmm, let me think."

"Let us just temporarily accept it this way," whispered One quietly in One's ear. Since his thinking didn't yield any result, One shrugged and nodded in agreement.

"Anyway," continued One, "this essence-you, it is so obvious, so self-evident, that we completely ignore it. And that's actually pretty normal, because it's that what's doing the looking after all. An eye rarely looks at itself, now does it? Unless you'd take it out and point it back at your other eye…"

"…or you use a mirror," coughed One in his fist.

"So that what's doing the looking is the transparent thingy?" queried Sven almost inaudibly.

"Exactly," smiled One (well, they always are smiling because of their masks, yet still, you could unmistakably recognize the smile in his voice). "See, it truly is transparent. It cannot be touched, it cannot be seen, yet it is undisputedly there."

"In a sense," spoke One, "it is always sort of concealed."

"As a matter of fact," gestured One some indescribable gesture, "it is pretty ambiguous in nature. It is plain in sight and hidden at the same time."

"Come to think of it," pondered One. "All these nebulous characteristics are exactly why it is the most enigmatic mystery of all. Mystics, scientists, philosophers, you name it, they all have tried to crack it and …"

"… mostly failed at it," finished One. "Simply because while cracking it, they just can't resist overloading it with sticky notes again."

"And before you know it, they see a pattern in those new sticky notes."

"And from that pattern, they develop a system."

"And a system becomes a path, a way, a method, or, for God's sake, even a religion."

"While in reality," One concluded softly, "the transparent thingy ever simply remains… the transparent thingy."

"But this is silly," objected Yvonne. "What you are referring to simply is consciousness…" Then she looked up and to the right. "…or awareness, I guess. I never figured out which is which."

"That is totally correct, Yvonne," replied One. "And yes, we have all learned about consciousness at school. And in the same class we immediately learn to take it for granted. Soon enough the lessons jump back to all the stuff we can be conscious of."

"You see," said One, "it's a bit like gravity. It is unmistakably there, yet nobody really knows how it truly works. Can you imagine that? Hence, we would rather focus on the effects of gravity because at least that is pretty obvious."

"Yes," nodded One so hard his hood almost came off. "Same with consciousness. Worse even. If they are not taking it for granted or forgetting all about it, they are blowing it out of proportion. 'The Witness', they call it."

"Or 'the Looker' ", chuckled One. "And before you know it, it becomes 'the inner guide' …"

"… our 'intuition' …"

"… our 'spirit' ", drawled One, giving his best impression of Gollum speaking about his precious.

"Please," hushed One. "Let's not step into all this folly. Night is falling, and we do not want to waste time." He paused for a moment, gazing around to check if he still had the attention of his audience. "On the other hand," One then continued while throwing a reprimanding glance at his companions, "we almost make it sound like we are throwing the whole thing out of the window just because some people invented a silly terminology on top of it. Let me assure you this transparency thingy is not to be discarded. Not at all. On the contrary, you will learn soon enough that it is crucial with regards to our wellbeing, our psyche, our inner peace and balance and how we navigate life and existence as a whole." (You should reread this paragraph in the voice of Sir Attenborough. Then, reread it again with the voice of Sir Hopkins. It's fun.)

"That sounds pretty important," whispered Sven from Sweden while bumping his shoulder against that of Kalle from Finland.

"Might as well name the transparent thingy now, no?" suggested One. "Am I giving it away too soon when I say we ourselves like to call it the $\overline{S}$elf?"

One slapped himself against the mask. "No, not at all," he grumbled. "And next you will probably reveal this is actually the $\overline{S}$elf, which is meant in Know Thyself."

"Now you're the one giving it away!" pointed One.

"Urgh", exclaimed One. "Anyways. As you all can see, words can be confusing, even when at first glance they appear to be illuminating."

"Precisely," said One. "Just as words like 'soul' or 'ego' are being endlessly debated, we can have the same problem with 'consciousness', 'awareness', 'the Witness' or 'the Seer', your 'True Self', your 'Essence Nature', etc. Any noun or concept gathers the weight of opinion or beliefs, while our transparent thingy needs to remain weightless… or transparent for that matter. So perhaps it can better be described by its active characteristics, using verb nouns like 'Beingness' or 'Isness'. 'Presence' might work too."

"Or… S̄elf," glowed One while drawing a capital S in the sky with a strongly emphasized horizontal line on top of it. (Henceforward, we will refer to this One as the glowing One, as her shining presence is as consistent as the radiance of the sun when you look at it from Mercury.)

"Or S̄elf," repeated One, still slightly agitated.

"So that's the self you need to know when they say Know Thyself," spilt the glowing One. "Not that endless hodgepodge of fears and worries, feelings and emotions, needs and wants, roles and responsibilities, characteristics, features, flaws and faults, but that thingy that is doing the looking, that thingy that is the absolute, most essential me when you say 'I' or 'me'."

"Did you do special breathing exercises before you uttered that sentence?" queried One. – "Me? No, not really. It simply came out from a deep passion within."

"Aaargh, will you all shut up!" One rearranged his cloak and hood, straightened his mask and recovered his poise. But then Kalle, who was eager to join the conversation for quite a while now, dared to speak out: "I still don't get it, guys."

"Argh, really?" muttered One biting his teeth.

"Consciousness is neath, I give you that," continued Kalle, "but surely I am my thoughts, no? Or at least, my thoughts are an expression of me. I mean, well, I don't know. It's a bit confusing."

The glowing One rose up. With the setting sun on her back, she almost literally appeared to be glowing. That got everyone's attention. "Hmmm," she pondered while pacing up and down. "How about one more little exercise? It's quick and easy, really. Yes? Very well. Gently close your eyes one more time for me."

Again, all closed their eyes, except Bram from Flanders, who had fallen in love with an Egyptian girl a bit further and just couldn't take his eyes off her.

"Okay, now try this: stop thinking for the next five minutes."

The glowing One took out her watch and literally set her timer to five minutes. All other Enigmatic Ancients of Infinite Zero suppressed a sigh of frustration as the 300 seconds passed by, knowing well enough that 60 or even 20 seconds were plenty enough to prove their point.

"Very well," cheered the glowing One. "Now, please raise your hand if you had no thoughts whatsoever during the past five minutes."

No hands were raised except that of the sleeping Scotsman, which his nurse had raised as a joke.

"Wait, hang on," the glowing One acted surprised, "so you say you are your thoughts, or rather, your thoughts are the most direct means to express yourselves, but you can't even decide to have none for a few minutes?"

Kalle blushed. "Yeh, I kept thinking about my dad, who's probably worried about where I am."

"I was thinking about the pizza leftovers I forgot in my fridge," said Charles. "Must have grown hair by now."

"And I was thinking how silly this all still is," said Yvonne. "I then tried to discard that thought to prove you wrong. But then I simply got a random thought about me going to Marrakesh next week. And when I discarded that thought, the thought of being afraid of dying popped up out of nowhere."

"So," concluded the glowing One, "whether you want to or not, you can't control your thoughts. Surely your thoughts are not y-"

"Hang on, hang on," interrupted the Scotsman, who turned out to be all but asleep. "Yer misguiding us there, laddie! Dar ndóigh, I can't stop me thoughts when I am me thoughts. They're me. If you'd ask water to not be wet, it wouldn't be water any longer, now would it?"

"That's certainly a good observation," concurred One. "However, just about 10 pages ago, you had a first glimmer of a thoughtless experience. And you didn't disappear, now, did you?"

"So," started the glowing One for a second time, "whether you want to or not, you actually can't control your thoughts. Surely, your thoughts are not you. It's just like you can't stop the hair on your head from growing, and you do agree you are not your hair, are you?"

"Attendez, what?" said Georges DuRien. Can you imagine he was still struggling with his pretzel-legs. "What has hair got to do with thinking? I mean, they are pretty close to each other, oui, but that doesn't mean there's a direct connection, is there?"

"May I please continue?" sibilated One between his clenched teeth. "I was about to make an important point."

"By all means," approved the glowing One.

"So, what I was trying to… What?"

"Nothing, nothing, carry on."

"Thank you." By now, One had calmed down again and actually sounded truly compassionate. "The point I was trying to make is that all this thinking, or any approach of a rational kind, is futile in order to truly understand this $\overline{S}$elf. It has to be experienced, not verbally dissected. You cannot approach it the way you'd approach the self. Any explanation or description is nothing but a distraction. The $\overline{S}$elf simply is."

"He's right," confirmed One. "In terms of knowing thyself, this 'knowing' is not to be seen as a mental construct like one can know persons or have knowledge about things. It simply is beyond regular comprehension."

"That's the thing," said One. "Any idea about this $\overline{S}$elf, in terms of concepts or thoughts, will immediately collapse into the self. It will once again become a sticky note like all the others."

"So 'knowing the knower', 'witnessing the witness' or 'seeing the seer', it's all a distraction. It only opens pathways to the realm of useless fantasies which will come to fester within the self."

"And as you have already proven, Yvonne, the rational part of us only

45

thinks little of this discovery. It simply can't find any practical benefit or use in it. The gravitational pull of the s̲elf, and its need for the practical, is simply too strong to withstand."

One suddenly noticed how the glowing One was stumbling around between the monoliths, holding her arms in front of her like a sleepwalker in an average comic book. "What's the matter?"

"I can't see a thing with this mask on," she replied. "Is something wrong with my mask? Or is it night?"

"I can't see a thing either," said One. "Must be night. Let's call it a day, shall we?"

"Why would you call it a day when it's night?" wondered One. "So weird."

That night, there was music. As it turns out, seekers always seem to carry a bunch of instruments with them. There was a guitar, a lot of djembés, tambourines, Bongo drums, tablas (it appears seekers like to hit stuff), a flute, some weird thingy with just one string, and a guy with bagpipes who was only allowed to play at a greater distance.

Torches were lit, casting a warm, wavering light on the standing stones. When the bagpipe turned silent, and the djembés took over, there was dancing too. The Enigmatic Ancients of Infinite Zero floated between the crowd and the standing stones, waving and whirling around like ghosts who had too much to drink. Even the mysterious woman in the white gown participated, playing hide and seek from stone to stone while gracefully sharing her radiant energy through the most sensual movements a woman could display in dance.

The nurse looked worried at the IV of the drooling Scotsman and decided to replace it with a new one. All filled up he'd surely last a bit longer once more, perhaps even long enough to finally come to know the Truth.

Chapter 8 This one appears to be something about diving into the $\overline{\text{S}}$elf from the s̲elf, if that makes any sense to those only reading the table of contents (and that's why there isn't one)

The next morning, the Boundless Seers of Infinite Zero, together with the crowd that got stuck to them like a sticky note, found themselves at the foot of a large nuclear power plant. Two enormous cooling towers cast their gloomy shadow over the landscape. The white, moist air they were both emitting inspired fathers to tell their toddlers how humans were actually responsible for the clouds.

Sven woke and looked at the two towers. He prodded Kalle against the shoulder. "Wow!" they both exclaimed. "Must have been some party."

The Boundless Seers of Infinite Zero were long awake, lying, sitting or standing around, being totally relaxed as they were. One even had a flower protruding from the smile in his mask. He gently nibbled on its stem and occasionally switched it from left to right and right to left.

"Good morning, everybody", beamed the glowing One. "How are we all doing?"

Nobody answered. All were still trying to find their bearings in the new scenery (actually, they really had trouble with that since none of them knew what a bearing looked like).

The glowing One was nowhere near giving up on them. A contagious enthusiasm took hold of her. "I can't hear you," she shouted. "Come on, everybody say 'Yeeee!'"

And when the crowd went genuinely 'Yeeee!' after the fourth attempt, everybody sat down with big smiles similar to the ones of the Boundless Seers of Infinite Zero.

"All yours," grinned the glowing One to One.

"Err," began One doubtful. "Didn't we agree not to lecture and only answer questions?"

"Well, I have one!" hollered Kalle Mihinkään. He then realized he was speaking out pretty loud and lowered his voice. "Yesterday... Err, I think yesterday, you said something along the lines of the rational part of us not being cut out to recognize the Truth. Could you explain that a bit, maybe?"

"Oh boy," said One. "It'll take me an entire chapter to answer that one."

"Well, better get on with it then," croaked ol' Cormac O'NoOne from his wheelchair.

"Traitor!" shouted Jimmy O'NoWhere patriotically from across the circle. "You're no bloody Scotsman! You're Irish! (Now, between you and me, Jimmy himself was actually born and raised in New York, just like his father and grandfather did.)

"Wheelchairs and nurses come cheaper in Scotland!" countered ol' Cormac in his defence.

"What!" exclaimed Nurse Erin O'Someone (actually, she migrated as well since living in Scotland is said to be 30% cheaper). "I don't come cheap!"

The sky was the brightest blue. No sulky nurse or angry Irish immigrants could change any of that. Two strings of man-made clouds floated towards the horizon with a natural ease.

"Right," sighed One. "Yesterday, indeed, we took a bit of a leap. Let's take a step back first."

"Indeed, indeed," added the One nibbling on the stem of his cosmos (there happened to be a botanist in the group). But as he spoke, the flower dropped from his mask on the ground. "Darn," he ended while he bent down to pick up the cosmos.

"Right," sighed One – again. "So we clarified that trying to know your identity-self, or self as we coined it, will not get you far in terms of trying to find the answers to the Big Questions."

"Indeed, indeed, indeed," began the One with the cosmos (this time, he was holding it in his hand while he spoke). "This identity-self, you see, it has both the privilege as well as the burden of constant doing and ceaseless choosing. It is never at rest, ever competing, striving, loving, complaining, enjoying…" He would have gone on if it wasn't for him running out of air.

"Exactly," One quickly came to the rescue. "And either choice or doing can lead to pleasure or frustration, growth or setbacks. Likewise, either event which befalls us becomes categorized as good or bad, with us or against us. Our entire personhood keeps us busy from the moment we wake up till we finally tuck in again."

"Even tucked in it can keep us awake for a pretty long time as well," added One.

"I'm not saying it is worthless to know or fathom it, nor is it fruitless to improve it and allow it to grow, not at all. It's all good. But we are aiming to answer the Big Q's, and that requires a different perspective, as we already said on page 3."

"But then we got stuck in new words like consciousness, or awareness. And 'Beingness' or 'Isness' couldn't help either, at least not at this point. Hence, we concluded a rational approach would not lead us any further. We are in need of something of a more experiential nature."

"Will we get to take ayahuasca?" whooped Andrea Klein with a heavy German accent. Her dreadlocks waved with joy at the thought alone. "Everybody go 'Yeeee'!" she exclaimed with her naked arms up in the air.

"There will be no need for ayahuasca or anything of the sort," hushed One.

Dreadlocks went down like they seemed to crave being watered.

"So," One continued. "At first glance, consciousness only seems to be like a tool of some kind. It allows us cognition, self-reflection and awareness of our surroundings among other things."

"One would also say it allows us to remember, to have an inner conversation, to think, to have volition and all sorts of stuff."

"Indeed, indeed," yes, with cosmos in hand, "and this way, all attention goes to the properties, while the thing itself, that what allows all that neat stuff in the first place, gets mostly ignored."

"Bottom line is this," said One. "In our ever upholding of our identity-self, in our 'I am this' and 'I'd rather be that' we totally forget about 'I'."

"True," said the One with the cosmos in a very relaxed manner. This time he kept the stem of the flower between his teeth while supporting it with his hand. "We simply don't realize how disconnected we have become from our purest essence, even to the point where we think the notion of 'essence' or '$\overline{\text{Self}}$' to be totally absurd. We fail to see anything practical in this 'I' itself. It doesn't appear to 'do' anything."

"One might say we mistake a hammer that is not hammering for being impractical."

"Yeh, but that's just stupid. A hammer not hammering is simply something which you never find when you are looking for it …"

"… and bump into when you are not."

"It's definitely not the same as consciousness doing nothing at all."

"Exactly," radiated the glowing One. "Consciousness not 'doing' anything at all is nothing but 'being' instead. And you can't imagine how extraordinary this is."

"Indeed, they can't," confirmed One with a friendly tone to his peers. "So let's remedy this and try something experiential for a difference."

Then One revealed a series of the most secret physical exercises. In fact, they are so secret they cannot be revealed here. While being ridiculously easy, the effect of the exercises was truly baffling. Not only did they bring everybody in a healthy shape, but they also caused everyone to be more present in the here and now. Somehow the exercises induced a higher awareness of the body, and through that increased awareness, the awareness of consciousness itself was raised significantly as well. This prepared them for the next step.

(At this point, you are probably wildly inquisitive about the nature of these exercises, making you willing to pay tons of money to practice them when the author of this work passes by your place. That's just lovely – looking forward to meeting you.)

(No, no, no, trying to skip ahead in the remaining pages will not bring any salvation.)

"Now, let's do something slightly different," began One. "It may seem silly, but please, indulge us for a moment."

"Close your eyes," asked One with a gentle voice. "Now, start noticing everything noticeable within you. Sweep through your body, from the most exterior parts like hands and feet to your trunk and your head."

"Very good," One continued after a short minute. "Now, become aware of the observing itself. I'd like you to try the following. I'd like you to try finding the exact location where the observing is taking place."

Some faces, if not most, developed a deep wrinkle between the eyebrows. The glowing One couldn't suppress a chuckle. Others stayed more relaxed, allowing the process to develop.

"Start with the obvious," advised One gently. "Are you, the observer, are you inside the nuclear powerplant in the distance? – No, it seems not, does it? – Are you in the adjacent field? – No, again that seems not to be the case. – Let's come a bit closer now. Are you in your feet? I mean, that what is doing the looking, that what is doing the noticing, is it in your feet? – No, it is not. – Maybe it is in your arms? – No, it is not there either. – In your tummy? – Please, allow this to be an effortless exercise. Let us gently try to do the simplest of all things: literally, find ourselves in our essence."

One allowed another minute of silence. Although most foreheads still developed a frown and wrinkles, some did seem to genuinely relax.

"Are you, that what is looking, are you in your head? – May seem the closest we got so far, isn't it? Still, let us go for precision. Are you in your chin? – No, not there. – Are you in your ears? – Definitely not there. – Not in the nose either. – Are you in the back of your head? – Try to pinpoint it to the very exact location. That smallest point from where the looking is taking place. – See if you can find it."

Again, One allowed a few minutes of silence.

With a joyful "Excellent!" the glowing One ended the exercise. All eyes slowly went open again.

"It's a trick," said Jimmy, just as he had on page 33. This time, however, he said it with a thick accent, trying to sound as Irish as possible to cover up the truth about him actually being an American. "I just can't seem to find it. Seems I'm in my eyes, but that doesn't sound right, does it?"

"I think I understand," said Yvonne. "No really, I think I do. I think it's all less about finding a specific location than it is about actually merging with that looking itself."

"Man," shared Sven Ingenson. "I mean, I have done meditation exercises before. They all sort of had the objective of meditating, but this one brought me straight into a state of meditation itself. Really amazing!"

"Same here," said Adebowale Unigwe from Nigeria. "Been doing the weirdest stuff, and honestly, with almost no effect whatsoever. And now, boom man, I have never felt this peaceful in my life!"

"I think I had almost found the exact spot," blurted Andrea, "but then I… Well, I fell into it. I can't describe it any else. But I know this for sure, my ayahuasca is going down the drain, I can tell you that. I mean… it felt like being as vast as the universe itself. And at the same time…"

"… it felt like being nothing… at all," finished Sven. "One could call it infinite zero."

"Ha! How silly," jested the One with the cosmos. "Who'd ever do that?"

By now, everybody was sharing their experience with their nearby neighbours, except for Nurse Erin, who was too occupied checking the pressure of ol' Cormac's wheels (the ones on his wheelchair, obviously).

It was the voice of One which eventually drowned out all others.

"Please," he gently hushed. "Let's avoid the mistake of placing a single fleeting experience on an altar, only to idolize it, and by doing that, lose its true essence forever. Let us rationally examine the irrational."

"So now you have seen," explained One, "by physically turning the light of the source of our being upon itself, we somehow managed to induce a profound awareness of Beingness itself, regardless of us finding its actual location or not."

"Indeed," said One. "When you'd direct your awareness to, say, your left foot, it would veritably increase the physical sensitivity of exactly that. But directing awareness upon itself does the opposite. It induces a peculiar, non-physical experience."

"And, somehow, by consciously directing awareness upon itself, the mental mind seems to become silenced significantly as well. Hence, a meditative experience spontaneously emerges, as you described yourselves."

When Yvonne raised her arm in a doubtful way, all went silent. Much to her own surprise, the sudden attention made her forget what she was about to ask. Luckily, it soon came back to her: "I think I understand it a bit better now. But, well, I somehow can't connect the dots between Truth and this little experience. Is that just me?"

"No, Yvonne," answered One. "As a matter of fact, you are completely correct. While what you experienced today may seem like a leap to some, it still is nothing but a small step."

"Still, however small it may be," said the glowing One, "it is a solid one in the right direction. So let us move on, shall we?"

"Indeed, indeed," said the One with the cosmos while standing up and straightening his cloak. "How about doing this by actually putting some real steps into it?"

All of the Boundless Seers of Infinite Zero agreed. And so, they went on their way again.

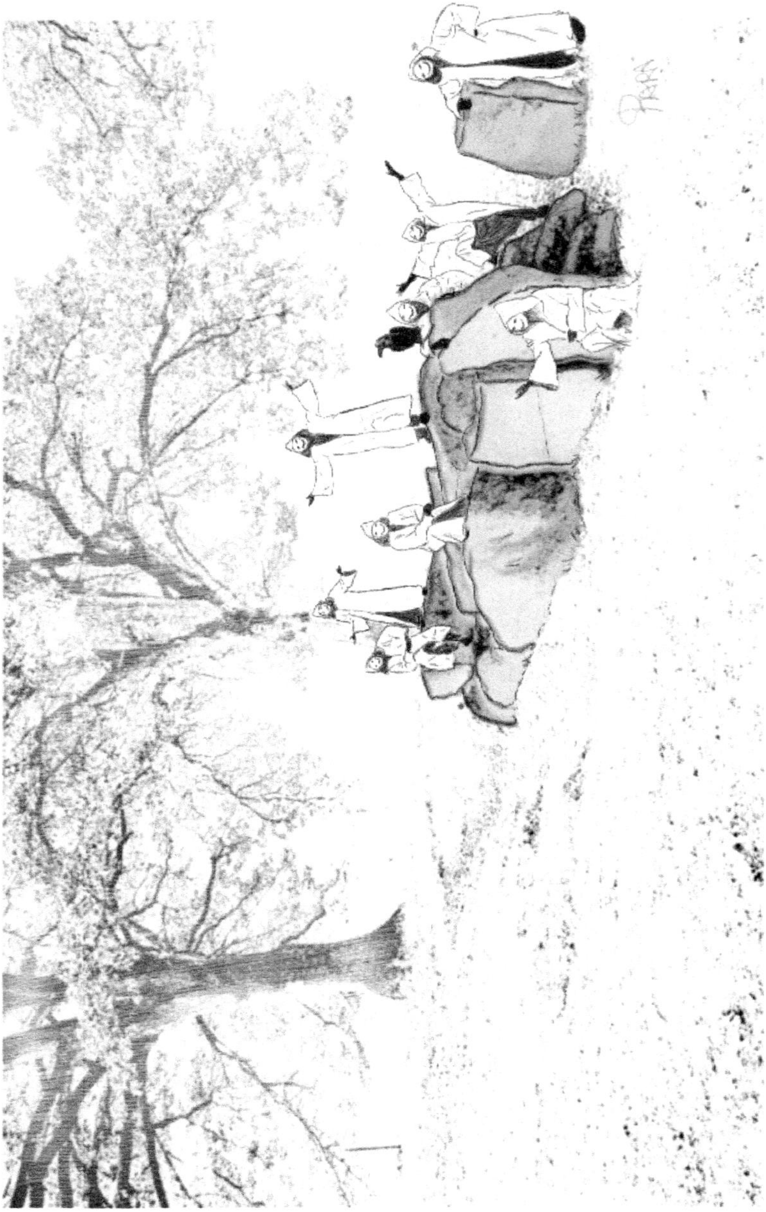

Chapter 9 **How the newfound S̄elf is neat for sure and to be cherished, but also, how it is merely the first step towards a more profound insight (oh, there's also a little trickery here)**

The Mystical Mages of Infinite Zero decided to take the white clouds of the nuclear power plant as their guide. Hence, as the wind came from north-northwest, they headed south-southeast (duh!). The walk seemed to go on and on for many hours. A light breeze, a gentle sun and a fairly blue sky kept all from complaining. On that account, the One with the ice cream van, who met them halfway, did his part as well. It was a beautiful day indeed.

After no less than 36 kilometres, they came upon the Dolmen d'Oppagne. It was here the Mystical Mages of Infinite Zero decided to halt. The dolmen found itself located in a sort of dent in the ground. It was as if the weight of the stones had made the ancient construction sink deeper than its surrounding landscape. Four majestic trees, arranged in a rectangular pattern around the dolmen, solemnly held guard while all gathered in their shadow (unfortunately, we could not identify the trees as the botanist of the group temporarily got lost).

Some of the Mystical Mages of Infinite Zero took a seat upon the capstones. Others chose to stand on them, lean against them or lie down underneath them. The crowd simply sat down on the higher ground between the trees. Shoes flew out, and feet almost literally sighed in relief, grateful for the freedom they were given after being held in sweaty darkness for almost the entire day.

From out of the blue, a raven landed on the right shoulder of one of the Mystical Mages of Infinite Zero. Both stared at each other for a brief moment, each assessing what to do with the situation. When the raven seemed to relax, the One, now known as the One with the raven, relaxed as well. Both accepted the situation as it presented itself.

"Boy, that was quite a walk," huffed ol' Cormac. Behind his wheelchair, Nurse Erin lay unconscious on the ground while a helpful lass from Bulgaria waved some fresh air at her.

The raven shortly released a gurgling croak as if soliciting a new question now all had settled down.

It wasn't sure if Andrea could understand the raven's language – she surely wished she could – but she appeared to take the hint nonetheless: "I assume we now need to learn how we should cast our ego and identity permanently aside, no? And then, we will deepen this experience of the S̄elf way up to enlightenment, right?"

"Uh oh," played the glowing One with a tone expressing sincere worry. "She said 'assume'."

Almost all of the Mystical Mages of Infinite Zero ostentatiously shook their heads, except for the One with the raven (he didn't want to risk his mask being filled with black feathers and whatever stuff was sticking to them).

"What?" sobbed Andrea worried. "What did I say wrong?"

"You said 'assume'," replied the One with the cosmos while holding it casually between thumb and index finger. "Very nasty word. If assuming itself isn't already the worst one can do, the word itself also implies you are making an 'ass' out of 'u' and 'me'."

"Err," faltered Andrea. "I… I didn't realize. I'm sorry, I am German. I don't speak very …"

"We're just messing with ya, girl", smiled the glowing One. "We always like to make fun of that silly word."

"Nonetheless," observed the One with the cosmos. "I don't think you can 'deepen' something 'up' to something."

"Anyhow," said the One with the raven against his cloaked and hooded companions. "Here I thought us being the ones going too fast at this. But from what I'm hearing now, it's them who should be given a ticket for speeding, no?"

"Yes, indeed," One agreed. "I think we once more need to take a step back."

"Like hell, I will!" exploded Nurse Erin while she spontaneously awoke from her little coma. She immediately slapped both hands on her mouth as if trying to put the words back in again. With wide eyes, she scanned left and right to see if she had really spoken aloud or just dreamed it.

"Now, before we answer your question, Andrea, it may be good to look a bit closer into the experience we shared this morning."

"Indeed, a good idea," nodded One. "Surely there's a lot of folk who just keep on reading instead of giving it an actual try themselves. They will totally miss the point and wonder what all the fuss is about."

"The problem, of course is, well, this experience is pretty hard to describe. I'd almost say we should leave it to a poet or other artists, no?"

"Even then, the best poem will never be able to pass the smell of a rose… to those without a nose." One chuckled. "Get it? Rose. Nose. – No?"

"You are right," agreed One after he slowly shook his head. "However, that doesn't necessarily render a poem or any other art about Truth pointless. From those who experienced it before to those who recently did as well, it surely can be an excellent means to reconnect, surely at times when we get lost again in our identity-self."

"Still, I'd call it a good challenge to describe the experience."

"Well," decided the One with the raven, "at least we can give it a try. I'm sure we can find an angle that works."

The raven cawed in agreement, prodding his newfound friend to continue. "Remember? As we already know, an inquiry into the self can trigger a range of personal feelings and emotions. And depending on your inner judgement, these feelings can be neutral or happy, exciting or disturbing, confusing or more of an epiphanous nature."

"But when we start looking at the self from outside the self," continued the One with the cosmos, "we produce a new perspective, being the one of the uninvolved spectator. This little trick on its own already allows a certain degree of ease to settle in."

"But then a new question arose, didn't it? 'What is doing this looking?' "

"And you simply answered, well, that's 'consciousness'. But such an obvious deduction, although perhaps true, is far from an actual experience."

"Which we then gave you via our secret exercises," added the glowing One. "You all fell into a state which some would describe as vastness, while the person next to you would call it emptiness… or both at the same time."

"But!" interjected the One without any particular characteristics. "Who is the one experiencing all this?"

That got them all silenced.

"You see," concluded the One with the raven, "as we told you before, and you now have experienced yourself, the 'knowing' in our infamous 'Know Thyself' is not a knowing like one would know their history, or how to knot a tie. This 'knowing' is a knowing of a different kind. It is direct in nature. It transcends thinking or feeling."

"That's correct", agreed One. "Unlike knowledge, which can be transmitted in writing or in person, this 'Beingness' finds itself harder to convey by more common means, even despite its simplicity and straightforwardness. From a strictly mental perspective, a state of identity-lessness seems rather unreal…"

"… utterly useless …"

"… or even outright bizarre."

"Thus, from the moment you get an actual glimpse of the experience – that is, if only you allow it to – you will spontaneously realize this consciousness, or rather, this 'Beingness', is 'That' what 'You' in your essence really are."

"And this 'really-you' will turn out to be the opposite of an identity-self. It's more something like a non-identity. That alone already, this disentanglement of our ever-needy personality, this reconnection with our true essence, inevitably generates this inexplicable ease – completely out of the blue! – without there ever having been the intention for it to happen."

"And when you continue to cultivate this connection, it will soon enough deepen this ease significantly. From that point on, you will find yourself in a slide towards more poetic descriptions like peace …"

"… or joy …"

"… space …"

"… gratitude …"

"… I'd even say a sort of …"

"… love …"

"… be it a love beyond our more common understanding of the word."

"And thus, when folks attempt to put it to words, you will soon enough notice how this state of Beingness is often illustrated with a range of superlatives of all kinds. Many will come to describe it as a state of bliss. Others will try to genuinely portray their experience with words like 'boundless' or 'timeless', and although these words seem both irrational and rational at the same time, they actually are a pretty good description of the $\overline{S}$elf, all because of the simple fact that when you find yourself emerged in Beingness all sense of time and space literally falls away."

"Come to think of it", pondered the One with the cosmos while the glowing One gasped for breath. "I'm really starting to consider coining it Infinite Zero."

Sven prodded Kalle with his elbow against the arm. "Hey, you hear that?" he whispered. "That was my idea!"

"Let's just say this Beingness is a bit of a 'non' nature," continued One. "It is a non-identity which emerges when the constantly nagging me-me-me is silenced. It is non-causal, as nothing actually happens in this state. It is non-dualistic, as there's only that and nothing else; in short, it is non-egoistic, non-personal and non-anything."

"Exactly! There simply is no trace of any doingness. Nothing ever happens in Beingness. It is 'happeningness' itself. And yet, without the slightest pause, all happenings continue to occur within it."

"That's the thing. It is unidentified and unattached, yet it is at all times involved in the deepest way possible. And while it can appear to be concealed to the fullest by our natural engagement in identification with whatever presents itself to identify with, still, at the same time, it remains ever as empty as a blank slate. You see, Sven, your transparent thingy can take on the colours of anything it becomes aware of, yet it remains ever transparent nonetheless."

"But wait, there's more to it," added the glowing One. "While the self – rational and practical as it always likes to be – thinks little of this pointless Beingness, the direct experience of it will allow you to discover a certain wholeness which is beyond anything fathomable to our rational mind."

"Precisely," said the One with the raven. "Merely touching this quality, as you all did this morning, and experiencing its expanding effect upon the identity-self, as you could witness afterwards, delivers a glimpse of its immense importance to our inner wellbeing…"

"…and how we interact with others and our surroundings," added One.

"That's the thing. Taking a frequent rest in Beingness somehow prevents all threads of identification from clinging together into inextricable knots. This repetitive reconnection with Beingness literally allows your personhood to maintain a healthy and enduring flexibility. It's the antidote to the mistake we too often make: we try to solve a general discomfort in the mind by applying this malfunctioning mind to itself. Such an approach will rather cause it to crack into a breakdown instead of finding relief."

"So, you see, the experiential state of the $\overline{S}$elf can release you from the burden of ceaseless preoccupation with the self."

"To resonate in your Beingness," quoted One from this page, "offers a calming, healing and energizing experience. It allows your physical and mental energies to flow naturally without any blocks or distortions."

"In short," laughed One, "dear reader, drop your rational approach of

Beingness for a moment and dive in as the rest of this lot did."

For some reason, the crowd started to applaud.

The Mystical Mages of Infinite Zero all scanned each person one by one, staring into their mesmerized eyes. It was obvious everybody took it in and believed every one of their words to be true. The crowd was straight out drooling for more and ready to appeal to others to agree as well.

"Yes!" the Mystical Mages of Infinite Zero all shouted loudly in unison. They all rose from their seated position and started giving each other high fives. Some even added a weird dance move or a dab.

"Hey, what's going on?" yelled Kalle, confused.

"You see what we did?" asked the glowing One cheerfully.

"We tricked you all," said the One with the cosmos.

"Indeed we did," said the One with the raven. "Here's what we did. We shared a little knowledge with you in words. Each time we said something, another agreed by nodding or saying 'indeed' or 'precisely' or 'correct'. This way, we induced a group-sense of agreement. Hence, you automatically agreed as well with all we said."

"Basically, if we were to say elephants are pink, you'd believe that too," chuckled the One with the cosmos.

"We acted a bit like musicians who add crowd-cheering into the song they record in a studio," giggled the glowing One. "Makes it all radiate success. You'd feel a fool not to be cheering yourself."

"Oh yes," remarked One, "we should definitely add a lot of praise quotes on the back cover of our book."

"Might as well do it on the front as well," suggested One.

All laughed and seemed to have pretty good fun while the crowd didn't really understand what was going on.

"So, above anything else, please," pleaded One, a bit more seriously again, "do not simply believe what we tell you. We are not CSDCs trying to trick you into a story we like you to believe because we happen to believe it ourselves. You need to test it…"

"… probe it …"

"… touch it …"

"… try it and experience it."

"But we already did!" said Andrea, bewildered.

"I know you did, Andrea," affirmed One. "I was more or less referring to those who still haven't closed this book for even a mere minute."

Kalle was confused. "So all you said before wasn't true?"

"Oh, we assure you, it all is," replied the glowing One. "We're just saying you're taking it too easily for granted. Remain vigilant."

"Okay, well, considering it all to be true, I still don't get it," sighed Andrea. "Well, no, I do, I do get it. But didn't you just prove my point that we should learn how to be in this state permanently? All the things you mentioned seem like a long advertisement for exactly what I said, no?"

"Ah, yes, that again," remembered the One with the raven. He paced up and down the capstone a few times as if looking for a good answer. In truth, he was wondering if it soon would be no longer allowed to stand on top of the dolmen. "Too bad," he muttered.

"What?"

"Ah! No. Not that. I'm sorry. Well, first of all, Andrea, this Beingness, or this $\overline{S}$elf, is not something you reach or accomplish. It's simply ever there. It wasn't ever not there. We have merely brought it back to your attention and offered you a means to frequently revisit it."

"Oh."

"Also," said the One with the cosmos, "it is not to be regarded as an improvement or an upgrade or something, you know, like 'superior' or a preferred state. You can't add muscle to it, and neither can you add intelligence or agility to it. It simply is 'That', and 'That' is perfect as it is. We shouldn't underestimate it, and we also shouldn't overrate it."

"I don't agree," said One.

"You don't?" The cosmos fell on the ground.

"Nah, of course I do. I just wanted to disagree for the sake of disagreeing. Was fun. Here, your flower. Shouldn't drop it like that. Poor thing."

"Right," sighed the One with the raven. "So when I said 'first of all', I said it with the intention of a 'secondly'. Here goes: And secondly, dearest Andrea&co, we haven't even come to the Truth yet. What you are suggesting is that we stop here and now. Close the book. Forget all about the 289 pages which are still waiting for us. Toss it out. Bury it on a shelf."

"At least don't put it between books of the CSDCs, please," pleaded the glowing One. "Put it on the shelf with the travel books. That'd be neat."

The One with the cosmos looked puzzled. "Why do you lot have this compulsive tendency anyway?"

"What compulsive tendency?"

"To jump into every cosy hole that comes across your path. It's like you are all geared up to climb the peak, and then you decide to stay in basecamp near the cosy fire with merry-fellow-climbers, comparing your fancy equipment and clothes, sharing stories about how you all one day will reach the summit for sure."

"Also, Andrea," continued the One with the raven, "when you express this need for permanence, you basically admit to being biased like ever before. You choose. You develop an opinion. 'This $\overline{S}$elf surely is better than the $\underline{s}$elf,' you conclude. So you like to vilify the ego in favour of this non-identity-self. But such a point of view is futile."

"Yeh, it leads nowhere."

"But why?" asked Andrea.

"Because it is a false idea. You can't cast your identity aside. What will you do? Sit on a rock all day with a big smile on your face?"

"Indeed," agreed the One who disagreed before, "the $\underline{s}$elf and the $\overline{S}$elf are not to be separated as two identities."

"They are like two faces of the same coin?" suggested Sven.

"No," replied One. "Such a view is most certainly incorrect. It will confuse you and throw you back into rational meanderings and logical deductions.

Before you know it, you are looking for means to balance it out and develop methods and techniques to do just that. It's a recurring theme in human history."

"And also," added One, "once again, before you know it, you're no longer connected with this Beingness, but with the 'story' about Beingness."

"So, choosing one over the other is like hopping on one leg," shared One. While imitating his words physically, he lost his balance and almost fell down from the dolmen. "Yeh, okay, some are way better at this than me. Thinking about it, many actually do this hopping-on-one-leg rather well. They even convince themselves that it brings them forward. But convenient?"

"Seems to me like you guys just made all our problems way much worse," concluded Kalle while Sven and many others nodded.

"Look," said the One with the raven. "Being withdrawn in Beingness may seem nice and a pleasant state to be achieved. But it becomes a precarious situation when you go hungry or need a new roll of ultra-soft, six-layered toilet paper in the little room."

"I don't understand," snivelled Andrea. "I thought I had it, but now I seem more lost than ever."

"Very good," nodded One. "Very good. So far we have only revealed the first glimpses of the Truth. It would be pretty awkward if you'd understand the bigger picture straight away."

"At this point, the actual experience of Beingness was the most important first step", added One. "Without that, we wouldn't be able to approach the Truth and recognize it as such. So better gird your loins, ya'll; there is more to come."

"Only the first step?" complained Nurse Erin. "That's a 36-kilometre first step! We're not going for another walk again, are we?"

"No need, Nurse Erin," assured One. "No need. Let's all start with a small break, shall we?"

Even before One reached the k in the word break, all spontaneously ran to the tree line across the field in search of some private space to answer nature's call.

"Oh, don't mind me," groaned ol' Cormac who had been left behind. "I'll hold it up."

The Mystical Mages of Infinite Zero remained in silence on top of the dolmen. Only the raven released another gurgling croak. By the sudden warm feeling on his back, the One with the raven realized the bird had released more than just a croak.

Chapter 10 **Something about a pudgy caterpillar's reluctance to become a butterfly**

An eerie fog rolled over the fields at the speed of a galloping horse. The fog had a thickness beyond compare. Andrea could no longer spot her dreadlocks in her peripheral vision. Sven couldn't see Kalle. Kalle couldn't see Sven. Nurse Erin was desperately searching for ol' Cormac, and some simply pinched others next to them to make sure they still existed.

When the fog started to dissipate, Andrea released a sigh of relief. Affectionately, she caressed her dreadlocks while Kalle and Sven both wondered who pinched them. It wasn't long before the Ancient Mystics of Infinite Zero were spotted as well. But then, each and every jaw dropped wide open. Looking over the hoods of the masked figures, they saw a mountain which appeared to be fully covered by a walled city.

The Ancient Mystics of Infinite Zero led the way across a wide plain of grass. On either side, the crowd could spot flocks of sheep scattered across the meadow. A clattering of jackdaws flew over and rattled unknown words at the raven of the One with the raven. On their far left, a young man's husky looked up at the sky with a questioning gaze. Not that the dog had any interest in the jackdaws. He was just wondering what happened to his squeaky toy, which the young man had thrown up (he actually faked the throw). What his master didn't realize was that the clever canine was on to him and faked his looking for the toy. Fooler fooled!

The One with the raven first looked at the jackdaws and then at the raven. The raven just shrugged. Clearly, it was of the opinion that the jackdaws should mind their own business. Nobody in the crowd really understood why the One with the raven was walking all the way at the tail of the group, nor did they get the giggling, guffawing and chortling up ahead amongst the Ones in hooded cloaks and masks.

Half an hour later they all reached the foot of the granite rock. At the entrance, it was as crowded as ever. But the Ancient Mystics of Infinite Zero seemed to know their way around. Instead of squeezing themselves and the crowd through the narrow main street, they soon picked an easily overlooked stairway to the left. This led them to a rather quiet place at the foot of the abbey.

While the crowd all relaxed and sat down, the Ancient Mystics of Infinite Zero mostly found their seats on the battlements of the broad ramparts. From here, they could enjoy an unobstructed view of all those coming to visit the mountain from afar. For a while, they remained silent. Everybody used that moment to simply enjoy being in this wonderful place.

But then, a little chattering started to emerge from within the crowd. Bram Van Nulandt – the Flemish guy, remember? – stated to his Egyptian neighbour how impressed he still was by the Dolmen d'Oppagne. "Can you imagine," he said, "how five thousand years ago people managed to move and position those enormous and heavy stones?" And Marwa Abadi matter-of-factly replied: "Hmm, I don't know. I mean, around that era, the people from my country already had the pyramid of Djoser. It's about 60 meters high." All Bram could reply was: "Oh."

In a similar fashion, Olivia Hart, a gal from Denver, Colorado stated how she happened to know about the local tides. "Can you imagine," she said to Jimmy, "that the incoming tides around here can cross the bay at the speed of a galloping horse?" And Jimmy answered with his fake Irish accent: "I'm not really impressed by that. I've seen fogs doing the very same thing."

"Excuse me," Georges spoke all of a sudden with his thick French accent. "You mentioned how you have only revealed a mere glimpse of the Truth. Would it be a good time to lift the veal a little more now?"

"Very good idea," answered One.

"Although I do suggest to leave the poor little cow on the ground," added the glowing One with a smile. "Let's do some veil-lifting instead."

Georges blushed while the native English speakers in the crowd couldn't suppress a sweet little chuckle.

Lost in thought, the One with the raven gazed at the golden figure atop the abbey's peak. "Up until this far, we spoke about 'perspective' and how we needed to switch it. Now that we've done that, or at least a little bit, it is time to re-evaluate our seeking."

"You see," started the One with the flower, who somehow had traded his cosmos for lavender, "in the beginning, our seeking for Truth started from the perspective of the self."

By the way, you may have noticed that self and S̄elf sound exactly the same yet have a totally different meaning. Therefore, it is vital that you know that each time One speaks out either one of both words, they always add a horizontal stroke to it in the air, being a low one at the height of the solar plexus or a higher one at the level of the eyebrows. Just so you know.

"Indeed," agreed One, "that's how it always starts. Each seeking for Truth, for meaning, purpose, direction or answers to life's questions unavoidably starts from within the identity. In other words, it starts from within you as a person. After all, it is our personality which longs and seeks. It is our individuality which runs into trouble or seeks out solutions for the many dissatisfactions it suffers."

"It is the self which ever chases this illusive joy and happiness which we always seem to be short of," added One with a poetic tone.

"And this is important to realize," emphasized the One with the raven, "otherwise you'll find yourself wandering on the paths of the CSDCs in no time: all you are looking for from the perspective of the self, is your personal need of what Truth should be to you, while that most likely will not be the actual Truth."

"You are simply ever on a chase to satisfy the self," summarized One. "But the self is insatiable. It will have you running from book to book, cult to cult or guru to guru, all because of this inexpressible sense of lack which makes us feel fragmented like we're never where we're supposed to be. We rather choose to dwell in personal fabrications instead."

"Hence," deduced the One with no particular characteristics more graphically, "as a seeker, you are a bit like a gluttonous caterpillar, crawling along all obstacles life and your ever-growing identity presents. This rampant growth comes at the cost of meeting ever more and larger obstacles on the way, if not on the outside, then certainly on the inside. So all you do is eat… in the hope that you grow wings… so you can overcome the many obstacles more easily."

"So the main question is," concluded the One with the lavender. "Will you eat my flower or leave it?"

One agreed. "Indeed." And then disagreed. "Wait, what? That's not the main question!"

"The main question is," said the One with the raven, "Errr… Darn, I forgot."

"I think," started Sven, "you were about to ask us if we are really keen on knowing the Truth or that we simply strive to satisfy our personal needs and worries …"

"… our doubts and our fears …" added Oliva, mimicking the tone the Ancient Mystics of Infinite Zero usually use.

"… our obsessions and our cravings," hissed Bram as Gollum, while the Ancient Mystics of Infinite Zero couldn't suppress laughing out loud.

"So we need to become butterflies?" concluded Marwa matter-of-factly while raising an eyebrow in the direction of Bram. Bram blushed and felt hopeful at the same time. At least he succeeded in getting her attention for the second time in a row.

It was as if, by magic, a butterfly that happened to visit le Mont-Saint-Michel on its holiday landed on One's gloved finger. It was a vanessa atalanta, if you must know, and it happens to be that even butterflies come with spiritual meanings, this one, in particular, having one which seemed very much appropriate for our main topic (look it up).

"Become butterflies?" repeated the One with Vanessa (most of the vanessa atalantas happen to name their offspring Vanessa). "Yes! But here's the difficulty. What the caterpillar will never be able to realize is that it needs to un-become a caterpillar to receive the gift of flying. There simply is no other way."

"And just as a caterpillar can't chóóse to become a butterfly," added the One with the raven, "we can't choose to switch to that perspective which allows an authentic recognition of Truth. It simply happens, given the right circumstances. And then the transformation is complete. It's done."

"One could mysteriously say," said the glowing One, "that the end of the seeking – you know, when Truth is actually discovered – also implies the end of the one who is seeking. Or, one could equally mysteriously say that the one who starts the seeking is not the one who ends it."

"Begging your pardon," said Charles. "I couldn't follow that last bit."

"I think I understand," sounded a new voice. It came from a random tourist who happened to blend in with the crowd shortly after they arrived. "What they are saying is that you start looking for Truth from your identity-self. You know, your personality. Or your ego if you like. The issue is the identity will never accept the real Truth. It will simply reject it because it seems very plausible that the Truth may render the self as something it never thought itself to be. So, basically, it simply goes against its instinct, like your caterpillar. It'd never voluntarily commit suicide in order to become a butterfly. It will do everything to protect its caterpillar-ness, while all the same, it will never stop longing to become a butterfly. Can you imagine that!"

People looked confused, going 'what?' and 'how?' at the words of the newcomer. But the Ancient Mystics of Infinite Zero's nodding prompted the newcomer to continue.

"You see, if you'd 'know' for sure that the end would mean a new beginning, you still wouldn't consider actually ending it yourself. There'd always be that 'naaah, not today, maybe tomorrow', or 'what if that promised new beginning isn't real after all?' "

"That's not right," protested Adebowale. "I've been a seeker for a long time already. And I know the ego is false and needs to be overcome in favour of enlightenment and liberation. I do accept my ego to die!"

"And did it die?" asked the newcomer. Adebowale was a bit lost for words. He meant to say it's a work in progress, but somehow, that seemed an inadequate response.

"Very good," said the One with Vanessa. Now Vanessa wasn't as placid as the raven of the One with the raven. Vanessa was rather a bit more restless, hopping around from finger to shoulder, from shoulder to hood and from hood to finger again. Yet somehow, despite its apparent restlessness, the butterfly seemed to be ever at ease.

Where were we? Ah, "Very good," she repeated. "So you may understand by now, the transformation of the caterpillar is met with great reluctance. And yes, a seeker may surely come to learn he or she is a caterpillar in need of becoming a butterfly. But this knowledge alone will not result in him or her turning into the winged little witch, will it?"

"Absolutely not," giggled the glowing One. "It will surely think itself to be a butterfly and pretend to have wings. And so, the seeker too will think to have reached enlightenment, filled with pride and satisfaction, claiming to have tossed the ego aside."

"And thus, all these folks will construct what one could call a spiritual ego. They fabricate an idea of being unattached, altruistic, humble, loving and liberated. While still, their ego surely is not likely to yield at all, albeit it will be cunning enough to tenaciously pretend it did."

"I see y'all nodding," said the One with no particular characteristics. "But I can assure you, it's exactly those with an elephant of a spiritual ego who always nod in understanding when this topic comes up."

As you can imagine, all stopped nodding instantly. You too, didn't you?

"The caterpillar will crown itself and put on neat jewellery," said the glowing One, "but it will ever remain a caterpillar. Chomp chomp chomp, eat eat eat."

"This is all too ridiculous," said Charles, clearly irritated. "You repeatedly accuse us of walking in circles, but you're not offering any possibility of escape."

"True!" shouted ol' Cormac who had become a bit restless. Nurse Erin hadn't switched his IV yet, and the plastic bag's sides were sticking ominously flat to each other. "Ye say all ur needs and wants are coming from this so-called self. But how can the identity come to forsake itself? Do we all need to turn urselves into a bloody cocoon or something?"

One laughed in a gentle way, as did some others as well.

"We may have made it sound more difficult than it really is," comforted the One with the lavender and Vanessa (you could have predicted yourself the butterfly would at some point land on the lavender). "But rest assured, and you'll discover this soon enough, it really can be easier than it sounds right now."

"On the other hand," said the One with the raven, "it is paramount you understand this chapter. Because most of you are still in this space where we could tell you the Truth in just a single sentence, and nonetheless, all of you would immediately reject it."

"Just imagine I'd say you do not exist," taunted the glowing One. "Just these four words: you – do – not – exist. You would-"

"I'd pinch me nurse in the butt," jested ol' Cormac with a rasping laugh, "She'd immediately prove ya wrong." All laughed except for Nurse Erin. She didn't.

"Laughter is good," said the One with the raven gently. "But we must pierce this issue at its core to remain open to the Truth as it is."

What??? The chapter ends here?

Chapter 11   From caterpillar to butterfly, and heck, from butterfly back to caterpillar again

A bit further, a five-year-old darted back and forth in seemingly random directions. A pink sweater, red trousers and brown shoes coherently flew around as if played by the wind. Her rather short blond hair was held together in a simple, one-inch-long pony. She ran about as if she didn't have a care in the world. Occasionally, she took a short break. While catching her breath, she leaned over a low stone wall with a joyful gaze that swept in every direction. Those who observed her well noticed how her eyes were fixed on a host of sparrows. The birds appeared to be engaged with her in what seemed like an intricate game of tag and hide & seek. For many of the older spectators, the girl radiated a joy that reminded them of their own carefree childhood. Some of them wore a smile which lasted until the end of the day.

"How can it be less difficult than it sounds?" pondered Mykhailo Niktonov from Estonia. Now, Mykhailo happened to be an Olympic athlete. He could hold his body suspended in the air using nothing but two metal rings on ropes. With his arms horizontally stretched out! Upside down! For three minutes! He was basically the guy who rewrote 'impossible' into 'I'm possible'. Nonetheless, despite all his strength, it seemed he had come across the biggest hurdle life could present: himself.

"I mean," continued Mykhailo, "here we are, caterpillars, munching our way around. We all want to become butterflies. We love to become butterflies. We even need to become butterflies. We…"

"… yeh yeh yeh, we get yer point," growled ol' Cormac. "Now get to it, will ya."

Unruffled by the old man in the wheelchair, Mykhailo continued. "We even come to believe we 'are' butterflies, while still… we remain nothing but caterpillars. It even seems that – when push comes to shove? – we actually don't really want to become butterflies because then the caterpillar dies. And we can't let go of our caterpillar-ness. So, I don't get it. How do we become butterflies if the ego prevents us from becoming one?"

"When you think of it like this," pondered Andrea. "it is actually utterly absurd. Getting rid of the ego is merely one of the many needs we have as a person. So basically, from within our ego, we decide we want to get rid of the ego. And then, when we embark on this ridiculous quest, we eventually sabotage ourselves. Of course we do. Because our ego never really had the intention to destroy itself. It was just playing along. Why, it's so silly! It's like Charles said. We are running in circles… and we love it."

"I'd say it's a good summary, no?" One prodded One.

"A very good summary indeed," agreed One while he prodded One in return. "And very important questions, too!"

"Wait a minute," interrupted Kalle. "Hang on. Hang on. It's too much at once. So… So we are incapable of becoming a butterfly?"

"On the contrary," corrected One gently. "You are all perfectly capable of becoming one. Even more, you've been there already."

"You mean after those exercises we did near Wéris?" asked Andrea.

"No," answered One. "Well, yes, then too. A little. Or a lot. Depends. But you have been there before that as well. It has happened to all of you. And it happens more frequently than you'd expect."

"It happens in those rare, little moments when the radiant light of consciousness outshines the searchlight of the identity," added the One with the raven. "These glimpses of butterfly-ness are touched when the identity-self drops the need of being in control, in those peculiar moments where it finds itself more or less at ease, untroubled by identification or maintaining any identity at all."

"An episode of wonder," said the One with the lavender. "Unattended contemplation. A state of flow. Dancing. Beauty. An experience of profound gratitude. It can essentially be any moment in which one loses the self in favour of something that evokes this transcendental state we call Beingness."

"This state of being," continued One, "is mostly reached unintentionally.

And still, it is more satisfying than any intention could promise."

"Absolutely," cheered the glowing One. "A subtle ease will envelop you, akin to a sense of calmness or even profound peace. Some will come to experience it as a serene interlude of untroubled joy."

"Others will feel it like a deep sensation of silence. It's not the absence of sound. It's rather a sort of silence which can even be found in the loudest environment possible. It's more like the inner chatter simply ceases to be. The thinking ones amongst you may think there is no existence without thinking, but in reality, there's no deeper existence possible."

"I remember," exclaimed Mykhailo with wide, happy eyes. "I do have experienced that! Oh my God, I've been a butterfly!"

Mykhailo laughed happily with his own silly expression, as did everyone else in the crowd. Each of them could recall having experienced such moments themselves.

"Wait!" shouted Andrea while raising her index finger. "I think I've got it. I've got it! The contradiction! It's not a contradiction at all."

"What contradiction?" asked Kalle.

"Why, us trying to destroy the ego, of course; it is basically the same thing as saying the ego is trying to destroy itself. It doesn't make any sense, right? But that's simply because we've got this all wrong. This intention of destroying or getting rid of something, it's nothing but a misinterpretation of something real but hidden underneath. You see, it's not about eradicating something, not at all."

"But what is it about?" pleaded Kalle, who got all anxious.

"It's our S̄elf longing for itself! It's a pure, instinctive longing. Wordless and natural. But then, our mind picks it up in an attempt to wrap itself around it. And then, the ego joins in because it feels frustrated and wants to solve it. But it can't. It's not that it's evil or is intentionally blocking us. It simply can't comply because ending the frustration means hitting a self-destruct button. And that button isn't there. It's futile. We really need to stop this silliness."

Kalle's mouth dropped wide open. "An.. Andrea? Are… Are you one of them without the cloak, the gloves, the hood and the mask?"

The Ancient Mystics of Infinite Zero exploded in laughter.

"Beautiful!" chorused the glowing One. "Well done, Andrea! Well done. We have finally found the right place from where to continue our looking for Truth!"

"Took us about eighty pages to get here," sneered One ironically. "About time, I'd say."

Charles wasn't the slightest impressed. "Continue our looking for Truth?" he queried. "By God, man, I thought we were there now."

"There?" reiterated the One with the raven. "My dearest Charles, we haven't even started yet."

Ol' Cormac's chin landed on his chest with a huge sigh. "Oi oi oi," he sighed for a second time. "All this walking around from hither to yon and all for naught."

Nurse Erin couldn't resist passing him an evil eye.

"Oh, but we made a huge leap forward now," encouraged the glowing One. "You see, this switch of perspective when we truly realize where our longing is coming from is of the utmost importance to discover and recognize the Truth. Without it, you would never be able to see it. You'd be wandering around following spiritual-this and religion-that, always looking for a solution from the perspective of your ego, ever claiming the path you're on to be the best, that is… until the next one appears."

"Yeh," nodded the One with the lavender. "Not to mention the CSDCs who are always lurking around to lure you into their silliness, even if you vowed to never do that again." He briefly took the lavender out of his mouth and rhetorically nodded at the other Ones. "True, isn't it? They all do."

"This switch really is important," concluded One while casting a never-mind-him glance at the One with the lavender. "From the perspective of me me me, want want want, need need need, you were only capable of seeing – and accepting – 'a' truth that meets your current state of personhood."

"In other words," added One, "your personal, opinionated and needy source of seeking for Truth could never allow you to actually find it. That's what we already said in the very beginning."

"Therefore," continued One, "you need to touch a sort of different dimension. A place from where your looking no longer aims to satisfy your needs. Once you connect with this ever latent and authentic source of seeking, Truth can be unveiled, or rather, It can be realized and experienced."

"And the ego dies?" tried Bram.

"No no, Bram. See, what happens there is that your ego is not obliterated or anything silly of the kind. Your ego, your identity-self, it will automatically yield. Simple as that. It will give in simply because the state of Beingness, the state of the $\overline{S}$elf, is so overwhelming."

"Overwhelming indeed, but note also, without being enforcing about it. It happens in the most gentle way possible and, at the same time, the most effective as well. One could say the seeker from that point on is almost literally reborn."

"Party!!!" shouted Andrea. And soon enough, the crowd picked up her silly dance moves. They cheered. They laughed. They were happy.

"The problem is…" Dancing stopped. Cheering too. You can imagine what happened to the laughing.

"Oh dear, yes, the problem," added the One with Vanessa to the One with no particular characteristics with a sigh. (That is, the One with Vanessa sighed. The sigh is certainly not characteristic of the One with no characteristics; otherwise, it would be plain silly to refer to him in such a way.)

"It doesn't last."

"What doesn't last?" asked Sven.

"The switch! The experience that transcends your identity and allows you to see and accept the Truth. It doesn't last. In mere minutes or hours at best, it will collapse again."

"It's like me pills!" croaked ol' Cormac. "At first, it's great. And then it all comes back again. And ya think this evil nurse here will give me a new one when I ask for it? Nooo, sirree."

"Anyways," said One. "After you collapse into the <u>s</u>elf again, you will soon enough – not immediately, I can say that, but soon enough – you will discover deep within yourself this lingering urge to return to that state of peace and happiness once more."

"It'll feel like you had this important dream, and the memory of it eludes you, no matter what you try. It's like Andrea said, your mind will try to wrap itself around it, but it will not succeed. You just can't get back to it."

"That's correct," nodded One. "Try as you may, this transcendence seems impossible to rekindle."

"I knoooow," enunciated Erin. "It's soooo frustrating. Why is that?"

"It's simple," answered One. "You're once again starting from the wrong place. Any intention you have, it starts from within the <u>s</u>elf. And any intention from within the <u>s</u>elf is ever accompanied by a sort of control. It's like you are clutching the reins and forcing the horse to go in any direction but the one it really needs."

"Oh, so frustrating," enunciated Erin again. She clearly needed to vent a bit. "I just hate it. I can feel so disconnected at times." Ol' Cormac peered up at her through narrowed eyelids. Usually, his nurse was the rather quiet one.

"Same here," confirmed Charles. "At times, I can have this puzzling feeling of unease. It's a pretty weird thing, actually. Everything in my life seems to be in order, best as can be, and still, there's that eerie feeling that something is missing. It's like amidst all that defines me as the person I am, I somehow have lost touch with the essential me, if that makes any sense."

"That's not a bad thing at all," comforted the glowing One with her sweet, feminine voice (you probably forgot she's a girl, didn't you?). "It's exactly that feeling of unease – that mystical longing – which will guide you homewards."

"That is if you are lucky," scoffed the One with the lavender. "More often than not, the reborn seeker simply reincarnates in the same idiot once again. Before you realize it, you're back to buying or selling solutions and fabrications that are trending in the moment."

"There, there," hushed the glowing One, the One with the lavender. "Let's not get gloomy. You sound like a broken record. Perhaps you'd better chew on a poppy instead."

"Indeed," said One. "Let's also not forget we claimed that people are perfectly capable of discovering the Truth all by themselves becau-"

"Wait a minute," interrupted Charles. "I think I finally get it. Basically, you are saying, this experience of Beingness is not the Truth, but a means to... be able to... see Truth, right?"

"Spot on!" confirmed the One with the raven. "And once you've really been there, I mean really, not as a judgemental spectator, but as pure Presence, the recognition of Truth is within arm's reach for sure. It will hit you when you expect it the least. It cannot not happen."

Charles squeezed his eyes shut while his face got all wrinkled. "But... I mean, why is that?"

"Because you merge with it. It's like meeting yourself in the street. 'Oh, I know you. You are me.'"

"So everybody can see this for themselves? Without any guides or whatsoever?"

"Absolutely, Charles. Like we already said, it all starts from this intangible longing from deep within. This hidden urge to reconnect with your source essence, so to speak."

"This longing," continued the glowing One, "is a longing beyond rational ideas or mental constructs. In its authenticity, it's a longing which no longer seeks to destroy or erase, fix or improve or change anything about anything at all. It's a longing which accepts. It's genuine and sincere. It allows. And in this accepting and allowing, it no longer meets resistance or needs to be fulfilled. The direction of your consciousness-energy is gradually changed from being limited, focused and constrained to being receptive, self-sufficient and unattached."

"And right here," said the One with the raven, "in this gradual transcendence of the perceptibly yielding ego, the Seeker Reborn can take flight. It is this peculiar openness which changes the game entirely. It brings us outside of the box with no boundaries whatsoever, simply because this particular kind of openness is not looking to be filled up again. It finds contentment in emptiness itself."

"But… But…," stammered Sven, "How?" That last word came out as a long, loud whisper if you can imagine a whisper to be loud. "I mean, do we simply wait for it to happen again?"

"That'll take ages," vented Olivia. "I mean, yes, I've had such experiences myself, yeah, but like, well, I can't even remember the last time."

"We're all doomed," mimicked One C3PO. Another One said the same thing in the language of R2D2 (but there is simply no way to write this down). The other Ones laughed. The crowd didn't. On the contrary, a disturbing chatter started to rise from several little groups. It was Charles's voice, which seemed the loudest, complaining about running in circles yet again.

"There, there, now. It will not take ages," shushed One. "It is actually far from impossible to fall into this state of transcendence."

"It is," assured the One with the lavender. "You can repeat it as much as you like. It's not even hard."

"But please don't expect any intricate methods or other sorts of spiritual cleverness," added One. "Simplicity is the key!"

"Let's stop all this lecturing for a moment and fall into it," suggested One. And so, after the glowing One gave some basic instructions to shake off all frustration, the One with the raven readied all for some exercises. Within mere minutes, all fell into this profound state of Beingness. The secret exercises were totally different from the ones given before, yet they were equally effective.

And no, they will not be revealed here. – Sorry, no can do.

Chapter 12 Through the eyes of the butterfly (which will feel a bit weird – adapted glasses will be offered in Part 2)

The Ancient mystics of Infinite Zero felt a short walk was exactly what everybody needed (except for Ol' Cormac, that is). They guided the crowd through narrow alleys, leading them further upwards. Just as before, it was Mykhailo and Adebowale who lifted Ol' Cormac, wheelchair and all, across the stairs under the supervising eye of Nurse Erin.

It wasn't long before they reached le terrasse de l'Ouest. There, they regrouped in the open space in front of the entrance to the abbey church. Tourists came and went, strolling around, looking over the ramparts and taking thousands of pictures and selfies before heading into the church.

The Ancient Mystics of Infinite Zero took a seat on the edges of the U-formed upper level. The crowd silently gathered on the most western side of the terrace. From there, looking down over the ramparts, they could see their previous spot where they had made 'the switch'.

The little sparrow-girl had also made her way up to the terrace. A man was chasing her, as well as a slightly older girl. Screaming for their lives, they zigzagged between the tourists to escape his clutches. Luckily, a woman appeared to be filming the whole thing. But the girls quickly got bored when the man needed to take a break. Only then did the older girl notice the Ancient Mystics of Infinite Zero. At first, she could only stare at them for a while. Then she decided to move closer.

"Are you going to perform a magic trick?" she asked while her younger sister came hiding behind her. Both had the same pink sweater and the same blond hair. Their cheeks were still red from running around.

84

"A trick?" replied the One who performs magic tricks (what a coincidence!). "Well, well, well. Why not?"

The One who performs magic tricks retrieved a deck of cards from inside his cloak, shuffled it and fanned it out. "Pick a card, please. But make sure I don't see it."

The girl picked a card and held it against her chest. Her little sister leaned over her shoulder to get a peek.

"Are you holding a red lady with hearts all around her?" guessed the One who performs magic tricks after he took a quick peek at the back of the deck.

The girl, however, had spotted the move. "I know that trick! My daddy already showed it to me. It's some Sy-Step-Ins-thing or something." She handed the queen of hearts back to the cloaked and hooded figure.

All Ones laughed while the One who performs magic tricks tucked his deck back into his cloak. "Damn fathers," he softly growled. "Stealing away an honest conman's living."

The girls giggled and ran off with their parents into the church.

"Anyone else a card trick?" begged the One who was about to quit performing magic tricks.

"Better not now," advised the One with the chicory flower (now, where did he manage to get that???). "Best to stay in this vibe of Beingness we just created."

"Aye, let's stay in the vibe and get on with it, will ya," croaked ol' Cormac. He lifted his cane to emphasize his eagerness. Nurse Erin managed to dodge it just in time. All were baffled by her agility. She clearly had a lot of practice.

"Ok, let's do this," started the One with the raven. "Now that we're all still in the zone, it's good to sit down for a moment and relax."

"Be warned," said the One with the chicory flower, "Truth is a bit like fire. The first contact can cause you to pull back in an uncontrollable reflex. But you'll learn soon enough to appreciate its warmth when handled properly."

"Very good," said the One with the raven, looking left and right at all seated. With a deeper voice, he continued at a slower pace. "Now, please gently close your eyes.

Let's go within first before we start with everything around us. Truth can be discovered within and without. So, please, allow yourself to come home again in the S̄elf, the non-identity, you in your essence, completely unattached from anything appearing within the self. Sense this Beingness. It just is. You just are. Nothing to add. Nothing to subtract.

Observe your thoughts. I am sure many of you didn't even notice you still had any. But you have. Notice their ceaseless appearance. Their rise and fall.

Notice how your most basic feelings are all there as well, somewhere in the background, ready to pop up whenever they like. See how they can be observed just as well within the field of your looking.

See how you and your thoughts are not the same thing. See how you and your emotions are not the same. It is not that they exist independently of you like you'd be able to amputate them or something. It is not like that. It's different. It is more like… they actually seem to be just a tiny fragment… within the vastness you are experiencing now.

Notice… how each and every one of these immeasurably complex aspects… used to appear bigger than life. They all seemed to be so all-encompassing, pressing and important… while in reality… in this vastness of your S̄elf, they are but mere grains of sand… each only pretending to be rocks… boulders… or even mountains. This illusory immensity… of all these identity aspects… is the main cause of your feelings of confinement... and lack thereof.

But not this time. From within the S̄elf, you come to experience how all boundaries and limitations are blown away. There is freedom... an actual liberation... and the joy experienced there can only be described as... a state of bliss.

Your True Self, your Essence Nature, it is not something you once more need to become... like yet again, an upgrade... or improvement. It rather is this quiet emptiness which was ever there... and somehow envelops all of what you call your identity, with ample space left. It simply is boundless, abundantly present... and timeless as well. There is no choosing between s̲elf and S̄elf. You are the S̄elf. And the s̲elf is merely a fragment of your totality.

You see, from within the s̲elf, you could never succeed in removing all the sticky notes. Removing one would only cause another to land on that spot. When you recognize and experience your True Self, it is as if the sticky notes all drop away at once. In reality, you will see, it's not that they really disappeared or dissolved. It's more like the radiant light of your purest presence simply outshines them all.

Immerse yourself deeper into this vibrant nothingness. Even the highest waves, all caused by your identity, are just tiny ripples in the ocean of this I am-ness. Linger there just a little longer... You as the Seer... purest presence... awareness in all its authenticity... you are ever dynamically at rest.

Notice now how this rising and falling of thoughts and feelings is less rich in number as you would dare to admit. You may believe yourself to have thousands of thoughts and feelings each day... in reality, they are but a limited series of possibilities... appearing and disappearing within your particular individuality. The same ones pop up in a constant loop, aiming to solicit for your attention once again after you only recently discarded them.

Now... look a little deeper. Try to see their origin. Trace each thought down to its roots. Did it just pop out of nowhere? Or is there a cause for their rising? Try not to collapse in the thoughts themselves now. Remain at a distance and simply observe the causalistic patterns.

Track them down... not only all the way to their source... but also to how they later on repeatedly are triggered, again and again. See how a complex narrative reveals itself if only you take enough distance. The cause of all your thinking... and feeling... and needing... it sometimes is clear as crystal... while on other occasions, it can seem pretty arbitrary. Arbitrary or impenetrable, obvious or straightforward, when you continue to look from beyond, you will start to notice how every inner event inevitably unfolds from the previous. No matter what direction it goes, there is always something pushing it in that particular way.

Look back at all the times when you did step into these thoughts and ran along with them. See the pattern. See how your running with it could not have gone any other way than it did. Regardless of it being causalistically either clear or undefinable, you distinctly sense every inner event couldn't unfold any other way.

Please, don't collapse into thinking or analysing. Simply remain present. Do not expect any immediate insights or conclusions. This type of observing needs more time... and frequent repetition. At first, your mind will spin numerous objections. Your observing is still coming mostly from your identity. The more you manage to shift into the position of the uninvolved seer, the less need there will be for impulsive objections. A peculiar clarity will dawn instead.

In time, this particular open-minded clarity… it will allow careful scrutiny during rational musings. It will also allow the non-mental experience to deepen. To sink in. Eventually, you will come to recognize how every occurrence within the s̲elf… is undeniably causalistic in nature. And at the very same time, you will come to recognize, as well, how the S̄elf … somehow seems to be free of these causalistic patterns. It simply is and ever remains as 'that'.

From a strictly mental perspective, this causeless state of being may sound as boring as hell. However, you will see, from within the experience, one can't find more aliveness and more presence than this. This S̄elf… this aliveness… this presence… this profound experience of Beingness, it transcends any causal event. It transcends love. It transcends happiness. It has a crystalline, heartbreaking purity which simply can't be shared by descriptive means – it has to be experienced, it has to be felt."

An all-encompassing silence fell over the terrace of le Mont-Saint-Michel. Even the tourists passed along in a respectful, subdued silence. It didn't last long, though. Ol' Cormac slowly lifted one butt cheek. The sound produced was of this particular nature, where one tends to doubt whether anything actually landed or not. The noses of those nearby went into the funniest wrinkles. Only Nurse Erin had managed to pinch hers just in time.

"Wow!" exclaimed Olivia, who missed the ol' Cormac commotion. "That was quite a ride."

"Quite a ride?" sneered Jimmy. "It's bollocks! This can't be right! It's a trick, I'm telling ya! I have no idea what you mystic-lot are trying to make us see, but it sure feels like a dirty trick!"

Andrea couldn't hold herself any longer. She hadn't even heard what Jimmy just said. "By god! You weren't joking all along! I really don't exist. And at the same time, I am nothing but existence."

"Ah, come on!" scoffed Jimmy. "They clearly paid you to say that!"

"Actually…" intervened the One who is writing all this. But then he faltered as all eyes turned in his direction. His majestic presence was simply overwhelming. The jaws of all men and women simply fell open when he started saying 'actually'. You didn't notice him before? How strange.

"Okay, okay, forget about me. Please carry on," he said when he noticed how all kept staring at him. "I have notes to take."

"It's no trick, Jimmy," said the One who quit performing magic tricks. "The only trick being played is the trick of our minds. Remember the two girls who saw straight through the card trick? They saw through it, and it took the magic away. However, seeing through the trick the self plays with us, does exactly the opposite. It reveals the real magic. It doesn't take it away."

"I must agree with them, Jimmy-boy," asserted ol' Cormac. "When the two of us look at one another through the eyes of ur silly, little identities, we only see two men who abandoned their country. But when I look at ya through the eyes of this beingness-stuff, we are the same. What'd ya think of that, lad! We are brooooootheeeers!!!" (imagine Sean Connery in Highlander).

The One with the raven couldn't stifle a chuckle. "Yes, my friend," he then nodded. "Beingness, the experience of the $\overline{S}$elf, it is consciousness in its purest form. And, as you point out so well, we all have this purity in common. It is, so to speak, colourless or transparent in nature — isn't it Sven? — whereas regular, identified consciousness is always more in a specific state, coloured by what we make of what we see, coloured by our thinking, coloured by our feelings and emotions. One could say Beingness encompasses a form of boundless liberty in contrast to the rigidity of all the patterns taking shape in our identity-self. — Hmm, with this last sentence, one could also say I'm not making any sense at all while I do."

"That's the thing," added One while ignoring that last bit. "We may believe these patterns to be of our own design. But soon enough, they prove to have this tendency to become rigid and sculpt us into a solidified state we call 'personality'."

"And there's nothing that consumes more life-energy than maintaining this personality-thingy. You'd think maintaining a house and having a family takes a lot, but you have no idea! Psychiatrists, mental coaches, and all people like that can testify this to be true!"

"Except that, as much as they want to, these specialists hardly help out. They only pass out different brooms and stuff to continue maintaining your identity. They hand you tools and methods to shape an even bigger one…"

"A better version of you. Happier, more efficient, more assertive, more, improved, and perfect. But all they do is give you even more to maintain. More to uphold."

Then the inevitable happened! In fact, it was already long overdue.

"Hi there," said a sweet-looking old man. He just popped up out of the blue from behind the seated Ancient Mystics of Infinite Zero. His cheeks were glowing red above his neatly trimmed, white goatee. He was a bit corpulent and certainly not the tallest person on the planet. The whole picture made him fit the profile of the merriest fellow on earth. "I couldn't help overhearing how you all discovered your True Self? How great is that! Absolutely wonderful!"

The Ancient Mystics of Infinite Zero sat with their heads propped on their hands and their elbows resting on their knees, deciding to sit this one out. They knew there was no escaping the CSDCs.

"My name is Gregg Tea. Doctor (!) Gregg Tea. But you can call me Dr. T."

Now, as it happens, Dr. T. was indeed a doctor. He got that degree at a university ages ago. He also got it on a totally different topic than the one he was about to sell now. It's a bit like a guy offering you to repair your bicycle and then charging you double because he happens to be an historian with a PhD. Basically, it's a clear tell-tale of a CSDC, yet we all tend to fall for it.

"I beg your pardon," said Dr. T. to the One who is writing all this, "but if I may just have a few words, I'd appreciate it, thank-you-very-much."

"So," continued Dr. T. while addressing the crowd again. "Isn't that wonderful! Your True Self! It's an a-ma-zing discovery, isn't it? Now, I happen to be both a scientist and an expert on spirituality. As such, I have developed this bridge between both, which is absolutely amazing. I, I mean 'we' – there is more of us – 'we' can help you to develop your True Self in such a way that you can actually heal all physical ailments you suffer. There simply are no limits to it. We can help you unlock…"

Dr. T seemed to be searching for words. He grabbed a deck of cards with keywords out of his pocket and quickly shifted through them. "Ah yes," he then said, relieved, "We can help you unlock your true 'potential'! Isn't that something?"

"Can this 'True Self' heal an illness like cancer?" asked Yvonne. She happened to have cancer, which was rather unfair given she only just celebrated her 38th birthday.

"Can the True Self heal cancer?" repeated Dr. T. as if it was the silliest question ever. "Of course it can! We use special quantum techniques which work on the cellular level. By using your mind, you can actually change your cells. How amazing is that! Thousands have done it before you."

By now, the crowd was completely mesmerized. Perhaps you are as well?

"Here's the thing. About twenty years ago we discovered an ancient code in ancient writings of ancient people with ancient knowledge. This secret code matches our recent findings on quantum mechanics in such a way it was astonishing. We were totally baffled by it. Even as we speak, many scientists are still trying to unlock these secrets, but 'we' already have. And 'we' can teach you to apply them for yourselves. If you just follow me, I will lead you on this most amazing journey for a special price."

Now, you there in your cosy hammock, reading this book only because you are unable to roll out of the clumsy thing. You probably think this is too obvious. You wouldn't fall for it in a zillion years, right? Rest assured. You would. You can take our word for it. And the more educated you are, the more likely it is. Really weird, isn't it?

"I'm in," Yvonne decided. Reinvigorated, she got up and joined Dr. T. on the upper terrace. Some others first hesitated, looked left and right, scratched the back of their heads, shrugged their shoulders and then got up as well. Soon enough, Dr. T. was backed by a small group of people willing to give this a shot: a girl, the daring questioner, the decent bloke, the husband and his poking wife, the archetype of nerdiness, a tall man, a short man, the long-bearded, old man, the blind spectator, a middle-aged man and nearly all of the Americans.

Jimmy stared at the people who followed Dr. T. For a moment, he didn't know what to do. Then, he addressed the Ancient Mystics of Infinite Zero. "I'm not sure, guys. I mean, I still think you lot are trying to trick us. But... following that other guy doesn't seem right either."

"Yeh," agreed ol' Cormac. "That sneaky fella up there is a trickster for sure. I can smell one over me own smell anytime."

"Well, alright," said Dr. T. undisturbed. "If you change your mind, just look me up. Dr. Gregg Tea. I'm always there for you."

And so, Dr. T. and his newfound followers left.

"How can you let them leave like that?" sniffed Olivia. "You should've stopped them."

"Remember, dear, we're not here to convince you of anything," clarified the One with the raven. "We only answer your questions with nothing less than the Truth. And you're free to do whatever you like with that."

"Now you're not only tricking us," chided Jimmy. "You're mocking us as well! 'Free to do whatever,' he said. While they just proved how our freedom has become a very shaky thing to say the least. Still can't wrap my mind around it. Ah, bollocks, where did that T.-fella run off to? I should've gone with him."

"Depressing conclusion that is." The One with no particular characteristics mimicked Master Yoda. "Much to learn still, you have."

"Much to learn, indeed," concluded the One with Vanessa. "I say it is time for the butterfly to lift off."

Chapter 13 The butterfly takes flight

"Vanessa? – Vanessa?" The One with the butterfly was walking over the terrace from left to right, up and down, looking over the ramparts in all possible directions. "Va-nes-saaaaaaa!!!" she yelled.

Clearly, Vanessa had taken flight at the exact moment she wasn't paying attention. The One without Vanessa – well, we can't call her the One with, can we? – was becoming more worried by the minute. She even ran into the church, asking people if they happened to have seen a vanessa atalanta.

Then the One without Vanessa came out again, sulking and head bowed down. "I just hate those chapters with the number 13."

The One who was writing all this didn't seem happy either. "Damn publishers can't even make such a chapter start on an odd page."

Chapter 14   This time, the other butterfly takes flight

Far south, on the road to le Mont-Saint-Michel, a double-decker bus approached. In front of it drove a classic VW Campervan. It soon became clear both vehicles belonged together as each carried the logo of the CLF.

"Ah," said the One with the raven. "Time to take the bus. Chop chop, everybody! Let's head down again."

When the crowd and the Mystical Mages of Infinite Zero arrived at the front gate, the bus and the VW Campervan stood already waiting for them, with doors wide open. Both drivers were standing in front of their respective vehicles, each wearing a hooded cloak and the typical smiling mask.

The crowd and some of the Mystical Mages of Infinite Zero serenely boarded the bus via the front door.

"Typical," muttered Jimmy while stepping back out of the bus, as all seats were already taken. "They even trick me into stepping into a bus that is already full."

The glowing One stuck her head out of the classic VW Campervan. "Hey Jimmy," she shouted while thumping on the side of the van. "There's one more seat in here!"

It turned out a seat became vacant as the raven refused to enter the Campervan. For the One with the raven, there was no other option but to sit on top of it. His legs dangled in front of the passenger seat window. For the One in the passenger seat, there was no other option than to stick out his head during the entire ride. And so it was that Jimmy sat in the middle of the Mystical Mages of Infinite Zero while the VW Campervan led the double-decker bus back to the mainland.

"Excellent," said One, mimicking Jimmy's fake Irish accent. "This way, we can keep a real good eye on ya, ye cheeky wee devil." All Mystical Mages of Infinite Zero chuckled. Jimmy didn't dare to utter another word. With arms crossed and shoulders lifted, he sat squeezed in between the glowing One and the One with no particular characteristics. All he could move were his eyes, and his eyes regularly went from left to right and right to left, eying the masked figures who were determined to keep an eye on him. The same thoughts kept spinning in his head: "They're going to dump me into some swamp. I'm sure that's what they do with those who disagree with them."

The atmosphere on the double-decker bus was much more relaxed. The One with the chicory flower had picked up the microphone in the front and used it for the typical silliness one can hear on those typical road trips.

"Ladies and gentlemen, when you all look to your left, you will not be able to see a husky being chased by sheep on your right." The sheep happened to be chased by a man. He desperately tried to keep his silly hat on his head with one hand while the dog's leash dangled around in his other. The man, in his turn was chased by the two girls we saw earlier. They giggled like crazy and seemed to be having the greatest fun. And last but not least, a woman was trying to keep up while holding on to all the coats and rucksacks of her company.

"Well how about that," was all Olivia could say while the frivolous train of humans and animals disappeared from sight.

"All feet up!" yelled the One with the chicory flower through the microphone when they crossed a river on the highway.

Instead of feet, a lot of right arms went up (there also were a few lefties here and there). It turned out the toilet was out of order, and a lot of folks simply had to go. Of course, they had just passed an 'Aire' with toilets. In the back of the bus, Murphy chuckled.

Luckily, the double-decker bus and the classic VW Campervan soon enough managed to park at the next 'Aire', which also had a gas station, a shop and a restaurant. The crowd stepped out less serenely than they had stepped in. Some dashed for the toilets, while others were more relaxed and went for a stretch between picnic tables on freshly mowed grass.

When all finally regrouped, the Mystical Mages of Infinite Zero invited the crowd to sit with them on a stretched-out hill edging the 'Aire'. From there, they had a good overview of the whole scenery. Somehow, poor

Jimmy found himself squeezed in once again between the glowing One and the One with no particular characteristics.

"What's with Jimmy?" Bram asked Marwa. Initially, as a way to start a conversation, he intended to ask her why the sky was blue. Luckily for him, he decided to go for Jimmy at the very last minute.

"I'm not sure," answered Marwa. "I am having difficulty with the whole thing myself as well. I mean, I felt it all the way, and somehow I 'know' it to be right. But on the other hand, I somehow fail to see the implications of the whole thing. It's like Jimmy's brain is working faster than mine and he already did. Or, he didn't 'feel' it the way I did. I just can't tell which one of both it is."

"Wow, Marwa," said Bram in admiration. "That's really deep what you say there. I bet you are expressing it exactly the way many of us feel right now."

This made Marwa blush a bit. She suddenly felt more inclined to stick to this Flemish guy who repelled her a bit at first.

But then Bram made a big mistake. Raising his voice towards the Mystical Mages of Infinite Zero, he asked: "I'm having trouble seeing 'the implications' of our last exercise. Could you perhaps elaborate on that a bit?"

"We certainly can", answered the glowing One delightfully while Marwa crossed her arms and looked the other way. "But perhaps we can do that later."

"Indeed," agreed One. "At this point, it's better to pierce through all the way."

"Let's take off and fly little butterflies," whooped the glowing One. "Time to look down at the world." (nobody noticed the slight sob of the One without Vanessa)

"Very well," started the One with the raven gently. "Return to being aware of your breath. Isn't it wonderful how it is always there for you?"

"Ol' Cormac?" prodded One. "You still breathing too?" All Mystical Mages of Infinite Zero couldn't suppress grinning out loud.

"Darn right, I'm still breathing," spat ol' Cormac back. "And I will not stop before the last page is written, that is, if it's up to me, of course."

"And Nurse Erin!" shouted Kalle from a distance. All laughed while Nurse Erin's face spoke 'Well, I'm not too sure about that'.

"Very well, very well," repeated the One with the Raven. "As I was saying, the breath. Notice its presence. Observe how the mere noticing of it has a tranquil effect on your state of being."

"Now, look around," he continued after a few minutes. "Consciously notice everything that comes in range of your sight.

Keep looking while you distance yourself. Distance yourself from each and every person in your view. Distance yourself from any opinion, any idea or any belief about anything happening in front of you.

Look how people arrive. Look how people leave. Look at their actions. See how some just get out of the car and stretch a bit. See the faces of reluctant teenagers. See people holding hands. See laughter. See frustration.

See what people buy or have brought along for the trip. See them talking. Keep looking without becoming involved in any possible way.

See the clouds pass by. See the leaves rustling in the trees. See a napkin floating away. See the smoking cigarette left behind on the ground. Remember, do not get involved.

Observe. Simply see how one moment flows into the next.

Now, ask yourself while looking at everything simply happening. Could it have happened any other way?

Is it all one continuous flow? Or can you detect certain glitches which change the outcome of the events as they occur?

Look deeper. See people's thoughts. See the food in their stomach being digested. See air flowing in and out of their lungs. See how their bones move. See the cells of their bodies. See the atoms vibrating in these cells.

See the continuous, uninterruptable flow of wholeness. One moment, flowing into the next, and into the next, and into the next. Unstoppable. Indivisible."

Many in the crowd were so absorbed in this observing that they didn't even notice how the One with the raven had become silent for quite a while. Then he continued.

"Very good. Now, allow yourself to become involved again. Notice your feelings when you see the hugging old couple. Notice your opinion about the unfinished French Fries being left behind on the picnic table. The burning cigarette in the grass. The unleashed dog taking a dump right next to it. The young boy stepping into it. The mother making a big fuss about it. The sister crying because she lost the attention of her mother. The father stressed out because he now needs to take care of his daughter while he was already craving a second smoke."

"Boy, I'm not having any luck here," the One with the raven whispered to One near him.

"Hang on," whispered the One who is writing all this. "Let me remedy this."

"Oh, cool," whispered the One with the raven, who continued in his guiding voice: "Notice the handsome young man proposing to his beautiful girlfriend. Notice the little girl handing a flower to the bearded musician playing guitar. Notice the wife sending her husband back to clean up his mess.

Notice the rising of your opinions. Witness how the feelings of others are mirrored within your own inner being. Notice how your inner reactions affect your body… your heart rate… your breath… Notice how all of that simply rises from within, in sync with that of without.

Again, ask yourself, could it all have happened any other way? Could your being judgmental of your judgmental-ness have happened any other way? Could your wishing-for-yourself-to-have-reacted-differently have happened any other way? See the flow of events, within and without."

Despite all the noticing around, none noticed how the One with the raven had become silent once again. But unlike most silences, which soon become uncomfortable in a group of people, this silence was of an almost timeless nature. All were more present than ever before in their lives. And at the same time, they all were as absent as a young child, lost in inner reveries.

The horn of a truck being blocked by another truck, which in turn was being blocked by a car that stopped for no reason, all brought them back to their selves. Cars stopping for no reason do tend to bring this about. Some would argue that it's the sound of the horn that triggered it. Others would say it was the food the toddler ate this morning, now exited all over the dashboard of the father's car. But all that's rather short-sighted. Then again, claiming they all were brought back to their selves by the Big Bang, however true that may be, would be too great a leap at this point, now wouldn't it?

"Did I just witness God being at work?" asked Adebowale out loud without realizing it.

"I think I experienced true oneness, didn't I?" wondered Andrea, truly astonished.

"I'm telling you," muttered Jimmy while still being squeezed in between the glowing One and the One with no particular characteristics, "it's a-"

"No, Jimmy," interjected the One who is considering doing magic tricks again gently. "It's not a trick. It's as real as it gets."

"I'm surely having trouble seeing the implications of all this," said Bram genuinely concerned while scratching the back of his head. – "You wouldn't even know how to spell implications," muttered Marwa inaudibly.

"Seriously," spoke Adebowale with a firm voice. "Did we just witness God's will?"

Adebowale didn't care much for Truth himself. As far as he was concerned, the Truth could dictate that the earth was created by dancing pink elephants. He would accept it all as long as he would receive an audience with those elephants to make sure it was real.

It turned out Adebowale Unigwe was on a mission. Back in Nigeria, his sister, Ayofemi, was suffering a terminal illness. All had given up on her except her eldest brother. At the risk of not ever seeing her alive again, he ventured out to search for a cure. As none could be found in conventional arts of medicine, he was about to give up. But then he came across a sentence which struck him in the heart: the Truth shall set you free. And so, he went looking for the Truth, for he wanted his sister to be free of illness, free of worry and free of her mother-in-law.

"God's will?" mused One.

"Oh, Him again," said the One with the red clover (found it right at his feet). "He can be annoyingly persistent, can't He?"

"Indeed," nodded One. "Even after all they have already experienced, still, this Dude is supposed to be behind it all."

"Let us explore that a bit, Adebowale," proposed One. "You see, as we all know, most theistic religions insist on a universe having been created by a higher entity. This entity had to be present before all that, of course. Before the dawn of space and time, so to speak."

"Most are pretty clear on that," continued One. "But then it becomes foggy. You see, to some, this Creator withdrew Himself afterwards. Sort of remaining as a Watcher or awaiting us all in another realm. To others, this Creator is still present, here and now, continuously available to intervene where needed or asked."

"There's many more views and theories and beliefs about that," said the One with the raven. "But the main point is that all these views have one thing in common. They separate God from creation. And this separation causes a myriad of questions and opinions, all pulling us in this direction and that."

"And so, some will not only come to their own personal conclusions. They will also develop ways to please God, to atone to God or even command Him. They will fabricate methods and techniques to influence creation and life's events by means of prayer, magic, voodoo or any other kind of ritualistic practice. Others, like philosophers or mystic theists, will ever try to guestimate how the balance between God's will and man's will is governed."

"But, as we all well know, none ever come to solid, irrefutable conclusions. Hence, we all are the greatest contradiction walking around on two legs. Whenever we accomplish something, it is achieved by our own volition and perseverance. Whenever it doesn't work out, or some ill fate befalls us, it suddenly is God's will. We simply pick which one of both suits us best in the moment."

"No!" boomed Adebowale. "I'm not here to pick what suits me best. I want the Truth. Not vagueness. Not inconclusiveness. Not the next story to believe in. The Truth only. Nothing less."

"Even if it's pink elephants?" the One with the red clover casually remarked. Adebowale's eyes went wide open. 'Are they able to read my mind?' he wondered.

"You lot aren't really fond of His Greatness, now are ya?" snickered ol' Cormac when Adebowale missed the next beat in the rhythm of the conversation.

"It's not about fondness, Cormac," answered One. "We're only exploring cracks and problems in any possible view. In the end, you can only figure it out by experiencing it. It makes no sense to tell you whether there is a God or not. Either way, it would just be another view, another opinion. It wouldn't break that silly, useless cycle."

Andrea raised her arm. She wasn't sure to speak or not, so she simply waited if someone would notice her and go with that. "Yes, Andrea," pointed One before she could even decide if she'd really go with that.

"I… I think I saw a kind of Oneness in everything", she faltered. "I mean… It was like I was staring at a river. And the water flowed by in one continuous flow. And all the waterdrops acted as one with the others, as if interconnected… as if they were all propelled by the unstoppable force of them acting in unison."

The raven croaked. There was no particular reason for that. It simply did, as ravens tend to do every once in a while.

"I felt humbled and privileged at the same time," continued Andrea. "I really did."

The raven croaked again. This time, it might have been trying to make a point.

The One with the raven sighed. It was a good sigh. "From a certain perspective, you are both correct, Adebowale and Andrea. One sees God's action. Another sees Oneness in everything. The thing is, both views have one common flaw."

"And that is?" tried Kalle.

"I know exactly what that is," croaked ol' Cormac. "It's the one in the wheelchair. That's 'that is'."

"You see right through us, wise ol' Cormac," answered One. "That is exactly 'that is'."

All faces in the crowd went puzzled. If Picasso had been around, he'd certainly have been inspired to paint something normal, as reality seemed abstract enough as it was.

"Let us have one more little visualization," suggested the One with the red clover. "Perhaps that will bring some clarity. Please, indulge us one last time here."

"More trickery," mumbled Jimmy nearly inaudibly (he was still being squeezed in between his two masked and hooded friends).

"Okay, try to relax again," started the One with the red clover. "How to go with this?" he mused. Then he stared at the red clover twisting and turning in front of him and had an idea. "Aha! Of course! Let's try this."

"Please, close your eyes for a moment. Breathe in – breathe out.

Imagine a closed lotus flower. It's in a large lake in Vietnam, surrounded by thousands of other lotus flowers that are all about to bloom.

Now, imagine each of you as a little, coloured speck on one of the petals of one of these many, many flowers.

In fact, the whole of the flower consists of countless little specks. You are just one of them.

Each speck, including the one you are now consists of billions of little particles, all consistently forming the little speck alongside the many others.

The particles are moving. The energy vibrates. Now, imagine the lotus flowers all slowly opening up.

See the oneness in this unfolding. No particle jumps out of line. No particle suddenly appears out of the blue."

You, as the speck on a petal, you simply unfold along with the whole of the flower.

It all is the flower. It all unfolds simultaneously, effortlessly in unison. All of them, all thousands, in that lake in Vietnam.

The ripples on the lake are part of the movement. The wind bending the flowers left and right is part of the movement. The spinning of the earth is part of the movement. The dance of the planets around the sun, it is part of the movement.

Do you see it? Do you feel it?"

"Blimey," gasped Kalle. "Ol' Cormac is right! He's totally right! The common flaw… It's us! It's each of us. Every single one of us. Despite all previous realizations, we failed to see the Truth of it all."

"I think I follow you," Sven said, still baffled. "We all make the same mistake. Some see God at work. Some see existence acting as One. But we always take ourselves out of the equation. The simple fact is that we all are part of this great, unifying equation constantly at work."

"My point exactly," concurred Kalle. "God, Something, Oneness, it's all nothing but interpretations. It's all the same thing. And just as much as we are part of this equation, so is God, or whatever you'd like to call It."

The Mystical Mages of Infinite Zero silently observed this realization rippling through the whole of the crowd.

"Mother of God," whispered Jimmy, who was no longer flanked by the glowing One and the One with no particular characteristics. "It's not just a trick. The whole bloody universe is one gigantuous, ginormous, right-in-your-face-and-ever-disguised megatrick."

Some laughed. Some were silent. Some had tears rolling down their cheeks. Some couldn't stop talking.

The Mystical Mages of Infinite Zero nodded. The whole process which was unfolding seemed to find their total approval.

But then there was a sudden shift. As daily reality penetrated their minds once again, so as well did doubt and confusion.

"I am totally lost here," said Nurse Erin in her sweet voice. "I mean, yes, I see it. I see it! I truly do. But still... I am utterly lost at the same time. I don't know who I am any longer. I mean, I don't even know 'what' I am."

"Man," started Bram, "Now I really fail to see the implications of all this. It doesn't make any sense at all. It all feels right. And at the same time, it doesn't. It's like I'm forced into..."

"... living in two conflicting worlds," finished Marwa, "one annulling the other."

"It's a paradox!" concluded ol' Cormac.

"A paradoxical existence," added Jimmy.

"Not yet!" spoke the One with the raven firmly. He clapped both hands strongly together...

and everything disappeared.

Chapter 15   The discovery of Truth (and how it unavoidably escapes us… unless you are willing to read Parts 2 and 3)

Everything was white. There was no horizon, no sky or no ground. There was only whiteness.

Ol' Cormac found himself alone in this whiteness. Disorientated, he looked left and right, up and down.

The same happened to Nurse Erin. She walked left, she walked right, only to discover how the whiteness had engulfed her entirely. Bram, Marwa, Sven, Kalle, Georges, Charles, Andrea, Jimmy, Olivia, Mykhailo, Adebowale, Márcia and all the others in the crowd suffered the same fate.

Mere seconds seemed like an eternity. Nonetheless, after just a few seconds more, the whiteness seemed to give way a little bit. All were able to perceive each other again. They all seemed to be in the same spot as they were at the edge of the 'Aire'. But the tourists and travellers were all gone, just as much as the slope, the gas station, the restaurant, the grass, the sun and the clouds.

At the spot where the hill was supposed to be, they suddenly saw a large Chesterfield Wingback sofa. It was a little curved and allowed three to five seats. On its left and right, a single-seat chair appeared in a similar fashion. The armrests had deep brown, wooded mouldings of the masks of the Timeless and Boundless Avatars of Causal Causality. The weathered oxblood leather gave all three of them an antique look and feel.

All present still felt disoriented. Totally flabbergasted they kept looking in all directions, desperately trying to find a point of reference. With all that looking around, they didn't notice how the Timeless and Boundless Avatars of Causal Causality appeared at the sofa and chairs. Some were seated in them. Others were standing behind them, gently leaning on their back and wings.

Somehow, the chairs and their occupants brought back calm and ease to the crowd. A combination of habit and deep consternation made them all take a seat in the whiteness. Some took a cross-legged position. Some, like ex-pretzel-Georges, simply leaned back with their legs straight in front of them. As such, they once again formed a semi-circle around the Timeless and Boundless Avatars of Causal Causality.

A cloaked and hooded figure appeared in the distance. While he slowly approached, a raven came down from high above. With its wings wide open, it glided low above the crowd. A careful observer would have spotted an oddity in its eyes. One had a red shine to it. The other blue. When the hooded figure came closer, the raven circled around one more time before landing on his shoulder.

The raven released a gurgling croak. It seemed totally unconfused by the white environment. The bird bend his head as birds do and eyed the crowd with its red eye. Its masked companion started to speak with exquisite clarity.

"Truth is all around us. Truth is within us. Truth is omnipresent. It is all-encompassing."

The raven made a few steps left and right on his shoulder. Then it peaked at the crowd with its blue eye.

"None of you came here for a truth which is merely about true or false, right or wrong, accurate or imprecise. Such truths, surely meaningful within their own realm, are never free of debate, opinion or doubt. They can be practical for sure, by all means useful as well."

The raven stepped back, turning its red eye once more towards all present.

"But the Truth you are looking for is rather of an existential if not spiritual nature. You are pleased only with no less than the absolute Truth. Irrefutable, straightforward, clear and without any compromises, which would only suit your personal needs and wants. Moreover, Truth must cover both the nucleus of your very own personal existence as well as existence in its totality."

"Truth is about you," added the One with no particular characteristics. He felt perfectly at home in this realm with no particular characteristics. "It is about who you are, what you are and why you are. It is about your purpose and destiny in life, as well as the very meaning of life itself."

"Truth," said the glowing One, "is about life, both before and after death. It is about whether there is a God or not. It is about all the major questions you encounter within and around yourselves at any given moment in time."

"You see," shrugged the One with the raven, "therefore, to be Truth, Truth must encompass everything in its entirety, the whole of totality, without the slightest exception. Hence, Truth and existence can only be one and the same. Consequently, you as a person and Truth are also one and the same."

"Truth is absolute in nature," explained the One without Vanessa. "Truth is complete. It transcends thought, logic, feelings, your ego and even something you'd like to call the soul."

"Yet despite all of that," said the One with the red clover, "Truth will never belittle you. Nor will it render anything irrelevant or inferior."

The One with the raven now walked towards the sofa and took seat on its armchair. "But let's slow down a little first," he proposed. "It is clear you all realized something significant in the core of your being. And now your minds are trying to catch up and simply don't know where to start. Yes, sweet Erin, this is absolutely normal. Nothing to be alarmed about."

Erin blushed. Ol' Cormac immediately noticed this and raised his cane: "Oi, get your own nurse, will ya! You better do some explaining instead of getting all sweet on me, Erin here."

"Very well, old, wise friend," chuckled One. "Very well."

"First of all, it is very simple, the creator and creation are one and the same. Every given moment in space and time contains the creative force and masterplan for the next."

"Exactly! Each single moment, shaped by the previous, continuously unfolds into the next. Existence unfolds itself in the only single possible way it can, by itself, within itself."

"You see, in the beginning of space and time, there was no masterplan.

There wasn't the slightest idea of what everything should be like in some distant future, let alone in this very moment where we now turn up to witness all this. And nonetheless, the very beginning of space and time contained the masterplan for the universe in its entirety."

"It's unfathomable, it's mindboggling, but it simply is nothing else than that. You can experience it. You can realize it. You can recognize it."

The One with the red clover and the glowing One exchanged a high five. With a courteous bow, the One with the red clover gave room for the glowing One to take over.

"Secondly, there is the you-thing. Oneness implies there is no longer any you either. You see? You simply can't have it both ways."

"Your observations in the previous chapter were very good, Kalle and Sven," complimented the One with the red clover.

"Indeed," clapped the glowing One. "Oneness is rather radical in nature. While many see themselves and oneness as two separate things, in fact, there can be only One in oneness. And we must agree, mentally, that this is simply impossible to grasp. The mind separates itself from all that enters it. Still, the mind can come to the most startling recognition when it can fall back on true experience, when it can rely on a knowing which is beyond words or ideas… and nonetheless penetrates every cell, atom and quark of your being."

"Oneness erases both God and You as separate entities. It's as simple as that. There can never be two in oneness, now can there? Not even you and God, or you and the universe."

"Indeed. You yourself are part of this unfolding, unseparated from everything else. Your actions, your thoughts, feelings, emotions, memories, aspirations, the whole of the self, it ever unfolds in unity with everything else."

"You understand now why we'd rather aim for the experience first instead of trying to exploit it mentally. It makes no sense without the experience."

"Hey, that has a nice ring to it," chuckled the glowing One.

"It makes no sense without the experience," repeated the One with the red clover in a played, formal tone.

"From a mental perspective, you'd only approach this oneness as a contemplation of causalistic patterns at best. From an experiential perspective, however, oneness is more like a sense of unicity of being."

"The sense of a strictly individual being can no longer be found. Where there seemed to be this and that and such and so, all of a sudden, an intuitive sense arises that there is only That."

"You see, it all may appear as a myriad of things to the eyes that look, but seen from the non-identity, realizing the non-existence of 'I' in favour of this oneness, only That remains."

"And the more you connect with this, the more you will sense it not only transcends space. It transcends time as well. Everything happens in the now."

"Yes," exploded Sven. "Yes, yes, yes-yes-yes-yes! I know! I just… My mind just can't grasp it. I need some rationality to all this."

The glowing One chuckled. "We are in the most irrational of all places, and you're asking for a rational approach now?" The other One's all smiled as well.

"Absolutely!" came Kalle to Sven's defence. "My mind is seriously objecting to all this as well. I sense it, yes, but it doesn't make sense."

"Very well," said the One with the dice (we'll get to that soon enough). From within his cloak, he pulled a rounded, red, acrylic die (see, that's one already!) and showed it to the crowd. "You see this die? Now. Is there a mathematician or an IT nerd in the room?"

Three people raised their hands. One was Marwa. Then there also was 방찬, a game designer from South Korea and a little fella from India called Ayush Amit. Ayush specialized in legal hacking, although he also likes to explore the darker side of his trade in his spare time.

"Excellent," clapped the glowing One. "Now we can throw the die."

"Ah, but before we do," said the One with the dice, "a prediction, anyone?"

"A prediction?" asked Marwa. "You mean a lucky guess, no? There is no way we can predict which face you will roll."

"Now, isn't there?" challenged the One with the dice. "Tell me, 방찬, can you simulate the roll of a die with a computer?"

"Of course," shrugged the game designer. "Easy."

"I mean in a three-dimensional, real environment," added the One with the dice. "Where it is actually thrown and rolling on a surface before it comes to a halt."

"Of... course," answered 방찬 a little less confidently. "It's a bit harder to code and calculate. But it surely is possible."

"So," continued the One with the dice. "If we would feed a computer with all possible parameters, like the size of the die, the surface it will land on, the movement of air, the angle and force it was thrown, and its original position in my hand…"

"… the computer could perfectly calculate which face it will land on," finished Ayush with a thick Indian accent.

The One with the dice rolled the die in front of him. It landed on the white surface with a four facing up.

"Everybody agrees with Ayush?" asked the One with the dice, looking left and right to all. All nodded in agreement.

"Of course," elaborated Ayush, "this little thingy would require some serious calculation-power. And you'd also need a robot hand to roll the die. The slightest tremble in your hand would ruin the calculation."

"Fair enough," said the One with the red clover.

Then, the One with the dice reached inside his cloak once more. With a quick, strong throw, he rolled a thousand dice out in front of him. They came in all possible colours and scattered all across the whiteness. After a lot of bouncing and tumbling around, all came to a halt, with their bright surfaces revealing their very own number facing upwards.

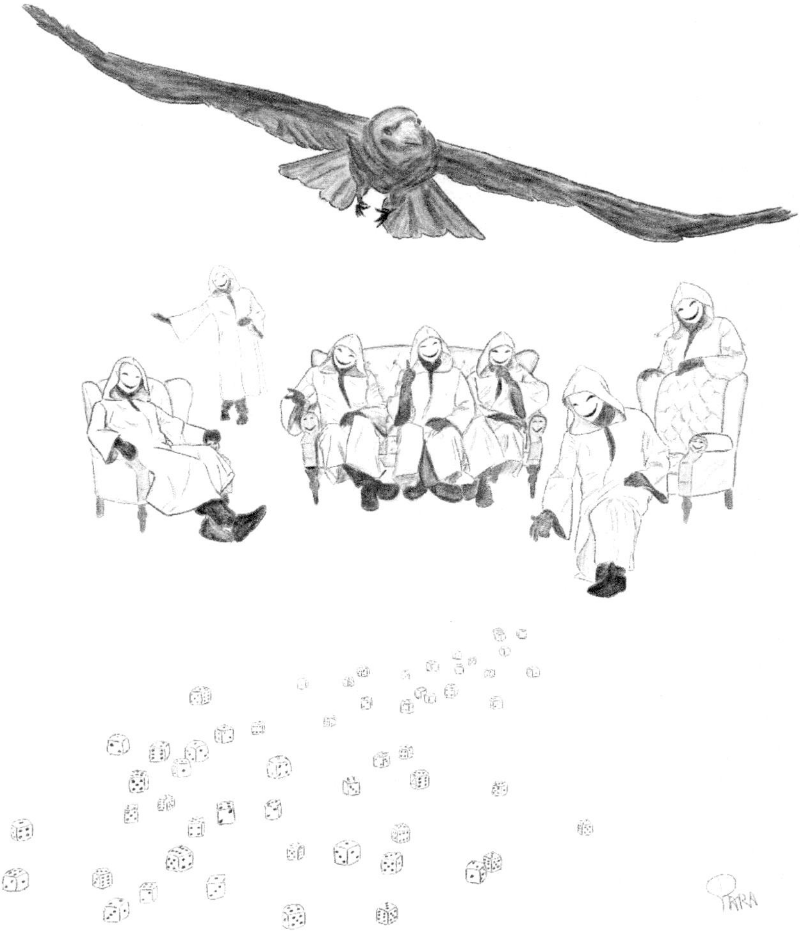

"How did he…" gasped Jimmy.

"It's definitely a trick, Jimmy," reassured ol' Cormac with a wicked tone. Nurse Erin and others had to bite their lip to prevent them from bursting out in laughter.

"So," started the One with the dice (now we're there, right?). "Tell us, Ayush, 방찬 and Marwa, would a computer be able to calculate this outcome as well?"

방찬 whistled a long tone, indicating this was heavy. Ayush wobbled his head in such a way that no one could figure out if he was indicating yes or no. Marwa held her index finger wisely against her upper lip. "I wouldn't say it is impossible," she said. "Difficult for sure. But not impossible."

"And what if I threw a million?" challenged the One with the dice. "Or a billion?"

"You will quickly hit limits there, my friend," said Wolfram. "The only computer that can calculate this is the universe itself by playing it out."

The one with the raven got up again and moved a bit laterally across the edge of the thrown-out dice. His arms were clasped behind his back. "The dice are just a simplistic example. The same goes for the leaves on a tree. The molecules of oxygen in the air. The neurons in your brain. Wolfram's universe computer will be able to determine all this. And it does."

Marwa moved in a bit closer to the One with the dice. "I see your point, Laplace. But the universe is not entirely deterministic in nature. You are forgetting quantum mechanics and entropy."

"True," agreed the One with the dice. "But then again, dear Marwa, I challenge you to lecture my dice all day long about the behaviour of the smallest possible particles in the largest possible space. When you are done, and I roll them again, you think our computer will have trouble predicting the outcome?"

"Errrr," groaned Kalle. "I'm not sure if this 'rational' approach is making me feel any better."

"I am also not pleased," bellowed Adebowale. "If this is the Truth, it is worthless to me."

With dramatic gestures, the One with the dice pulled his thousand dice in as if they were all attached to some invisible thread. When all disappeared again within his cloak, he still had two left in his hand. "Let's see," he said and dropped both dice on the whiteness.

"Hmmm, the signs are not in our favour," he pondered, seeing the blue die showed a six and the red die a one. He silently wondered whether or not he should throw them again.

The One with the raven ignored the musing of the One with the dice. "Let us take some steps backwards first," he proposed. "You see, it appears we are facing an issue here which we need to address. But first, we need to see the issue."

The One with the red clover took the red clover out of the smiling slit of his mask and pointed it at the crowd as a way to draw attention. "See, there is a perfect paradox in all of this. But instead, all of you sort of instinctively choose to live a contradiction."

"Like we pointed out before. One moment you say it all is God's will; the other it is yours."

"One moment, you want to see cause and effect in perfect alignment. The other, you seem to prefer your thoughts and actions to be governed by some quantum-ness in your brain."

"One moment, you want to fulfil your divinely ordained purpose. The other you wine about free will."

"One moment, you look into the stars, bones or cards for the future. The other you complain about all the appointments you have in your agenda right up to the next year or two."

"When you consider it strictly rationally," said One, "it makes no sense at all. Just look at those folks saying the universe is not deterministic in nature because of quantum-this and entropy-that. Now, imagine it'd be a fact that your actions and decisions are influenced by spooky quantum stuff or chaotic randomness. How can this make you feel any better when it comes to your precious free will?"

The One with the raven nodded. "You see, such a take on life is clearly full of discrepancies. When spoken out in examples, it's obvious to see, yet we all prefer to ignore this for the sake of maintaining our comfy-zone."

"Think about it," poked One. "Would it truly work like this? Can we ourselves decide how things are determined based on our personal preferences? Then written from above, then written by our own hand? Or... should we acknowledge there can be only one of both?"

"Kalle doesn't like it," said Sven with arms crossed. "And neither do I. We don't like it."

"Like it or not, Sven," sulked Kalle. "As terrible as it all seems, I'm afraid we have to accept it for a fact."

"Wait," said Marwa. "There has to be a way out of this stalemate."

"Stalemate, chains, prison..." listed One. "Looking from the realm of reason, when you see the unfolding of existence, with yourself as being separate of it, you will all experience yourselves as mere prisoners in a vast bastille of cosmic proportions."

"Stalemate, chains, prison..." reiterated One. "See, Marwa, now that we have tackled Truth from a strictly rational perspective, using dice or whatever other observation one can make, you can perfectly deduce how the causal flow of the universe governs your personal realm of existence. But that's just the thing. As long as you habitually keep seeing yourselves as being separate of it, you will ever experience yourself as mere prisoners in a... well, yes, a vast bastille of cosmic proportions."

"On the other hand," said One. "When you'd retreat back into the experience we had during the bus stop – you remember when you truly managed to touch this Beingness and Oneness? – you were all perfectly at ease. There was no trace of inner conflict."

"At peace," added the One without Vanessa. "You'd even say you all got pretty close to the true meaning of spiritual concepts like Surrender... Trust... Acceptance... and Freedom."

"Oi!" It was ol' Cormac. "Oi! You're not going soft on us now, are ya!?

Soon enough you'll be talking of love and stuff. But I rather see ya explain one thing, ye cheeky wee devils. How come this truth-stuff of yers is not widely known and accepted? Gotta be something smelly there if ya ask me."

As a response to that, the One with the red clover raised his arms and ostentatiously sniffed under his armpits. "Nothing smelly here, ol' chum."

The others chuckled and grinned as some copied the gesture. The One with the dice seemed to be examining the two dice in his gloved hands. Then he looked at his old friend in the wheelchair. "Nothing smelly about my dice, ol' chap. This truth-stuff is widely known. It has been discovered countless of times, and likewise, it has gone lost again and again."

"Exactly," said One. "It has been known for thousands of years. And then it suddenly evaporates. Not only throughout the ages, but also within the same generation, and, as you lot already experienced within yourselves, Truth even tends to get lost again within a single lifespan."

"You see," continued the One with the dice, "Truth is extremely transient when it comes to recognizing and integrating it within ourselves and our lives. One moment, you've got it, and it all makes perfect sense. The next, it eludes you again, when thoughts and emotions, goals and objectives and do's and don'ts overtake you in your day-to-day lives."

"We could speak quantum, like the CSDCs," chuckled the glowing One, "and say the wave of recognition collapses once it touches self-reality again."

"Let's not bring them into this, will you," objected One. "We're lucky enough they're not popping up in this place."

"But they did pop up throughout the ages, though, didn't they? Every single time Truth was discovered, they arrived fast enough at the scene to twist things around."

Bram raised his hand. "But can't you tell us then, how to prevent this… this wave from collapsing?" His question was so genuine and aimed at those near the sofa and chairs that he didn't notice how Marwa looked at him with some astonishment, perhaps even admiration, in her eyes.

"How to prevent…" One stammered without finishing the sentence. "But-"

"But that will take us the same amount of pages as we already used," finished the One with the red clover. "What about all the trees and the climate and stuff?"

"Enough," said the One with no particular characteristics. He loudly clapped his hands and…

nothing happened.

He curiously stared at his hands, trying to figure out what went wrong. Then he looked at the One who is writing all this. "Hey, we need a new scene for this one. After all, we promised to answer any question, and this one definitely needs a new scene."

"Try again," suggested the One who is writing all this.

The One with no particular characteristics clapped his hands firmly. And this time…

they all disappeared.

Well. Not all. Adebowale was still there, and so was the One without Vanessa.

Adebowale looked left and right. "What?"

The One without Vanessa walked up to him and put her hand gently on his shoulder. "It is time for you to leave, my good friend. Your presence is needed elsewhere."

"But…" protested Adebowale. Then tears welled up in his eyes. The tall man suddenly looked small and fragile. "I failed. Ayofemi. My sweet little sister. I failed her."

"You didn't fail her," comforted the One without Vanessa. "Adebowale, you are the most courageous man in this group. And you have a big heart, my friend. But the best thing she needs right now is you to be by her side."

Then the One without Vanessa took a tone which was still gentle but more firm. "Come now. It is time!" She clapped her hands and …

not even the whiteness remained.

When I see that I am nothing, this is Wisdom. When I see that I am everything, this is Love. Between these two valleys, my life flows.

– Sri Nisargadatta Maharaj –

Part 2

Interlude   **The talk show**

And so it happened that the Ancient Mystics of Infinite Zero were invited to a television studio for an interview.

An elderly man, pretty much past retirement, but more virile than many half his age, eagerly greeted the live audience and the cameras.

"Good evening, ladies and gentlemen! Good evening to you all. Thank you! Thank you. – Thank you very much. Today, we have…

the Ancient Mystics of Infinite Zeroooo with us. How about that!"

The audience cheered and clapped while the figures in hooded cloaks and smiling masks walked up the stage. The elderly man went to greet them and shook their gloved hands. Then he noticed the One with the raven. Looking at the bird, he asked, "So, what's with the raven?"

The One with the raven shrugged. "Beats me as much as it beats you. But look, it could have been worse. Could have been a baboon for all I know."

"I see," answered the talk show host. "I also noticed in the back studio how you never turn your back to anybody. What's with this lateral moving you always seem to do?"

"Yes, there's that," replied the One with the raven while looking at the bird on his shoulder. "Still, if it were a baboon…"

"I can imagine," chuckled the talk show host.

"I'd rather not," said the One with the raven in monotone.

The talk show host invited his peculiar guests to take a seat in a set of lined up, rusty-orange couches. Then he himself sat down on a white, spherical couch which was capable of turning round in all directions.

"So," the talk show host started, "I'm a bit mys-ti-fied here. You call yourselves Ancient. How ancient would that be exactly?"

One scoffed against the Others: "Who is this funny fella? Clearly, he should know the Ancient-word is a metaphor for a state of timelessness without beginning or end."

"Perhaps he simply wants to know our birthdays, no?" the glowing One grinned. "So he can send us a card and presents."

"And here your question is answered, I believe," said the One with the raven.

"Perhaps you can elaborate on that?" persisted the talk show host. "Timelessness? Without beginning or end? That's a bit God-like, no?"

"Well, Jim… Can I call you Jim?"

"It's Bill, actually."

"Well, Bill. Let me explain that to you. First of all, you see, time itself, it doesn't really exist."

"It doesn't?"

"Nope. Time is nothing but an abstract means to measure something. Somehow, it has been turned into an actual thing in our minds, but that's actually pretty silly."

"It's a construct," elaborated the One with the sea thrift (it took him ages to decide which flower to pick for the TV show). "It is a mental invention to serve a measurement of how things unfold."

"And it's an extremely practical one too," added the glowing One. "It allows us to sit here together in the same moment. Would be pretty awkward, wouldn't it? Us being here without you, or vice versa. Without time, the odds are it would most likely be just like that."

"Would be devastating for the ratings, wouldn't it, Bill?"

"So, so long to time travel," concluded the talk show host.

"Only for mathematicians and movies, Bill. But heck, I do love to watch mathematicians."

"If you'd really want to travel backwards in time," explained the One with the sea thrift, "you'd have to rewind the entire universe. Like a videotape."

"Only problem is, Bill," added the One still without Vanessa, "you're on the videotape as well. So even if you could pull that off, the rewinding, I mean, you'd also need to figure out how to prevent yourself from getting rewound along with it. Wouldn't be much point to travelling backwards otherwise, now would it?"

"Still, the fact remains", continued the One with the raven, "in reality, there is only now. Only this moment exists. And this moment is timeless in nature. If you can free yourself of the continuous hops in events and see this now as it is, you'd actually be able to experience this absence of time."

The talk show host stared straight into camera 2 with a well-played frown. "Would there be any, like, practical benefit to that?"

The One without Vanessa shrugged her shoulders. "What? Apart from the actual experience of timelessness?"

"You can only ask this question when you have not experienced it yourself, Bill," said the glowing One. "You see, in this state of timelessness, you not only drop all worries and to-do's for the future…"

"…or all troubles from the past…"

"… anxieties and regrets …"

"…you also drop the you-ness which is maintaining all this stuff."

"And hence you are able to indulge a timeless moment of actual peace, an unmistakable liberation of all that stuff that binds and constrains you."

Bill tried to comment on that, but One was faster: "It's not just a lazy moment of peace, Bill. Abiding in timelessness can actually be very beneficial. It's an undefinable moment where your mind and body aren't running from one instant to the other. It creates an opportunity for restoration and revitalization to take place, something which your you-ness, with all its resistance and inner conflicts, wouldn't be able to do."

"The point is," said the One with the raven, "if only you lived in the present a bit more, the benefit would be enormous. Not only would you be able to seize things in the moment, you'd also live more vividly, more alive. Life would be more intense, more real and way more appreciated."

"Yes," added One, "look at it as fishing in the rivers of life, Bill. It's not about catching any fish; it's all about that river."

Bill coughed. It is a trick he always uses to get a grip on the conversation.

"So, basically, you are saying we humans tend to search for the practical in practical stuff, while there's a lot more practical stuff found in the impractical, correct?" He briefly stared into nothingness, puzzled about the sentence he had just thrown out without having thought it through first.

"You nailed it, Bill."

With a smug look Bill took his next question card. "So, okay, we handled the timeless bit, I think. But you lot also seem to talk about, how you call it, 'boundlessness'?"

"That's absolutely right, Bill," the One with the raven complimented the talk show host again.

"Well, I must admit I'm a bit puzzled by this. I take it you are talking about out of body experiences, right?"

"Well, Bill, now you are completely missing the nail," answered the One with the raven. "Hit your finger instead, my friend."

That took the smug away instantly. "Enlighten us, please."

"Well, it's actually hard to describe," admitted the One with the raven. "It's more like an experience. You have to feel it."

"Well, please. We'd like to, very much."

"The One with the raven tilted his head for a moment. "Hmm. Aiming for boundlessness will be a bit high in this context here. But we might be able to give you an idea."

Then he leaned forward and looked at the One without Vanessa. "Something for you, maybe? Would get your mind off the butterfly for a moment, no?"

"Very well," the One without Vanessa sighed. She changed her slumped position, sat up straight and regained her radiance.

"Okay, ladies and gentlemen in the audience. Boys and girls at home. Here we go. Please sit up nicely like me. Relax. It's not going to take long at all.

Now, close your beautiful eyes for a moment, please. Take a brief moment to linger in silence.

Very good. Very, very good. Now, try this as vividly as possible. Retrieve a memory from deep inside—a memory of anger, sadness or grief. Go deep into it.

Splendid. Okay. Now, take a moment to look at the feelings that came with that. Evaluate them in relation to the feeling of space or wideness. Did you feel yourself to be spacious? Or did it feel rather narrow, like confined or something?

Good. Take some time to breathe. Clear the floor of feelings and emotions.

Now, retrieve a memory of joy. Of love. Wonder. Happiness. Once again, go into it vividly, like it's really real.

Wonderful! Now, one last time, evaluate these feelings in relation to the feeling of openness or space.

Beautiful! You can all open your eyes now."

"Got it, Bill?" queried the One with the raven. "I wouldn't say you experienced boundlessness. But I do think at least you have experienced how the psyche can feel in relation to space, no?"

"Well, that was pretty amazing indeed," testified the talk show host. "One moment, I really felt all confined and locked in. And then I felt all opened up. Like free or something. As if I was somewhere in an open field in nature."

Camera 4 glided over the audience in the studio. Most faces depicted a smile as if people experienced an inner sweetness in which they were still lingering a bit. (To emphasize the success of this exercise, we will not mention the people who were swiping, pinching and spreading on their phones during the exercise. You know, the lot that always looks up all of a sudden and goes 'What? Did we miss something?')

Camera 2 again. "So you're saying if we'd just dig into this a bit deeper, we actually could land in a feeling of boundlessness? Regardless of whether it is in the body or out of the body. Just the feeling, right?"

"You nailed it once again, Bill."

"Excellent!" finished Bill with a big smile. Not that he necessarily captured those last words. It's just that he received the signal for a commercial break. Ending with a wide smile for the Ancient Mystics of Infinite Zero, Bill looked straight into camera 1. "It's time for a commercial break, ladies and gentlemen. I wonder if there will be good hammers for sale."

The commercials weren't about hammers at all. Ever seen commercials for hammers in prime time? Of course not. It's not like you'd walk to the fridge and start some hammering, would you? So the commercials were all about the stuff in your fridge or the stuff that'd soon end up there anyway. – Hurry now; the Ancient Mystics of Infinite Zero are back on the screen!

"So here we are back again," started the talk show host with exuberant enthusiasm, "completely in the moment with the One and onlies…

Ancient Mystics of Infinite Zeroooooo."

Applause.

"Tell me, has anybody ever told you folks you talk a bit funny? Where're you all from?"

"Lots of different places," the One with no particular characteristics mimicked Conner MacLeod.

"Well, that explains it." Since the question wasn't actually in his notes, Bill decided to skip that and jump straight back to script. "You are all wearing these ever-smiling masks. Why is that? Why hide your faces?"

"That is because our true faces would be too disturbing for people to see," the glowing One simply replied.

The talk show host hesitated for a moment. "What do you mean? Are your faces ugly? Or maimed?"

"No, no, nothing of the sort," waved the glowing One. "Our faces reveal a continuous state of bliss. You see, we have this constant smile frozen upon our lips while our eyes are ever wet with tears of utter joy. If you'd get to see that for even a minute, you would revel in our light. But here's the thing: the minds of those not knowing the Truth would soon become gravely disturbed by this. Hence, we decided to hide our smile behind a smile. Simple as that."

"What?" whispered the One at the far end against the second last One at the far end. "Is he for real? Are we all wearing these silly masks just for that??"

Bill was a bit flabbergasted by this response. While his mind was digging for the next question, the One with the raven intervened: "Nah, she's just messing with you, Bill. We hide our radiant faces because otherwise, we would become nothing but the same as our eternal enemy, the CSDCs."

"Yeh, you see, Bill, we don't want to be gurus of some sort. There are plenty of those already. And all of them are frauds. People shouldn't follow other people. It's completely ridiculous to look for Truth in others, surely, when Truth can be found by everybody themselves. People just don't realize how ridiculous it is to worship or respect or look up to some dude or gal who claims to be enlightened."

A bit uncomfortable, Bill shifted position in his chair while he unconsciously touched the picture of his guru in his pocket. "Why would I… I mean, why would 'we' do this?"

"Because you… I mean, because 'we' all talk ourselves into this. Unhappy or bored by the places we grew up in, we dive into a custom of a faraway country and recommend it to ourselves and others: 'It is so great'…"

"… 'it is so much more authentic' …"

"… 'we live in our heads too much' …"

"… 'we need to surrender' …"

"… 'a wonderful transmission will take place.'"

"We scam ourselves, trading a little peace and comfort for abuse, lies and a lower bank account."

"People who bask in the light of their gurus ever remain in the shadows themselves. Even when you spend a lot of time in the spotlights, Bill. Even then."

"Right." Bill shuffled through his question cards for another topic. He picked the card with four letters on it. "C. S. D. C.? What's the deal with them? You make them sound rather ominous."

"Ah," answered the One with the raven. "The Charismatic Self Delusional Charlatans! We also call them the 'See As They Sees'. They ever lure you into some concocted or distorted truth for their own gain."

"A story they were lured in themselves before," added the One on the far end while leaning forward.

"And the more people they trick into their web, the more they believe their own nonsense."

"It's a tricky thing," said the One who is considering doing magic tricks again. "Because they are extremely adept at mixing nonsense with actual facts."

"Dangerous." – One.

"Misleading they are." – Yoda.

"They trickses good peoples and ensnares them in their sticky webses." – Gollum.

"You're absolutely not fond of them, are you?" concluded Bill with eyes wide open.

"Absolutely," answered One defiantly. "We hate them!"

"We despise them!"

"They are our number one enemy!"

The One at the far end shrugged against the One second last. "Shouldn't we admit we're just having a bit of fun with this?" he whispered. "A little rivalry always makes an interesting story, but in the end, we don't really mean it, right? Like the little German guy with sleepy eyes, who speaks so slowly, I always nod off in merely a minute. He happens to be my best friend. Especially when I suffer insomnia."

The One second last at the far end dropped his shoulders as quickly as he lifted them.

"And they never go in debate with you?" Bill asked.

"Mostly, they tend to agree with all we say," answered the One with the sea thrift. "It's pretty clever, actually. By doing so, they confirm that there's a lot of abuse and lies. And since they are the ones confirming it, they can't be the ones doing it themselves. It's as logical as can be. Hence, they gain even more trust amongst their following. It allows them to propagate themselves as the zero point one per cent of those actually not being part of the whole trickery."

"But in fact, none other than you lot are the zero point one per cent telling the Truth as it is?"

"Spot on, Bill. You nailed it again."

"Right," said Bill while passing a wink to the camera. "And what about how you guys call yourselves…"

"Oi, there's girls here too," groused One.

"I was going to say that," replied the talk show host apologetically. "Anyways, what about how you boys and girls call yourselves?"

"See, now you're changing it," insisted One. "You started with 'you guys' while everybody knows there isn't a 'girls' following guys! Wouldn't ring, now would it? Ladies and gentlemen, boys and girls, but not guys and… and what?"

"Look, I'm really really, really sorry. What I meant to ask is this: You call yourself the CLF. Now, first of all, I'm a bit confused because you all are… the Ancient Mystics of Infinite Zero, right?"

"Correction, Bill," answered the One without Vanessa. "We are 'also known as' the Ancient Mystics of Infinite Zero."

"Some also call us the Enigmatic Ancients of Infinite Zero," added One.

"I prefer the Timeless and Boundless Avatars of Causal Causality," said the One with the sea thrift. "Sounds rather neat, no?"

"Right, but the C.L.F.?"

"Yes, that," answered the One with the raven. "In general, we are the Causalistic Liberation Front."

"And when you like it all sweet," said the glowing One, "you can also pronounce it as See Luv. How about that."

"Causalistic Liberation Front', the talk show host repeated each word with heavy iteration and a clear pause in between. "What's the deal with that?"

"Well, if you had read part 1, you might have gotten a pretty good idea about 'the deal with that'."

"Hmm," doubted One. "May as well be that this particular bit only gets cleared up in part 2 or 3."

"Yeh, I'm not sure either. Is it 1? Is it 2? Or 3? Which one is it?" They all stared at…

"Hey, stop harassing me," said the One who is writing all this. "I'd love to get to that, but I need to do this scene now. It's confusing enough as it is."

"Right!" the talk show host noticed he was looking into the wrong camera and needed to stay focused. "Right!" (this time in the right camera, which happened to be on the left). "Let us have a look at the message you are spreading."

"We're not spreading any message, Bill. We simply answer questions. That's all."

"I stand corrected. Still, the answers you give to life's questions are somehow a bit deterministic in nature, aren't they? It seems you g… people adhere to a view where free will is rather absent. Now, I wonder, if that were true, what would be the point of getting out of my couch?"

"Well, quite honestly, Bill, the missus would kick you out soon enough."

"And if it's not the missus, it will be nature calling you out in no time. And while you're at it, you can also go for a refill on nuts and beer."

"Of course, you need to buy those first."

"And, of course, you need money for that."

"So you'll also need to go do that talk show thing you do."

"You see, Bill, plenty of reasons to spend only a little time in that couch of yours."

"Okay," replied Bill. "I see your point. Yet still, without free will, how can we make criminals accountable for their actions? If it weren't really their choices to begin with?"

"There, there, Bill. It's the same as with the couch. The missus will certainly not have murderers running around free, now wouldn't she? Pretty annoying if they do, wouldn't you agree?"

"Yeh. While you are sulking on your couch, the missus will surely apprehend or convict those culprits, regardless of your silly pondering on free will."

"But seriously, Bill," said the One with the raven. "The whole 'couch- and criminal arguments' are the typical eructations of those picking a fight with determinism. While the deterministic stand is pretty silly itself."

"I'm not quite following you there."

"The deterministic view always starts from the perspective of a person being victim of the whole thing. But there simply is no person to begin with."

"Your couch is empty, Bill. Nobody there."

"Basically, Bill, you are nothing but a word written on a page in a book. Have you ever seen a word on a page complain about where it appears in a sentence?"

"You are the actor on the stage, Bill. There is no-"

A cheery old lass in the audience stood upright and started cheering midsentence of the conversation. Then she sat down again and chuckled against her neighbour: "I am definitely liberated from causality. Look how

I did something for no apparent reason whatsoever."

She brought her hand to her mouth in a concealing manner – she forgot her teeth at home – and added with a whisper: "And it's not even illegal."

"As I was going to say," continued One while eying the One who is writing all this, "there is no audience."

"But that's the thing," objected Bill. "I act my act. And it seems I really have a say in the role I play. It feels real. So… So you are saying it's all an illusion?"

"It's certainly not an illusion, Bill. It's all very real."

"It's a bit paradoxical, isn't it?" whispered Bill. "How to make sense of such a paradox?"

"Will you all get off my back," ranted the One who is writing all this. "I was about to start explaining this in the second part of this book. But somehow, I ended up in this silly interlude. I'll get to it as soon as we're done here!"

Bill just stared at the floor for a few seconds. "I'm a bit lost here, to be honest." Awkwardly, he went through his question cards and even dropped one. When he picked it up and read it, his eyes lit up again.

"Aha! Here's a fun one. Do you believe in extraterrestrial life?"

"It's not really about belief, Bill," answered One. "Last thing we do is believe something. But it surely is a possibility."

"Likely a probability," added One.

"Any idea why they haven't visited us yet?" probed Bill.

"Well, Bill," started One while switching from one buttock to the other. "If they'd be capable of visiting us, we'd be speaking about an advanced civilization, wouldn't we? So, starting from that assumption, let's look at this from their perspective."

One went silent there for a moment.

"See, we have over half the population on this planet believing in the actual existence of higher deities, more often than not with contradictive narratives. We have leaders of nuclear superpowers, each publicly claiming they believe in God. We have warring factions, each proclaiming to have the same God on their side. We have millions of people following some dictate or dress code, imposing physical mutilation or hairstyles on innocent children, all simply because they believe a God or a bunch of Celestial Beings directly or indirectly told them to do so."

One went silent again for a moment.

"We have all sorts of people believing in mindreading, astral projection, clairvoyance, levitation and other supernatural powers. People who believe they can manifest stuff when they just think about it hard enough. We have folks, wealthy folks, famous and influential ones, who believe there is a confederation of planets and worship some extraterrestrial being and stuff."

"We have tailgaters and people littering cigarette butts."

"Of course," added the One on the far end, "there's also the Prime Directive."

Another pause.

"I mean, seriously, Bill, would you make contact with such beings?"

The raven croaked.

"It all looks a bit grim if you ask me," concluded the talk show host. "Humanity seems all wrong."

"You're back on your couch, now, Bill. Remember, there is no one there. We simply tell Truth. No need to go all judgmental on things. All is fine as it is."

"Ooo-kii-dooo," frowned the talk show host. "Perhaps we could take a question from the audience? Anyone out there having a fine question for these Ancients here?"

A man wearing a casual sweater raised his hand.

"Yes, young man," pointed the talk show host.

"Hi, I'm Sam. I was wondering what your angle on AI is. Could it become conscious like humans?"

"Hi Sam," greeted the One with the raven after the talk show host gave him a nod to reply. "AI. See, here's the thing, Sam. Humans like to look at this from their own perspective. From there, they measure AI against themselves. 'Will AI become more intelligent than us?' – 'Will it become aware of itself?' – 'What will the consequences be?' – Stuff like that, right? That's all pretty nice, sure. However, as AI will develop further, and perhaps, attain what we call 'feelings' and 'consciousness', we first of all, and most importantly, will come to learn much more about ourselves and Truth than we anticipated."

"Does that answer satisfy you, Sam?" asked the talk show host.

"Not sure it does," replied Sam. "It sounds a bit mysterious if you ask me. Perhaps even ominous, maybe, I'm not sure. I think I will need to toss it around a bit in my head. But thanks."

"Well," summarized the talk show host back into camera 1. "I guess that's what mystics do, right? Make you toss around ideas in your head. Too bad we need to wrap this up, as we have our next guest eager and ready to join us on the stage.

Ladies and gentlemen, the CLF!!!, also known as the Ancient Mystics of Infinite Zero and many other names! Give them a warm round of applause."

Warm applause.

Chapter 1 The meaning of life?

"I don't know," sulked Andrea Klein. "I mean, what now? I mean, so they told us the Truth and… Well, I don't know. It should all make more sense now, but it doesn't. It doesn't make sense at all."

"Exactly," agreed Márcia Ser Nada, the woman from Brazil, remember? The one whose belly was about to explode unless either the bomb squad or a midwife would come to defuse the whole thing. "It's like life has lost all meaning, as if there is no meaning to life at all."

"I agrrree," said Georges. "And that is saying something, as I didn't know the meaning of life in the first place. Mais c'est vrai, it seems there isn't any."

All of the crowd could do nothing but stare at the waterfall which landed a bit further. They all were seated comfortably in a meadow on its left side. It was still early. Most tourists hadn't arrived at the Krimml yet, but that would soon change, as the place was a popular hotspot.

With a total height of 380 meters, this tiered waterfall is one of the largest in the world. More than 500.000.000 litres of water drop down in a single hour. If it weren't for a favourable wind, the sound of the water crushing down would be deafening. Luckily for the crowd, the large clouds of tiny waterdrops floated in the other direction. Rainbows popped in and out against the backdrop of the scenery.

"Yeh," pondered Sven. "What's the meaning of life anyway? Is it happiness?"

"To grow, to develop, to improve ourselves, that is the meaning of life," divulged Mykhailo.

"Helping out others gives life meaning," shared Marwa.

"It's one great mystery if ye ask me," said ol' Cormac. "I guess me nurse is all the meaning there is in me life. If it weren't for her, I'd be all alone in me cold house near Edinburgh."

Nurse Erin blushed like she had never blushed before. Despite the gloomy mood, a smile appeared on most of the faces in the crowd.

"I guess life itself has no real meaning," tried Bram. "But 'we' do, don't we? We have meaning. So, we ourselves are the answer to this silly question. I think."

Marwa looked up with a rekindled glow in her eyes. Bram first thought she fancied his remark. But then it turned out her gaze was fixed on something else behind him. She stared right through him. All heads turned towards the other side of the Krimmler Ache. Some in the crowd stood up and cheered. With both arms waving, they made the obvious even more obvious.

On the other side of the river, the Enigmatic Seers of Infinite Zero waved back at them. Soon enough, the group of masked and hooded figures rejoined the group and sat down with them.

"Well, well, well," started the One with the sea thrift. "Been pondering about the meaning of life, have you?"

"You heard that?" asked Kalle.

"No, actually we didn't. But we quickly read the first page of this chapter before we got here."

"So," started the One with the raven while confusion and a cerebral explosion could be read in Kalle's eyes. "You've learned the Truth and all you do is sit gloomy in the vicinity of nature's great wonders?"

"Well, yes," said Sven. "What meaning does life have once you know the Truth? It's all pretty pointless. And you can't expect us to become monks being meditative all day in some remote monastery, now can you?"

"Iwouldn'tmindthat," said 방찬 who next to being an IT geek, also happened to be the fastest rapper in the crowd, if not in the world. "Iwouldn'tmindthatatalltobehonest.Rappingandmeditatingalldaylongwith nothingelseonmymindbutanendlessstreamofwords,andendlessstreamofw ords,anendlessstreamofwords."

"Let's take things a bit slower, shall we," chuckled the glowing One.

"And let's remember to not take our words for granted on the point we are about to make," added the One without Vanessa. "So, how about we go for an actual experience? Please be seated and relax. But fasten your seatbelts, for we are all about to commit suicide."

"I freakin' told ya," grunted Jimmy. "It's a cult. It's a trickster-cult, and now they're going to trick us into killing ourselves."

"Just indulge us here one more time, Jimmy. It's all safe."

"But just don't do it at home, ok."

"And also, just to be safe," stipulated the One responsible for legal, "if you have a medical condition like high blood pressure, a heart condition, mental problems or anything else, it's best to consult your physician or therapist first."

"Very well, here we go. Allow a couple of gentle, natural breaths, with awareness of the inhale and the exhale. Then, allow your breath to become a little deeper and close your eyes.

Imagine this is your last minute. Imagine you are about to release your last breath, and then that's it. You will cease to live. Imagine this very vividly.

Now, inhale deeply one last time, as if it really is the last one.

Now, exhale completely. It's really your very last exhale.

Leave the breath. Accept you are dying. Do not inhale. Be conscious of these last few seconds before your body drops down dead.

There was an intense silence for about ten seconds. Then, a sudden staccato of inhales burst out, with chests swelling more than ever before.

"Very well," said the One without Vanessa. "Please keep your eyes closed a bit longer. Let your breath normalize again. Féél your breath. Féél your heartbeat. Féél the blood coursing through your veins."

"You see," said the One with the sea thrift. "You can ponder life all day long and discover a myriad of possible answers. But one thing is for sure. Life longs for you."

"When questioning the meaning of life, life itself has both the most gratifying and the most satisfying answer there can be."

"Exactly. Whether you yourself long for life or not, it is obvious and crystal clear: life longs for you."

"If there'd be any calling in your lives, it'd be life itself calling for you."

"I know, I know," said One warmly towards ol' Cormac and others. "This call of life surely has its own particular peculiarities, quirks and eccentricities. It's certainly not all roses…"

"… nor a walk in the park …"

"… or sunshine and rainbows all day long."

"Life can be demanding. It can be upsetting. And at times, we may rightly conclude the hand dealt to us doesn't offer a great game to play."

"We may find ourselves bereft of many qualities coming natural to others."

"And that's even without mentioning the many, unexpected tragedies which can befall us and deprive us of the good hand we had."

"Fair enough," said Charles. "But life's longing on its own doesn't give us meaning, does it? Let's be frank: Is there or is there not a meaning to life?"

"Some of you have given that answer already, Charles. There are many answers possible, and each can be appealing to one and appalling to another. You can find what appeals to you by being a little more accessible and a little less tense in life. It's not rocket science or anything."

"If you'd like one common denominator that suits all, you can use it in one single word: movement."

"Movement?"

"Movement. You see, everything in the entire universe is possible only because of movement. Nothing is without it."

"It encompasses all of existence, be it organic, material or energetic. The smallest possible wave or particle, in a stone, in a living being or invisibly passing through the air, walls and our very own bodies. It all moves. It all vibrates and-

OMG! Vanessa!"

The One without Vanessa held out her hand with her index finger extended. Promptly, Vanessa landed on its tip and gently flattened her wings in the sunlight.

"Can you believe that! She's back!"

"That can't be Vanessa," shook Jimmy.

"It's her for sure," countered the One with Vanessa. "My little red admiral can fly thousands of kilometres; did you know that?"

A school of children was chirping and cheering near the waterfall. All of them were soaking wet, daring each other to come the closest to the clouds of water that bounced up from the rocks where the waterfall came down. An elderly couple overlooked the play with joy in their eyes. Higher up, a handicapped boy in a wheelchair put out his hand to a Labrador and got a lick in return. Both were full of happiness in this simple exchange of their existence.

"Movement," exulted the One with Vanessa. "From our very own, personal perspective it allows us meaning and purpose. To move others. To be moved by them. To touch others in their hearts and to be touched by them. To see the outcome of the interaction between us. It all gives meaning to our existence."

"One simply cannot not move," said the One without any particular characteristics. "Even when you'd be in a seemingly state of perpetual motionlessness, you'd still move others by this apparent lack of movement."

"Right," said One while clearing her throat. "Point is, you cannot not move."

"Said that!"

"Complete absence of movement would correspond to complete absence

of being," explained the One with the raven. "Movement allows aliveness. It allows existence. And most of all, it allows you. In its state of doingness, there is Beingness. And this Beingness is as complete as can be."

"Recall the exercise we just did," advised the One with Vanessa. "It is extremely powerful and completely harmless. See it as a key to be touched by pure aliveness itself. You can repeat it whenever you need it."

"Indeed," glowed the glowing One excited. "After you can no longer hold your breath anymore, it is this spontaneous, bountiful inhale which allows you to reconnect with life in its utmost pureness. It can genuinely be perceived as a renewed invitation to sense and purpose in your day-to-day existence."

The raven croaked, tapping the hood of its partner to speak. "Oh, is it my turn? Err, okay, so, yes, exactly, this simple, untenable inhale brings you in touch with life and all its qualities. It allows your ever identifying self to merge with the $\overline{\text{S}}$elf in its bare essence. And as such, my friends, a reciprocal relationship emerges in which the identity-self, from the experience of the non-identity, will find itself rejuvenated with a sense of merit, value and worthiness."

At that point, a baby screamed its lungs out. All heads went in the direction of Márcia, who was flanked by Nurse Erin and Wendy Wiehart, a single midwife from Pretoria. Soon enough, some tourists approached who happened to have babies themselves. And so, even faster than in the best hospital, the newborn found itself cleaned, with a set of diapers and fresh clothes to enter the world.

"Why flicky-dee-flack darn," exclaimed ol' Cormac. "Will ya look at that little bugger? Never thought I'd witness a beautiful sight as this one."

The baby had his first milk on a soundtrack of the sweetest oooh's and aaah's of all bystanders, young and old. At this point, Nurse Erin approached the Enigmatic Seers of Infinite Zero. She informed them that the current venue was a bit damp and chilly for the baby.

"Of course," nodded the One with the raven. "We will take care of that."

As soon as the baby's belly was filled, the Enigmatic Seers of Infinite Zero suggested the crowd follow them. Via a hidden path, they walked all the way behind the waterfall. Here, there seemed to be a hidden passage in the mountain that led straight into darkness.

After a little hesitation, all followed and

    disappeared from sight.

Chapter 2 **Fundamentally, we all have needs, and these needs are fundamental, regardless of Truth or any other silliness claiming otherwise**

"That was rather neat," said the One with the Viking horns.

Led by the Timeless Mystics of Infinite Zero, the crowd stepped out of the tunnel only shortly after they had stepped into it. In front of them, a large canyon wall towered high above them, stretching out from left to right as far as the eye could see. Looking upwards, they immediately noticed they had come out of a similar canyon wall from their side. By definition, having a canyon wall in front of them, as well as behind them, they found themselves to be in a canyon.

A gentle breeze blew comfortable, warm air through the Narrows Bottom Up. The sun was at the perfect spot to cast the most ethereal light throughout the canyon. A couple of thin trees grew on the side of the river bank. Their leaves lit up like bright green, little lampions. The water of the North Fork Virgin River passed by with a gentle rushing sound.

"What's with the horns?" asked the One with no particular characteristics while the crowd was still trying to adjust to the new scenery.

"Oh, that! You just can't believe what stuff they sell at the Krimml. It's one little gift shop after the other. I simply couldn't resist."

"But how did you manage to stick them through your hood?"

"Dunno. I simply put them on. And then I pulled my hood real tight until the horns decided to protrude."

"I also want horns like that!" trumpeted One who was just One up till now. She ran back into the cave and disappeared from sight in a split second.

Meanwhile, Márcia's baby was being passed from one set of caring arms to another. When it reached Bram, it started exhibiting peculiar behaviour.

"Hey, look at that. It's trying to kiss me on the cheek."

Marwa discretely held her hand before her mouth while she chuckled. Márcia approached and took the baby over from Bram. "It's not trying to kiss you, Bram. It's trying to suckle you."

"Oh."

"Hungry again, that little fella," said ol' Cormac. "Needy little thing, isn't it."

"Talking about needy," said Andrea. "I'm still not comfortable with this Truth. Unlike this little baby, it seems we need to drop our needs in favour of – I don't know – being all blissful in our response to the aliveness of life itself." She had to take a breath after that one. "Or something like that. But what kind of a life is that?"

"Exactly!" said Jimmy. "What kind of a life is that? Are we still to become monks or something? Living on a mountain. Meditating all day. Is that what you expect of us then?"

"Hang on a minute," hushed the One with the Viking horns, clearly in his element to take up a more prominent role. "Perhaps we should sit down a bit first."

The Timeless Mystics of Infinite Zero huddled down on a slope against the canyon wall. In a semi-circle around them, the crowd took seats on the many rocks and boulders scattered across the left bank of the shallow river (of course, if you'd approach from the other direction, the left would be on the right – it sounds obvious, but you can't imagine the confusion which comes from the most obvious).

"We're listening," probed Nurse Erin. "Like to hear the answer to that one."

"Look," nodded the One with the sea thrift in the direction of Márcia, who was breastfeeding her baby. "You see, the baby clearly has fundamental needs. Without them being fulfilled, it wouldn't last a day. So we can agree its needs are vital for its survival, right?"

The glowing One couldn't suppress another 'oooh' before jumping into the conversation. "And while growing up into adulthood – hey, we're adults in hoods, ain't that funny? – err, so, while growing up into adulthood, we continue to have needs which are fundamental to our daily existence."

"You mean we should continue to suck the nipple?" prattled ol' Cormac.

"Well," remarked Nurse Erin, "some men would surely be satisfied with just that."

All the women laughed. "Free porridge bottles for all men," shouted Olivia. "In the shape of a woman's breast! With a fake nipple! The solution to many if not most wars." The applause that followed echoed throughout the canyon.

"Err," continued the glowing One. "That was not exactly what I was going to say, although it surely is a good suggestion. What I wás going to say is this. Err, now what was that?"

"Truth doesn't require us to drop our needs," said the One with Vanessa. "In fact, it's the opposite. Truth can only thrive when it meets our most fundamental needs."

"Yes, that," confirmed the glowing One. "The identity-self, the s̲elf, must be able to find its needs fulfilled in Truth. Otherwise, Truth surely would be discarded in the blink of an eye. It'd be utterly useless."

"Even worse," added the One with Vanessa. "It would be perceived as obstructive to the flow of life we all try to create and shape for ourselves."

"Indeed," said the One with the raven. "Even if we'd all be nodding and agreeing to Truth to be true, we'd soon be forgetting all about it if it doesn't meet us in our day-to-day existence."

"Yeh, okay," said Andrea, "but how can Truth meet our needs?"

The One with the Viking horns slapped himself with a loud clap on the thigh. "A good question!" Then he looked left and right to his masked companions. "So, how are we going to answer that?"

"Perhaps," suggested the One with the sea thrift, "we should first take a closer look at those 'needs' we all have."

"Excellent idea!" said the One with the Vikings horns rather enthusiastically. Then his voice lowered again. "And, err, what are these exactly?"

"Well," started the One with Vanessa while staring with tilted head at the baby. "Starting off easy, I'd say we all have the need for nourishment. That's pretty obvious."

"Yeh, and that's immediately one which keeps us pretty busy on a daily basis. Nicely prepared food, not to forget dessert, is not falling from the sky, is it?"

"Next to that, I'd say we are all in need of physical, mental, and emotional comfort as best as is possible."

"Then there's our need for freedom. Hmm, yet also security and certainty."

"I'd toss in love and joy and social interaction in general."

"Purpose and meaning are good ones, too."

"And how about self-confidence? Being accepted in a group? The feeling of being supported?"

"You think those enlightened fellas in a cave on a mountain all don't have those needs? Most of them probably were introverts, to begin with, anyways."

"Then again, the extroverts among them blab all day long to crowds gathering around them from hither and tither."

All chuckled. The One with the raven ahum'ed briefly to keep them in check.

"Last but not least," said the One without a raven (it just decided to fly off for a bit), "I'd throw in wonder. And awe. And a need for transcendence, that one too."

"And perhaps, perhaps some mystery too?" suggested One.

"Yes, we also are in need of mystery. In a sea of facts, we all secretly yearn for something inexplicable. Something unsolved which we can share thoughts about. Have opinions. Propose ideas. Find solutions or answers. It's a bit like the American dream. Each and every one of us has a chance to gain fortune, fame, and the Nobel Prize. A good mystery allows many gaps which we can try to fill in by ourselves, regardless of our background."

"Or we can simply leave it to be a mystery and revel in its mysteriousness. You know, sometimes we are just fed up with answers. A bit of mystery also allows a bit of humbleness in a society which tends to push us to assertiveness and self-righteousness."

"Then again, when a mystery enters the domain of the spiritual, it becomes mystical. Wait! Is it mythical or mystical? Or both?"

The One without the raven shook his head (now that the raven was gone, he finally could). "The transcendental and mystical bits certainly are something highly misunderstood. You should definitely ask us about those later. Nonetheless, these last ones, and all else of a similar kind, are surely not to be forgotten nor to be underestimated. After all, it's these that brought most of you in this canyon here, didn't they?"

"Bottom line is," spoke the One with the Viking horns loudly. And then softer. "Well, yes, what is the bottom line?"

"Bottom line is," helped the One with the sea thrift, "it is futile to ignore or suppress our fundamental needs. They are the very fabric of our human nature.

You can't expect a flower to unflower after you explain it the Truth. Nor can you ask a stone to unbecome a stone. And so, as well, you will ever remain as you are, despite anyone saying otherwise."

Chapter 3   That pressing need for having no needs (whoever came up with that anyway?)

"But that goes completely against what I always believed," exclaimed Andrea. "Aren't we supposed to seek a way to escape our humanity…"

The Timeless Mystics of Infinite Zero looked confused.

The volume of Andrea's voice went down with every word she uttered. "…like, reach a higher vibration… …ascend into the light… …enter a higher dimension… …leave on a spaceshi-"

The Timeless Mystics of Infinite Zero turned to each other, hoping one would have an answer. But all remained silent, tilting their head this way or that, looking up, looking down, left or – yes indeed – right.

"I'm sorry?" One finally said.

Now, it was Andrea who felt really awkward. Then, she managed to recover her poise. "Okay, forget about the spaceship. What I mean is, well, isn't it obvious? Just look at those needs we always have. Look at all the trouble they give us. All this…"

"The endless cycle of pain and suffering," helped ol' Cormac. "You know, that Saṃsāra stuff of this Gautama fella. I read all the books about that one. Only cycling I got from that is me wheelchair."

"Yes, that! He escaped it, didn't he? – Ouch!!! Verdammt noch mal!"

"Like to see him escape that one," said the glowing One after she pinched Andrea in the arm.

"Smack you in the fa… mask I should," snapped Andrea.

"But then you'd be hurting both our feelings," snivelled the glowing One. "That wouldn't end your suffering, would it?"

"Wise ass," scoffed Andrea while rubbing her arm.

"Peace, sisters," pacified the One with Vanessa. "Perhaps we can take a closer look at this escaping stuff before we go sit under a tree for the next decade or two?"

"I strongly agree," said the One with the sea thrift. "Nothing good comes from that kind of asceticism anyway. You do know he ate himself fat after he finally got up from under that tree, don't you?"

"Now that's a common mistake," corrected the One with the Viking horns wisely. "Siddharta and Pu-Tai, the latter being the chubby one, are often confused with each other. But they both are totally different characters."

"That's true," admitted the One with the sea thrift reluctantly. "As true as Vikings never wore those silly horns."

"Can we please break this atmosphere of bickering?" intervened the glowing One. It's making my glow go gloomy."

In the background, whispering and muttering echoed throughout the canyon. "The Vikings didn't wore horns? – The jolly fat one isn't Buddha? – Next thing you know, fortune cookies aren't really from China. – Or the Great Wall of China isn't visible from space after all. – I think we better not trust anything coming from China. I'll dig into Zen as soon as I get back home. – That's also from China. – Ah, com'on!"

The voice of the One with the raven (ah, it's back) silenced all. "Listen, folks."

All listened. They only heard the pause in his words. Apparently it was exactly this silence which caused them to listen even more. It was a pretty enjoyable moment, listening to silence, and the One with the raven deliberately stretched it a bit.

"So, let's be clear about one thing. Finding Truth, realizing It and integrating It has nothing to do with escaping or transcending our humanity. So let's not fall for cult-like behaviour like denying ourselves stuff or start to forbid things."

"No need to practice abstinence."

"Or demonizing the body. Or the ego. Or the mind."

"Or marrying five wives."

"Bollocks!"

"Now, what would you do with five wives?" whispered Nurse Erin with a wide grin. "You can't even handle a single nurse."

"Yeh, ol' chap," laughed Jimmy, "you'd be desperate to escape that pickle if you were in it."

"So, hopefully, you can get this all in your thick skulls," said the One with the sea thrift. "All those needs and longings, your joys and pains, your pondering and brooding, your physical appearance and your continuous imagining, it's all irrevocably part of who and what you are."

"Exactly," said the One with Vanessa. "All that stuff that makes you human and defines you as such, it simply is the greatest wonder of all. It would be plain and utterly silly to even embark on an endeavour leading you out of this reality. All it'd do is nurture nothing but fantasies where you'll be an easy catch for the CSDCs."

"I may be the broken one in a wheelchair," mused ol' Cormac. "But in ur heads and hearts, I guess, we're all a bit like wounded dreamers looking for castles in the sky."

"That sounds about right," agreed Bram. "I think we all have this tendency to look for the better place beyond. Heaven. The next incarnation. A higher state of consciousness. Or, I don't know, some elevated vibration of somethingness. While it's all more about being fully human, as present, authentic and whole as one can be."

Marwa's face clearly expressed she just couldn't figure the boy out.

"It needn't even be thàt fairy tale-ish," said the One with the sea thrift. "Most people seek the greener grass in ideas like 'one day I'll…', playing the lottery or beating the stock market. Easy ways out, easy promises."

"It's like we are constantly trying to escape what we are," realized Erin. "It sounds plain silly if you think of it, but basically, that's exactly what it is. Why do we do that? It seems pretty fruitless."

"That's the thing," added Bram. "It's pretty useless, also because many of us are seeking a way out in directions where there isn't any. Just look at all those people pretending to be happy and complete with their new method, or their new book, or their new guru. While it always only lasts a little while. And then they dive into something different. Another book, another method, another… what do you call it? CSDC?"

"Why is it that being human becomes so difficult when we grow up?" wondered Márcia while she held her still-nameless little boy. The little infant was sound asleep and seemed to be enjoying being human as best as he ever could in this life. "What is it that will turn my son in a person that starts seeking for something beyond or afar?"

"That's a big question," answered the One with the Viking horns. "If we're to answer that one, we'll be flash-flooded in this canyon before we even get near anything. There's books and books about the difficulty of being human. Talks and talks. And as there ever keep appearing new ones, none appear to hit the nail."

"Well, basically, it boils down to one little thingy," said the One with Vanessa. "Being human is pretty difficult. To summarize a lot of books in one sentence: in its current state, the human brain allows a myriad of stunning possibilities, including them to be in conflict with each other in the most frustrating ways conceivable. Or inconceivable, for that matter.

Besides, if it were only the body getting bruised and broken, it would still be manageable. Well, more or less, I guess. But it's our mind, our psyche – our innerness, so to speak – that also gets its fair amount of bruises, pains and hurts."

"And on top of that," added the One with the sea thrift casually, "we have this knack to be pretty hard on ourselves. While most of us will never literally smack ourselves in the face, we do have the tendency to smack our inner selves like all the time."

"Come to think of it," wondered the One with the Viking horns, "if some were to display the same hostility towards others as to themselves, they'd be in jail for sure."

"Look," concluded the One with the raven, "we've already established that we have fundamental needs. The difficulty lies in how we cope with them. And I'm not talking about the most acute ones now, like food or comfort. Hard as they may be, they still are the easy ones. They only require work and determination, unless, of course, there's circumstances which are hard or even impossible to overcome.

More troubling, and more difficult, are our inner needs. The needs of our psyche. It's literally bombarded by external as well as internal stimuli on a daily basis. The lot of them either nourish our innerness or disturb it. Over time, we accumulate a lot of disturbance to our innerness. We collect needs that were never ours. We please. We try to stand out. We try to belong. And in doing so, we fail to put our experiences to the test of our inner compass. Our self-attention, our inner contemplation, it is all consumed by daily patterns which come to control our lives. Thus, the needle starts to divert."

It was Charles who happened to carry a compass with him. He took it out and looked at it in shock. When all faces went like 'Really!' Charles gave them the typical prankster smile. In return, he received a lot of you-are-a-real-goofball faces.

"Now, this diverting of our inner compass needle needn't be a bad thing. There is a certain stretch to it. And for every single one of us, this stretch is as unique as the original position of the needle. Like you, Bram, you could become a florist or a stockbroker. It depends on the circumstances, but you'd be able to thrive in either direction. However, being colour-blind, you will never become a jet pilot. That option lies beyond your stretch."

"And I wouldn't advise you to become a therapist either, my friend," chuckled the glowing One. "Somehow, you got talked into this, but I suggest you really contemplate this a bit more and check it with your inner compass."

"So," queried Bram with a slight blush on his cheeks. "basically, you are saying that this feeling of discontentment I have came from not following my original path?"

"It's not like there is an 'original' or 'perfect' path, Bram. There might be, but it's you in a big world. There are multiple paths possible. Some will work. Some will not. Still, when your personal compass points north, and wind ever pushes you south, discontentment is inevitable."

"But life is so complicated," objected Bram. "I hardly know north from south, let alone which way my needle is pointing."

"I know, Bram. Yet the problem is not always in all the winds blowing us around. If only you could recognize, attend to, and nurture your uniqueness and its fundamental needs. If only that would come to you as naturally as breathing, life might surely be a lot less complicated, right?"

"Instead," said the One with the sea thrift, "more often than not, we cross this uncrossable line – the really uncrossable line, I mean – and we come to construct a persona which lies too far from what we comfortably can sustain. We suffocate our uniqueness and its simple but fundamental needs. It will drain us and lure us into a vicious circle of doubt. We start to lack self-confidence and a loving self-esteem for the living being we are."

"Bwaaaahhaaaahaaa!" The glowing One erupted in inconsolable crying. "This makes me even more gloomy! I need a break!"

Chapter 4   How good ol' Truth can meet our good ol' needs

Cloaks and hoods flooded towards the gloomy One. Some went on one knee beside her. Others stood behind her and patted her on the back.

"I'm sorry," sobbed the gloomy One. "Don't mind me. I'll be glowing again in no time."

"I'll invite ya to my place," comforted ol' Cormac. "Tell ya Irish and Scottish jokes all night to get your glow going again. Will save me a fortune on electricity."

All laughed. The gloomy One regained her glow a little. After one final sob, she addressed Andrea. "So, Andrea. I'm sorry, could you repeat your question one more time? What was that?"

Andrea was a bit frustrated. After all, her question started in chapter 2 (page 145), and we're at 4 now. "Oh, don't mind this silly cow. You guys and girls just rant on."

"Please, Andrea," insisted the glowing One gently. "I'm sure this time we will nail it."

"Well, okay, one last time then. How can Truth meet our fundamental needs? And, because you started it, how can Truth help us deal with all these other needs which suffocate us instead of serve us?"

"How can Truth meet our fundamental needs?" pondered the One with the sea thrift sincerely, as if he never thought about this before. "Tricky thing. I mean, Truth, as we have discovered so far, is rather adamant in nature. Even worse, not only does it seem to transcend us, but it also kind of disintegrates us. I mean, it does have a way of rendering ourselves as a non-existing existence, no? How can one reconcile that with our personality, our aspirations, our emotional and rational driven actions, relationships… our needs? It seems like an impossibility if you ask me."

Andrea rolled her eyes. "Dude! I kno'ow!"

"It doesn't offer many options, does it?" poked the One with Vanessa.

"We could all start living as hermits, like Jimmy proposed. Abide in Beingness the way everything abides in pointlessness."

"W-w-what," sputtered Jimmy. "I proposed no such thing! I merely-"

"Or," continued the One with Vanessa, "we could succumb to multiple variations of spiritual vanity – you know, go all pretentious about having discovered Truth and show everybody how enlightened we are."

"Yeh," noticed the One with the sea thrift. "Of course, any such attitude only displays how far one can drift from the realization of Truth. Even if that person once may have 'had it', poof, it's gone once more."

"Then again, going all rational at it doesn't work either. See, the avenue of reason and logic is ever walked with the feet of one's individuality. Reason can contemplate I, but reason cannot be I. Failure will once more be inevitable."

"It seems rather more likely we would simply reject the whole thing. And then we're back to square one. Back to finding mental and emotional refuge. Steps here, methods there. Happiness. Self-love. Away with stress. Become more successful. Manage time. Spiritual commodities. Pseudoscientific deceit. Same, same. Boring, boring."

"Either way," smiled the One with the sea thrift, "existence itself simply continues to unfold without the slightest agenda. It will push unrestrainedly ever forward without the slightest care for any schedule or plans we may have ourselves."

Andrea rolled her eyes as far as eyes can possibly roll. The One with Vanessa pretended not to have seen it, which might have seemed plausible were it not for Andrea's loud sigh echoing throughout the canyon.

"Nonetheless," emphasized the One with Vanessa, "even when Truth is experienced and recognized as such from within the $\overline{\text{Self}}$, it will always be the identity-self that works with it, plays with it and comes to accept and even cherish it. Therefore, from our personal perspective, it is paramount for Truth to meet the fundamental needs of the identity-self in order for us to be able to apply and integrate It in our daily lives."

"Been there, done that," Andrea sang like an ambulance.

"Really? Oh. Right. Still, it is imperative that we are well aware of our fundamental needs-"

"and that we recognize their value," added the One with the sea thrift with a raised finger.

"Why would we? Many religions preach abstinence or-"

"And see where that usually gets them. See, the importance of our most intrinsic needs in life exceeds these typical religious or even rational reasons for abandoning them. It's a futile fight. No matter how hard we try – and how hard we can get on ourselves while doing that – most of us will be unable to discard these human needs we have anyway."

"So, my dear Andrea, we can assure you, Truth will certainly not meet our needs by belittling or controlling them. Hence, you surely agree it is a good thing to come to a healthy relationship with those needs we have. After all, without that, and as you very well know, being human can become pretty problematic at times."

"Speaking about that, this actually brings us closer to Andrea's question. Here's the thing: when it comes to the difficulties of being human, we all have a pretty standardized approach to solving things. We already mentioned it on page 60, remember, but it's an important point. We typically tend to approach the problem from within the problem."

"You know, where the person – a.k.a. the problem – is trying to fix itself. Now, don't get us wrong here. We are not implying to drop all that. We're sure there's plenty of good methods and good people to assist with this."

"But there's one perspective often forgotten."

"What's that?" Andrea seemed puzzled now.

"Why, the perspective of the $\overline{\text{S}}$elf, of course."

Marwa slapped herself against the forehead. "I should've known. Of course indeed!"

Andrea was puzzled. "Of course, what?"

"It has no needs," explained Marwa.

"Indeed, Marwa, that's correct. From the perspective of the $\overline{\text{S}}$elf, we are talking about fundamental experiences rather than needs. And here's the thing. These fundamental 'experiences' in the non-identity-self are basically of a singular nature. It's a bit like the transparent whiteness of light.

"Precisely," added the One with the sea thrift. "And just as the whiteness of light can be broken into many colours, likewise this singular nature of pure Beingness can be broken into a multitude of experiences when seen from the perspective of the identity-self."

"Huh?"

"When you, your consciousness, dives into the pureness of Beingness, you are white light. But when your consciousness is more focused on your environment, it takes the colours of your environment."

"Ya turn red when ya feel ashamed," shouted ol' Cormac, who thought the whole thing was pretty obvious. "And ya turn pale when ya're scared."

"And you turn blue when you feel blue," added Jimmy sarcastically.

"Very nice," remarked the One with the oxeye daisy, dryly, while he gently put his sea thrift on a rock. "Another analogy could be the lightbulb versus the torchlight. Imagine yourself in a large room. It's totally dark, and all you have is a torchlight. But the torchlight only brings light to a small area. You can wave it around, but you never get the whole picture. That's when your consciousness is narrow and confined. So you frantically wave the torchlight around in search of a bigger picture."

"And then there's the lightbulb," smiled the glowing One. "Once you hit the switch it goes on. All of a sudden, you can see the entire room without a problem. Nothing is hidden. All is clear. Now you can finally relax."

"So, you see," said the One with Vanessa, "where the identity-self is always in a causal flow between need and fulfilment, the non-identity is rather in some perpetual state of abundance. It's fulfilled on its own. You, in your essence, are fulfilled on your own."

"And from that perspective, Andrea, you will come to recognize and accept how existence in its entirety is fulfilled as it is. Truth integrates and pervades our individuality through Beingness. And it's exactly here where

Truth meets your fundamental needs. It's here Truth also helps you deal with those typical needs that tend to suffocate you."

"That's the beauty of it," said the One with Vanessa. "This state of contentment and abundance, within the $\overline{\text{S}}$elf, has the capacity to somehow shower the identity-self with its bounty."

"So you see, we're not saying you should sit on a mountain and abide in beingness 24/7. Yet a little lingering in Beingness during the day will prove far from useless or a waste of time." – The One with the daisy – (since we tend to repeat stuff, our editor decided to cut 'oxeye' for the sake of keeping the book within an acceptable number of pages)

"Exactly, if you'd only be able to do that once in a while, you will learn soon enough how this bounty of Beingness will meet your most essential and deepest personal needs." – The One who performs magic tricks (it's decided!) –

"Even better, I dare say. You will soon see how the light of Beingness will brighten the needs of the identity-self. You'll be reconnected with your authentic needs so you can distinguish and nourish them. And at the same time, you will identify those silly, useless needs that you constantly get shoved up in your noses. Put them in perspective or even drop them all together." – The One with the dice –

"In short, from the pure and simple experience of Beingness, the grace of this non-identity will truly uplift your identity-self. Most of the confinements and impediments we experience as individuals will either dissolve or turn into manageable challenges." – The One in shorts – (actually, this is the One with the daisy who is wearing shorts underneath his hooded cloak)

"And thus, you will find a frequent dive into Beingness to be most practical for being an authentic and sane human being, living a fulfilling and meaningful life. It's not a leap into escapism. It rather is a solid jump straight into a satisfying existence, regardless of accomplishments or disappointments." – The One with the raven –

"You see," chuckled ol' Cormac to his nurse, "we're lucky. No need to push me wheelchair up a mountain to live as hermits."

"We are lucky, you say?" she said, astonished. "How'd you like it if I pushed you down that mountain of yours? See how enlightened you'll be then."

"Oh, can you take us along for that one, please?" pleaded Calvin. "Sounds like an awesome idea! We could probably also install a warp drive to make it go even faster!"

"I'll stay with the nurse," remarked Hobbes dryly. "Love to help her with collecting all the bones." Somehow, nobody heard that last bit.

Bram raised his finger. "So basically, you are saying we shouldn't struggle with Truth but go along with it. And on the way, we'll find exactly that what we were always searching for, right?"

"Exactly," answered the One with the Viking horns cheerfully. "The thing with the identity-self, your personality and all, is that there is always some causal flow between need and fulfilment. The need is always long, while the fulfilment is frustratingly short. A new need arises even before the previous one is fulfilled. The non-identity, the $\overline{S}$elf, you, in your essence, is rather in some perpetual state of ease and contentment. And it has the capacity to shower the identity with that bounty."

The One with the Viking horns looked oddly upwards. "Hey, I think I'm experiencing a déjà vu."

The Timeless Mystics of Infinite Zero all sighed and smiled at the same time.

"What? What?" sputtered the One with the Viking horns.

"It's fine," said Marwa. "I wouldn't mind going on repeat about that bounty. And I'm sure Bram here didn't get it the first time anyway."

Now it was Bram going, 'What? What?'.

"Thank you, Marwa," said the One with the raven. "So, Bram, and all, this bounty-showering, it expresses itself in different ways. It can simply be felt as contentment…"

"… or peacefulness…"

"... joy..."

"... deep gratitude..."

"... acceptance..."

"... trust. I mean, in its purest way. Not in a way like you're sure the outcome of things will be exactly to your liking. Just trust, in its essence."

"Compassion... freedom..."

"We could blab about it all day in a poetic way. The experience is all. This frequent abiding in Beingness, with an involvement which transcends the identity-self, offers peace, solace, comfort, vitality and health to the troubled mind you carry along all day long."

"So, dearest Andrea. Truth is Truth. It's just that. However, it's in the experience of Beingness that you'll come to meet Truth. And from this special acquaintance, Truth will meet your needs. Not by fulfilling them or making them happen, that's the talk of the CSDCs, but by showering them with enough-ness. In this state of not needing, in this state of all-is-good-ness, you are offered a fresh perspective. Perhaps you will regain the vitality needed to carry on. Perhaps you'll intuitively shift your expectations. Or perhaps, your identity-self, your personality will come to accept the situation and drop all this pointless struggling."

Somehow, all got a little silent, each innerly musing and brooding in their own hearts and minds over the words spoken.

The Timeless Mystics of Infinite Zero decided it was time to move on. Each of them took one of the many wooden sticks positioned against the foot of the canyon wall.

"Usually you only find them near the temple of Sinawa," said the One who is writing all this. "But I took the liberty to put some of them at this spot for our convenience."

"He's an odd fella, isn't he?" whispered Erin in ol' Cormac's ear. When the Timeless Mystics of Infinite Zero stepped knee-deep into the river, with their cloaks floating around them, she somehow decided to follow without any reservations and pushed Cormac's wheelchair straight into the river. Ol' Cormac was about to scream 'Nooooo', but from the moment the wheels touched the water, a yellow rescue ring spontaneously inflated around the wheelchair. A second later, ol' Cormac found himself floating on the water with Nurse Erin desperately trying to hold on to the handles of the wheelchair.

"Feels like I'm freakin' James Bond!" whooped ol' Cormac excited. "Perhaps I can eject nails and oil and stuff as well."

"It'll cost you a good nurse!" yelled Jimmy. "Hey Erin, better let go of him. We all'll take turns bumping him in the right direction."

And so, ol' Cormac found himself spinning left and right while floating along the river. He never had felt this much joy in his entire life.

The Timeless Mystics of Infinite Zero waded through the canyon. The crowd merrily followed, continuously stunned by the intense colour palette of the majestic walls on their left and right: brown, pink, white, salmon, gold and vivid ruby; it was all there. Those who looked straight up could spot a sapphire crack as if blue lightning had split the rocks in two.

Then they heard wild splashing in the back. "Oi! Wait for me!"

It was the One with the magician's staff trying to catch up. Soon enough, she found herself panting next to the One with the Viking horns.

"So, you didn't go for the Viking horns, did ya?"

"Well, at first I wanted to. But then I saw this beautiful staff, and I just couldn't resist. Bet ya I can cast fireballs with this one!"

"No, you can't," said the One who is writing all this. "And that's the end of it!"

A little further, the Timeless Mystics of Infinite Zero and the crowd came upon a series of bamboo boats. Each of them came with a fisherman or fisherwoman wearing a purple áo dài tunic dress. Underneath the elegant, silky dress, they wore equally impeccable black trousers. They all had the same typical conical nón lá hats and a pedal (you can imagine which one they had on their head and which was in their hands).

The Timeless Mystics of Infinite Zero embarked in about four of them.

And so, the crowd decided to do the same thing. Only ol 'Cormac was floating along behind the last one while Nurse Erin was sitting comfortably in the boat, keeping the Irish Scotsman on a long leash.

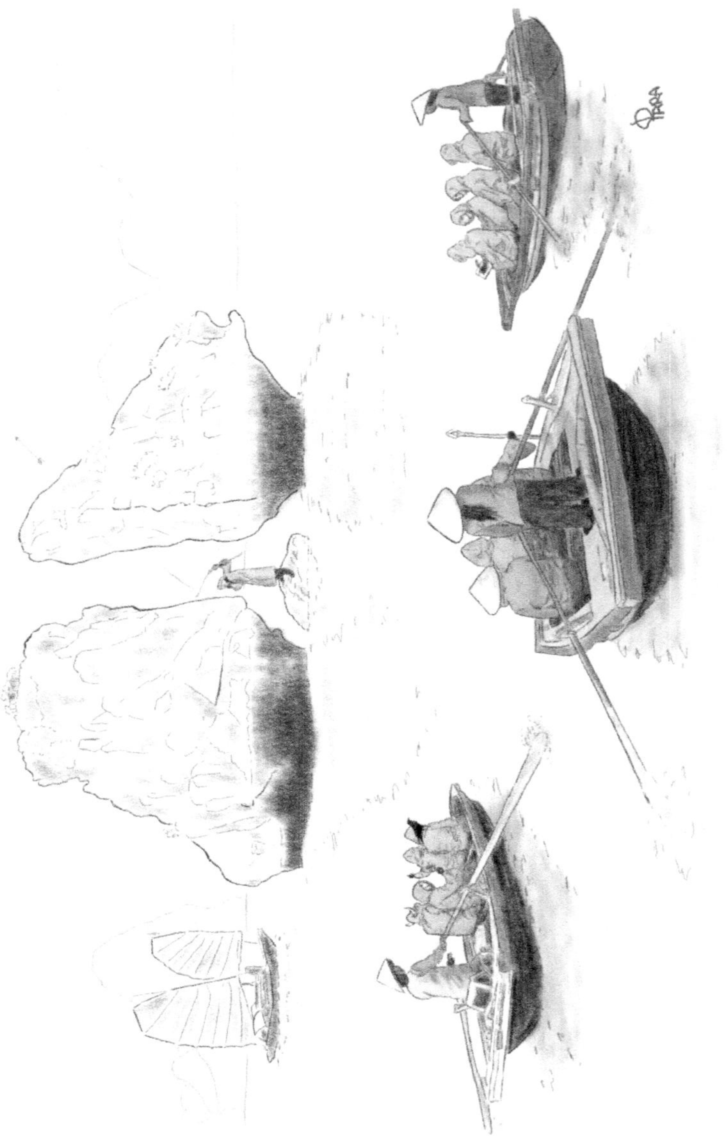

Chapter 5   **Paradoxical stuff**

"I don't get it," said Kalle. "I just don't get it".

"It blows my mind as well," said Jimmy with a mix of surprise, shock and wonder. "How the fricky-di-frack did we get here all of a sudden?"

While the river grew wider, the bamboo boats all floated gently into Ha Long Bay. Limestone pillars and islets, all sparsely covered with tropical trees, rose in front of them like gigantic pebbles in shallow water.

"I don't mean that, silly. That's the least of my I-don't-get-its. I mean this whole sales talk about Truth and Beingness and how it benefits us as a person, our personality or whatever."

"What's not to get?" Actually, Jimmy hadn't the slightest clue either. He cleverly decided to keep that to himself.

"Don't you start that crap, Jim! It was you who said it's pointless to begin with."

"I did no such thing!" (That's actually correct.)

"What's not to get, you ask? All that Truth-usefulness, of course. Why bother? It's all pointless anyways. It's all fake! Whatever we say or do, however we feel, it's all preordained as it is."

"I feel the same way," added Sven. "Kalle is right. The whole of existence is simply a predetermined field in which we are trapped for all eternity. We're like these self-conscious victims; aware observers, yes, sure – but nonetheless, we are all sitting helplessly in this boat while we watch the movie play until the lights go out."

"Precisely," agreed Kalle. "The outcome of things, the end of the movie, it is all written in stone since the beginning of the universe. What purpose can we possibly have if nothing can be changed?"

"Ah," said the One writing all this. "Finally, we're getting back to this subject. Took me a television studio, waterfalls, a canyon and a bay to get here."

"Kalle, Sven," the One with the raven said quietly, "we understand what you say. Truly. It's completely alright and normal to think this way. But… it's also wrong."

"How can it be wrong?" asked Kalle and Sven simultaneously while they almost tipped their boat over.

"If I may," started the One with the magician's staff. "Okay, let me start with a small recap of the previous part in which I was only known as One. See, on the one hand, you have the s̲elf. You know, that's the doer, the wanter, the needer, the taker, the giver, the lover, etcetera. On the other hand, you have the S̄elf. That one is simply that. It's being Beingness, just being aware, non-judgmental, non-interactive, simply content in contentment and all that. And then there is the universe, continuously unfolding with an unstoppable momentum in which every single little moment endlessly gives rise to the next."

"Whoooo," cheered the glowing One. "That sounds like a holy trinity. We should exploit that! Can you imagine the sales we'll make when we turn that into a necklace? Naturally, it will also have our image on it. And millions of people will wear it over the T-shirts we design along with it. And every time our followers encounter one another, they will exchange a high five and tell bystanders 'well, the universe made us do it'. "

Kalle ignored the glowing One's pun and kept focusing on the One with the magician's staff. "But that's exactly my point! This unfolding includes the s̲elf and all it is doing. And I feel it does that in such an encompassing way that it radically renders this s̲elf as utterly useless."

"Yeh," added Sven, "We simply suffer everything that happens to us. Your Truth only turns us into helpless bystanders. This s̲elf, as you name it, simply is non-existent in the way we think or perceive it to be. It's more like a cog in a giant mechanism or something, nothing more."

"Well, there goes our trinity necklace," sulked the glowing One. "Kalle and Sven kicked one out. And I don't like duos. It gives a dualistic ring to it. And that will surely put us in a tight spot in part 3 when you start using a word to which we are allergic."

"Too bad indeed," shrugged the One with the magician's staff. "But still, here's the thing. That helpless-watcher-in-the-couch... err... -boat view is the most egoistic there can be. Really. You came soooo close, Kalle. And then your ego got the best of you. You see, even if we rationally understand the Truth, we still persist in thinking ourselves to be outside of this causalistic chain of events."

"You claim to be non-existent," said the One with the daisy, "and at the same time, you complain about it. Don't you see, that's just plain silly? We can't repeat this enough. Because it's simply not correct."

"Why's that?" asked Sven.

"There is nobody watching the movie. There are no bystanders. We are all in it. Each and every single one of us is a character on this cosmic, multidimensional movie screen."

"Yet regardless of all that, the movie is playing," said the One with the daisy. "This s̲elf, it no less continues to believe itself to be the doer, all while the S̄elf remains absorbed in timeless presence as ever. Our identity and non-identity, both of them, remain as present as a stone which suddenly would come to realize it is nothing but a stone."

"And just as the self-realized stone wouldn't run off or start dancing, you and your ego, your psyche and your Beingness, won't disappear as well, regardless of what escape plan the CSDCs might offer you."

"I just don't understand," sighed Sven. "It's the worst catch-22 I've ever faced in my life."

"Oi," shouted ol' Cormac uncomfortably from the back. He was still floating on top of the yellow rescue ring while his IV dingle-dangled above his head. "I can't hear a word you're saying."

"Oh, sorry, my bad," replied the One who is writing all this. From that point on, ol' Cormac was able to hear everything being said.

"Basically, there's two ways out of this," noted the One with the daisy. "There is utter frustration where you keep approaching this rationally, and you'll only find it all makes sense... without making sense at all. Or...

"Or???" went the entire crowd.

"Or, there is the experiential approach, where your identity-self gradually comes to terms with Truth, when it finds itself engulfed with those deeper feelings of humbleness, surrender and gratitude. When it, you, no longer feel threatened by persistent little thoughts. When you find solace in something bigger than yourself, 'you' will give way easily, just as you would be willing to give your life in a split-second if that would save your children or loved ones."

"The realization of Truth does not need to be of a destructive nature, not for the identity-self, nor for the non-identity-self. And at the same time, it is. It's not a catch-22. It's a paradox!

"And here's the beauty," said the One who performs magic tricks. "You can dive into this paradox. You can live it. You can breathe it. And by living and breathing it, you will step into a realm of continuous wonder. It's magic! It's a trick. While all at the same time… it isn't."

"A paradox?" queried Kalle.

"But paradoxes are by definition impossible, no?" wondered Sven.

"Fair enough," answered the One with the daisy. "A paradox is indeed a seemingly impossible situation. But it nonetheless appears to be true, however absurd it may seem to be."

"Exactly," affirmed the One with the bow and arrow while nocking the arrow. What, you never noticed her before? You really should pay attention!

The One with the bow and arrow grasped the bowstring and then drew the bow. She aimed at the sky and released the arrow. The arrow flew out. But then it all of a sudden seemed to remain suspended, hovering motionlessly above the water.

"You see," pointed the One with the bow and without an arrow. "The arrow has a problem. The distance between me and the point where it will dive into the water can be divided in two. Thus, it has to cover that first half to get to its target. But, once it reaches this first half, the remaining distance can be divided into two parts. If we keep doing that, the arrow will never be able to arrive."

"Another nice paradox is how a mathematician can prove that $1 = 2$. (No need to elaborate on this here. It's all on YouTube.)

"Of course," explained the One with the daisy, "the solution to such paradoxes is to reveal how they inconspicuously circumvent certain laws which simply can't be circumvented. In reality, it is pointless to divide zero, and equally, reality will simply not allow to divide by zero. Sure, our imaginative mind may, at first glance, have no problem with such a minor trifle. But reality itself will be relentless in its behaviour: one will therefore never be equal to two; the arrow of Zena's bow here will irrevocably land in the water."

While his words were still entering the ears of the crowd, the arrow disappeared into the water.

"Oh, my," gasped the glowing One. "Hope it doesn't hit a fish down there."

A familiar warmth flowed down the back of the One with the raven. The fisherwoman steering his bamboo boat had to bite her lip not to burst into laughter. "That darn raven," grumbled the One with the raven while a shiver went over his spine.

"Anyways," continued the One with the daisy. "It's basically the same with our perceptible trinity of self, $\overline{\text{S}}$elf and the Universe. In Truth it's no trinity at all. It's a unity, as it always was and always will be."

The glowing One quickly intervened as she felt this last sentence to have come too soon in this story. "But as you can see," she said with both arms spread wide open. "Here we are, pondering these words, mesmerizing life and trying to make sense out of it all. It's as if we are the ultimate division by zero as if we have escaped the very laws that shape us and everything around us."

"So basically," concluded the fisherman of the boat which held Kalle and Sven, "even while we all are part of an interconnected unfolding in an undividable oneness, we still have the undeniable experience of being separated, self-conscious beings with a disposition of free will."

"Exactly!" applauded the glowing One. "Deep, man! Deep."

"Really?" murmured Sven softly while staring at the fisherman in wonder. Then Sven shook his head. "I'm confused again. So, we are an illusion? We aren't? Which one is it?"

"Seeing ourselves and everything around us as an illusion is pretty silly," answered the glowing One. "It's this typical, obsolete way of thinking, over and over again. When we try to bend our minds around Truth we usually end up with a view that we are pulling ourselves out of the equation. I can think of myself to be an illusion; ergo, I am not, but everything else might be."

"My thinking exactly," said the fisherman while gently steering the bamboo boat. "And just as much, there surely is no point to any form of denial of ourselves as we are. Dismissing our human experience as an illusion is just as well part of the illusion as agreeing with it."

Sven's eyes almost popped out of his head.

"Stop staring, dude," whispered Kalle. "And please, close your mouth."

"In the end, it always boils down to the experience," the fisherman ranted on. "The experience itself is real. It's surely not solipsistic in nature. And neither is it merely subjectively present in your mind. A neurosurgeon could cut it away with a scalpel. And so, as well, there's many ways to induce hallucinations or out of body experiences if you'd like that. It's just a matter of stimulating the brain in the right way."

"Hey Steve," shouted the fisherman's wife from the other bamboo boat in Vietnamese. "Ngừng quấy rối khách du lịch với những điều vô nghĩa của bạn, được không!"

("Stop harassing the tourists with your nonsense, will ya!")

"Tôi chỉ đang cố gắng giúp đỡ, người phụ nữ. Những người này hoàn toàn bị ngắt kết nối với cuộc sống. Và sau đó họ đang nhận lời khuyên từ những người đeo mặt nạ và mặc áo choàng, người ta có thể điên đến mức nào?"

("I'm merely trying to help, woman. These people are completely disconnected from life. And then they are taking advice from folks with masks and robes; how crazy can one be?")

"Now, now, let's not overcomplicate things," suggested the glowing One while the marital quarrel went on. "We all share this experience of being separate and mutually interacting living beings. And in this experience, we can move and inspire each other in many different ways, for better or worse."

"Can't be avoided," shrugged the One with the daisy. "To be and not to be, it's happening at the same time. Might as well go along with it, however paradoxical it may be."

"And why wouldn't we?" suggested the One with Vanessa. "$\overline{S}$elf and $\underline{s}$elf both have the capacity to have a tremendous, wonderful experience, each in their own realm and all its governing aspects. Wouldn't waste that with sulking all day, would we?"

"And as said before," stated the One with the Viking horns wisely, "Truth is meaningless if it is incapable of meeting the fundamental needs of the $\underline{s}$elf. Likewise, it is just as meaningless if it is not capable of allowing the fundamental experiences of the $\overline{S}$elf."

"But how does that even work?" wondered Andrea.

"Well," chuckled the glowing One, "it's all about not making a choice at all and diving straight into this paradoxical existence."

"Hang on, choice between what?"

The One with the dice juggled his dice in one hand for a moment. Then he looked Andrea straight into the eyes. "Once you truly understand you are a character on the cosmic, multidimensional movie-screen, once you realize there is no observer, you may get the impression that you have to choose between two contradictory options. Either you decide to be the character and forget about the movie. Or, you decide to be the light that's projected on the movie-screen. Be one with everything and abide by that stuff. Not much of a choice there."

"But there's another option," said the One who performs magic tricks. "A magical third: you may as well actively participate in the play while recognizing it is a play. A paradoxical state of being."

The One with the Viking horns clapped his hands. "I'd say even more: a paradoxical existence!"

That created a bit of silence. Somehow all the Mystical Mages of Infinite Zero seemed to glow.

Eventually it was Marwa who decided to break the silence. "Could we explore this a bit more?" she asked.

"Perhaps," pondered the One with the dice doubtful. "Or maybe it might be fruitful to examine the fundamental essentials of our humanness a bit more in detail, no? And while we're at that, we might as well do it from two perspectives. The one of the self and the one of the $\overline{\text{S}}$elf. And somewhere in between the lines, you'll find that paradoxical path as well."

The One with the Viking horns seemed puzzled. "Might be hard to spot that one, being between lines and all."

"They'll figure it out."

"Anyways," ended the One with the raven. "We should proceed. After all, it is exactly the lack of this dual perspective that gives rise to a lot of misunderstanding and confusion. No magic can happen in such cloggy-foggy, now can it? Surely, Truth deserves a clarity in which it becomes obvious how It can offer a meaningful and joyful existence. And simultaneously, this clarity can elevate us. It can enable us to rise above this duality, allowing us to harmoniously resonate with It at all times."

"Oi," shouted ol' Cormac in the back. "You, with that butterfly. I think I may have found some of its friends."

When all looked back, they saw how ol' Cormac was covered head to toe (and wheelchair) with vanessa atalantas. The Irish Scotsman held out his hands helplessly while he shrugged his shoulders. This caused the red admirals to head straight for Vanessa.

"Oh, wonderful!" said the One with Vanessa to the butterfly on her index finger. "Your family has arrived!"

Love

The bamboo boats serenely traversed the jade-green water. Limestone mountains towered left and right. Their pristine, majestic presence induced a tranquillity which could only be disturbed by the troubled minds of troubled human beings.

When they reached a quiet area without any currents, the fishermen steered the bamboo boats in the shape of a star. All were facing each other now. Even ol' Cormac got neatly lined up for a nice conversation.

"Don't I look awesome!" beamed the One with the nón lá (one of the fishermen gave him a spare).

"I wouldn't know," mumbled the One covered with red admirals. "I'm in the midst of a family reunion."

All laughed except Marwa. "Family," she sighed. "There's an example. How can I ever love my family again? And also, how can I ever fall in love... when falling in love is nothing but pre-determined, built-in chemistry serving no other purpose than to procreate?"

"There there," comforted the glowing One while Bram's mood hit ground zero. "You stuffed a lot of silly science in one sentence there, now, didn't you?"

"Well, it's true, isn't it?" cried Marwa. "What's the point of love? There is none."

"Well, to be precise, there's more to it than just procreation," explained the One with the daisy. "There's a lot of neurotransmitters, there's the role of the vagina nerve, there's that stuff called oxytocin, there's endogenous opioids, there's dopamine, there's-"

"Can you cut that out!" chided the glowing One angrily. "It's not helping, dude! And besides, it's the vagus nerve, you silly! The other one is where they put those eggs for-I-don't-know-why!"

Then, the glowing One came back at ease and directed herself to Marwa. "First of all, dearest Marwa, you're going a bit mental on us. And you know there's more to us than being mental, right? So let's just relax a little."

"Observe your breath for a moment," guided the One with the magician's staff calmly. "Now that you do, see, while becoming aware of it, you all of a sudden are trying to control it. While all along, it was happening – all by itself – before you came to notice it.

Very good. Now, try to allow your breath.

Simply allow it.

See. It automatically becomes deeper. More relaxed. Like inner tensions are no longer disturbing it."

"It's the same with love," glowed the glowing One. "You can allow it exactly the same way. You understand? It's important. Because the s̲elf needs love just as much as the body needs to breathe. It needs to love as well as it needs to be loved. You can't just reason that away with some mental realization. Of course, you can still fall in love, Marwa!"

Bram could have sworn the mask of the glowing One turned him a wink emoji for a split second.

"Humanity may still be a long way from transcending stupidity," said the One with Vanessa. "But mankind surely has proven itself capable of transcending mere procreative objectives."

This had Bram glowing even more than the words of the glowing One.

"Exactly," cheered the glowing One. "And love comes in so many different shapes and forms. There's the unconditional love of a mother. There's the conditional love amongst lovers. There's love for friends, and there's love for family. There's passionate love, and there's habitual love. There's love for trees, clouds and light. Love for animals or love for a cause. Love between two humans can even reach a level that can be called spiritual when there's this mystical spark between two persons that goes totally against common standards or understanding. Yet there it is."

"Seems to me we need as many different words for love as the Sámi have for snow," concluded Sven.

"And ideally," added the One with the magician's staff, "when it's all balanced out, it's the most satisfying situation one can be in. You feel accepted. You feel open to receive. And from this place of receiving you are equally willing to give. Love is nourishment for the s̲elf. There is care. There is commitment. There is connection and bonding. It's absolutely vital for our mental and emotional wellbeing."

"Of course," added the One with the daisy dryly, "there is a bit of a dark side too. It can become toxic, so to speak."

"At times, love can become demanding," explained the One with the nón lá. " Like an obligation or a directive. And just as well, it can turn to disappointment or frustration when it lacks mutual interaction or bumps into conflicts. Circumstances and our personality can bend and stretch it in many, many ways. It can become ever more beautiful, but unfortunately, it can become ugly also."

"So I guess one can say love can become distorted?" pondered Bram. "Can that be avoided, too?"

"Not always, Bram," answered the One with the magician's staff. "Friction is inevitable in human interaction. We're not living in Lala-land, are we? Then again, it does have the tendency to become distorted where it didn't need to be like that. Like when there's a lack of communication or understanding. But mostly at times when we are disconnected from our inner ease."

"Also," said the One with Vanessa. "The two most perfectly fitted seeds can meet with the greatest joy while floating in the air – and still hit unfertile land."

"Biologically speaking," remarked the One with the daisy, "that last example doesn't make any sense. But I see what you mean."

"Yes, yes, yes, the love experienced within the s̲elf can become distorted too," said the glowing One, a little annoyed. She eagerly wanted to skip ahead, and here she does:

"And that proves the beauty of Love all the more. I mean, Love with a capital! The Love experienced from within the $\overline{\text{S}}$elf. When you reconnect with the $\overline{\text{S}}$elf, when you briefly linger there – or when you timelessly abide in it, if only once a day – you discover a quality which exceeds the love we usually experience. From within this pure experience, there is nothing but Love. You see, it's no longer an interaction in need of balancing. This may sound very weird but… One simply becomes Love."

"Really?" was all Andrea could utter.

"Really!" affirmed the glowing One. "It can happen to you. It can happen to priests with weird toilets."

Many hands and arms went up into that typical 'what?' serif W-shape with heads going left or right.

"But shouldn't we love ourselves a bit more?" tried Andrea. "Isn't that what they always say?"

"I don't think you heard me there, Andrea. When you've become Love, when that pure feeling of Love vibrates in your core being, there is no loving yourself. You are Love."

The One with Vanessa nodded. "In the experience of the $\overline{\text{S}}$elf, you are as sweet as can be. You are sweetness itself, without any ingredients coming from others. You are complete."

"Loving yourself surely has a nice ring to it," added the One with the bow and without an arrow. "But it's pretty silly psychology if you ask me. I mean, how can you love yourself? How many of you are in there?"

" 'To love yourself' is just a statement. It isn't based on real experience," elaborated the One with the magician's staff. "It's a mental, rational approach to the Love we just talked about. But it's a dead end. You can linger a bit in this love-yourself reasoning, sure, but it will never be satisfying."

"Exactly," said the glowing One. "You all here have had goosebumps, no?

At a concert, for example, when the music, the players, and the crowd touched you so deeply, the hair on your arms came up, right? Telling yourself to love yourself is a bit like telling yourself to have goosebumps. You can't reason yourself into this. It needs an actual experience."

"You could empty your freezer and go sit in it," suggested the One with the Viking horns. "I always get goosebumps from that."

"Right," said the One with the raven while the raven shook its head. "Anyways, you cannot love yourself. But you do have the capacity to be Love. As you will learn soon enough, the leitmotiv of this whole thing is always the same: reconnect with your essence, with that untainted Beingness. In this experience, when you are Love, you are complete. You are fulfilled. From that Knowledge, from that regained strength, you get an all-new perspective on the love situation you are in with your identity-self."

The One with the nón lá looked around at all in their boats. "From abundance within the S̄elf, you can work with lack within the self. It's not that this lack will be automatically solved or anything. But you do have this foundation from where you can deal with it in a more constructive way. Even when you lack love, either from family, friends or a partner, this Love in Beingness is ever there."

"It's not that Love is all," said the One with the raven. "Relational love still remains crucial in our daily life. Both states can be there at the same time. The paradox doesn't need to collapse."

"Look, simply put, the experience of the S̄elf allows those who still long for a relationship to experience the purest Love, which is non-relational in nature. And this experience takes that typical pressure away, which tends to block us even more in our state of loneliness. Those who find Love radiate love. And that will rather facilitate a relationship than block it."

"As long as you don't fanatically start to radiate love in order to obtain a relationship," chuckled the glowing One.

Erin's head wobbled a bit as if she was close to agreeing to what was being said. But then she shook her head determinedly. "Yeh," she said with a cynical tone, "love is all, and all is love, that's what they say, right? Just try to sell that when there is killing, rape, torture, neglect or abuse in this all they speak of."

"Ah, I see," answered the One with the magician's staff. "That's actually a common mistake, Erin. 'All is Love' is an expression which arises from the experience of Beingness. Since it is a boundless and timeless experience, one can correctly say 'all is Love'. But when you project this experience onto your daily existence, of course, it will meet contradiction."

The One with the raven nodded his head. The black bird did the same. "The trick is to live the paradox. If you choose one over the other, it will only give rise to misconceptions. The realization of Truth, the experience of Love, the state of Beingness, it will not eradicate the many states of doingness we experience from within the identity. Nor does it ask us to accept such stuff or do nothing about it. Nothing will prevent you from acting, as a person or as a collective, when there is a situation like you described."

Freedom

"You're pulling our leg, right?" sobbed Nurse Erin, losing her poise. "Act you say? By what choice? We have no freedom. It's all decided already! It's fixed..." Her voice lowered to a whisper. "...and I feel broken."

"Yehyohfreedomhadtogoyouhadtomakeitgoandnowwearestuckstuckasarocknotknowingwhattodowhenalldoisalreadydecideddecidedlikeabillionyearsagoallbecauseoftruthallinthenameoftruthnochoicefixedstillbrokennochoicefixedandbrokennochoicefixedstillbrokennochoice."

"Say what?"

Mykhailo shook his head. "방찬, you really need to take your medicine, man."

"No freedom?" uttered the One covered with Vanessa's with a muffled tone. "From my current position, I can relate to that, like totally."

"Freedom," sighed the One with the Viking horns. "That's a big one. We're definitely going to be late for supper now."

"No better time to dig into that one than now," smiled the glowing One.

"Right," started the One with the dice voluntarily, "let's dig in, shall we? Freedom it is. Freedom... Hmm... Freedom is most likely the most fundamental need of us all, isn't it? But here's the thing. This freedom, it's rarely truly understood."

Bram took the bait. "What do you mean?"

"Well, when we say 'freedom', we usually refer to having a choice, right? You know, free will and stuff. It's what society and philosophers tell us. It's what the law and the government tell us. It's what our mother tells us. We like to have the freedom to choose and act, and we are obliged to accept the catch as well."

"The catch?"

"Well yes, we also have to take responsibility for the choices we make, don't we? We are accountable for our actions, if not by the laws of mankind, then surely by the laws of nature... or our mother's. And if it's not law or nature being the judge of our actions, then surely we have a pretty good knack for judging ourselves."

"Oh."

"So, you see, this ability to choose freely is a bit overrated to begin with. Our choices are strongly shaped by habits, imprints, social standards, etc. Some scientists even claim that our choices are made before we are conscious of them. So the whole thing is a little overidealized if you really come to think of it. And it gets worse."

"Worse?" Bram was on a roll in taking bait.

"Well, we have to admit it: choices can often be anything but fun. Just think of the avalanche of decisions we all have to make on a daily basis. It can bring us to the brink of frustration or despair. At times, and more often then we dare to admit, it can all simply get too much."

"Well, calling it an avalanche is not really an uplifting way to go," commented the One with the nón lá.

"Yes, I must admit," testified Olivia, "at times, I can feel pretty paralyzed by all these choices I have to make. And then I'm not even mentioning the big ones, like what I'd like to do with my life. What to study? Which profession to aim for? Which guy to marry? Children? No children? What to make for dinner? The damned colour of the new car! The pattern in the freakin' new front do'oor!"

"Exactly," said the One with the dice. "One could say the luxury of freedom can be a real burden as well."

"You wanna know the funny thing?" whispered the One with the nón lá. "We truly are a contradictive lot when it comes to free will." Then his voice turned back to normal levels. "Here we are, all wailing about free will. 'I like to be free to pick my own chocolate.' – 'I wanna be free to decide how long I can be on TikTok.' – 'I like to choose where I'm going on a holiday all by myself.'

But when it comes to the big decisions, we suddenly start to waver. The ante of failure, guilt, responsibilities or a multitude of other consequences is upped as well. So we rather leave the big choices to chance."

"Or providence," added the One with the dice.

"Or providence," concurred the One with the nón lá. "Suddenly, we become all humble and would rather have God decide our paths than do it ourselves. Husband? In the stars. Job? Must be in my hand palm. Left one or right one? I'll need a face reading for that one first. Fortune? My next tarot card reading session is already booked."

All laughed in that particular way when one agrees something is obviously silly while one secretly knows one is guilty as well.

"Fair enough," objected Nurse Erin, "but now you make it sound as if free will is only a terrible burden, like we should throw it overboard altogether."

"Hey!" warned a fisherwoman waving her index finger, "You not throw anything in water, you hear. Keep clean!"

"Not at all, dearest Erin," replied the One with the dice. "We merely are digging our way to the essence. Otherwise, we will only remain stuck in superficial opinions. Free will, real free will, in its raw essence, is more about having the unrestricted possibility to freely choose than it is about actively making the actual choice itself."

"Say what?"

"Having free will is more a feeling than it is an action," explained the One with the nón lá. "It is about not féélíng pushed or influenced in a certain direction. It's about the ability to féél you can decide for yourself instead of a decision being imposed or forced on you. The decision itself is less important than the féélíng of being able to choose. Even when we give this freedom away to God or providence, then at least that is still in agreement with our feelings about it. So, it's more about the idea of having all possibilities open to oneself, even the possibility of forfeiting this possibility, if you get my meaning."

"Oh."

"You see what we are trying to say, Erin?" checked the One with the dice. "Most of you make it all about actual choices or decisions and their moral implications. But that's a bit of a short-sighted view which solely comes from the position of the self. It's understandable, yes. And we are not saying this is not important. Of course it is. But there's more to it than that. Being able to choose left from right may be practical in navigating this world. But it hardly offers a true connection with who we truly and essentially are. More often than not, it leads us away from it."

"Hang on," intervened Mykhailo with his thick Russian accent. "That's not right. 'Navigating' should bring us closer to our destination, not away. You are talking in contradictions."

"You are absolutely right, Mykhailo," chuckled the One with the magician's staff. "But the contradiction is on you. Most of you believe all is jolly fine when you manage to navigate the universe of things and do's. You talk yourselves into thinking you can be 'yourself' if only you can make choices which are truly yours. It is as if choices made by yourselves, for yourselves, are equivalent to making a true connection with the core of your most authentic personality. But that's a rather utopian, if not plain silly, idea."

"Not to mention, an idea easily exploited by the CSDCs too," commented the One with the daisy. "They will offer you tons of means to assist with just that. Navigate the world. Be successful. Find happiness. Be yourself. But all that stuff is superficial."

"So what's beneath the surface?" asked Nurse Erin. "What's at the core?"

The One with the magician's staff placed the middle of the staff on her index finger. "At the core of our most inner psyche, it comes down to how we feel," she stated while trying to keep the staff balanced. "And one can categorize all possible feelings we have into two simple categories. That's what categorizing is all about, isn't it? One group of feelings leads to the sense of being contracted or contained. The other group of feelings leads to a sense of expansion and freedom."

"There's a great talk show on the telly about this," said the glowing One. "You should watch it. It's fun."

"Anyways," the One with the magician's staff continued while pointing to the left and right part of the staff, "when it comes to choices and decisions, our self tends to waver between these two like all the time. Trouble is…"

"… trouble is," continued the One with the daisy, "we tend to make choices which throw us in the wrong direction of our missy's staff here."

"How's that?" wondered Olivia.

"Mostly without us realizing it, our decisions are based on two inner needs which we try to keep balanced. One is the need for security and self-preservation. The other is the need to be free. To be fearless and audacious. To not be bothered by consequences and dive headlong into anything wild popping up. One is safe, cosy and comfortable. The other is prone to risk and the unexpected."

"Precisely," agreed the One with the nón lá. "Some will absolutely love the unexpected and the unpredictable. Others will avoid it like hell."

"So, as a result, some will find themselves at times failing to make that choice which would have been to their greater benefit. Then again, some will jump straight into paths which weren't theirs all along."

"Thing is," said the One with the dice, "we do have the tendency to linger in the safe zone. And while it's all pretty safe there, our levels of happiness aren't particularly spiking, are they? Even worse, our lives can eventually become incredibly dull and boring without us even realizing it."

"Thus," concluded the One with the daisy, "while we are always aiming for the feeling of expansion and freedom, we do have the tendency to end up contracted and contained all the same."

"And that's exactly the spot where you become vulnerable for those charismatic lot on stages and YouTube. In this contained state, you're simply not open to the actual feeling of expansion. It sounds impossible. So instead, you only find yourself addicted to quick sweets on Snapchat and other sugar media."

"Oh."

This was Bram's third 'oh'. And as predicted by a Peruvian shaman in 1925, a rooster crowed. (This was even weirder than you would first imagine since the nearest land happened to be further away from their boats than the sound of roosters can carry.)

"Errr," tried Olivia, "so we should avoid making choices? Or… we need to learn how to make good choices? Or… hmm… I don't think I get it."

"You can't avoid choices, Olivia. And there's no need either. Free will, the freedom to choose, and the feeling that comes with it, is an inseparable part of the self. It is vital. When the realization of Truth dawns, you may at first come to believe there's no choices to be made. You can use it as an excuse for procrastination or 'Oh, whatever'. Yet still, one way or the other, you will never ever be able to avoid them."

"We understand," empathized the One with the magician's staff, "making choices is often difficult. But let's not forget, humanity does have the capacity and willingness to help one another. And if your peers or community are not able to help out, you can still seek out professional help. Ask for personal assistance. Acquire useful techniques. There's plenty of ways which can facilitate your making the harder decisions."

"Or," countered One, "when needed, come to terms with the consequences that inevitably follow them."

"Dealing with choices no longer available is certainly part of that as well."

"Indeed, indeed. Life has this peculiar tendency to simply give as blindly as it takes. And somehow, we always have an inclination to take it personally. Doesn't help a single bit, now does it? Only makes it all worse."

"Seems like… there's… no way out," sobbed Nurse Erin, who couldn't get a grip on her sombre mood. "Like we're screwed two times over."

"Language, Erin, language," reprimanded ol' Cormac while looking up at her.

Erin exploded while tears jumped from her cheeks. "Oh, sod off, will ya! Don't you see? Here we all are, in this causalistically closed universe, having no actual freedom at all. And still, we suffer from making choices that have actually been decided since the beginning of it all. On top of that, we also get to suffer the consequences of these so-called choices. It sucks!"

"Now, see what ya've done," ol' Cormac grunted helplessly towards the masked culprits. "You've broken me nurse!"

The Mystical Mages of Infinite Zero looked at each other in a way like they seemed a little disappointed.

"They are not getting it, are they?" remarked the One with the magician's staff.

"Give them time," suggested the One with the Viking horns.

"Time is not the issue," disagreed the One with the dice. "What matters is how deep their realization of Truth sinks in. A superficial realization will only lead to more mental-like conclusions: 'Why would I care?' or 'Nothing I do matters.' Stuff like that."

"Or there is the more emotional response of nihilism or despondency… apathy… lethargy," added the One with the daisy while looking at his confraters. "You all remember how I won our last game of Scrabble with these fancy words?"

They all rolled their eyes. (Well, from the movement of their heads, one could conclude they all did. The mighty sighs gave it away also.)

"Anyways, once you're in that lane, where all sense and meaning is lost, you end up in a self-reinforcing cycle. Your moods grow dark. And Truth becomes nothing but a villain in a bad story."

"It's all 'think – think – think'," spoke the One with the magician's staff. "It's the 'me – me – me' which we overly identify with, over and over again. But our true identity is not 'me – me – me', now is it?"

"Sometimes I just want to be freed of all this 'me – me – me'," lamented Erin. "And free from all this freedom nonsense as well. Can't I just be a little?"

"There there, Erin!" hushed ol' Cormac. "If it helps, bonnie lass, there's a lot of me in yer life also, now, isn't there?" Erin gave him that particular look, which clearly indicated that it wasn't helping at all.

Meanwhile, the One covered with red admirals managed to raise a finger. "I dare say Erin does have a point there. Butterflies are nice, but too much of them can be overwhelming indeed." She stood up and allowed a shiver to run through her spine. The butterflies flew straight up and collectively decided to form a cloud above the bamboo boats, whirling around as if violent winds pulled them in the craziest directions. All looked up in awe. Except Erin.

"My dear Erin," comforted the One without red admirals. "I can't help noticing you are in a pretty contained spot there. Trust me. Truth is there with you. But it's impossible for you to truly let it in from your position. Moreover, this place of confinement has the tendency to pull in those around you as well. It's like a nasty black hole, really."

"But not to worry, not to worry," sang the glowing One. "Yesyesyes, emotions and thoughts, I know, I know, the ego and all, sure sure, all these silly little things, they do have this tendency to haphazardly lead us into confinement, yesyesyes. But!"

"Yeh, mine is aching too," announced ol' Cormac.

"But! Here's the thing. Never forget. You do have the capacity to actively subdue this sense of 'me – me – me'. I'm telling you, you all have it! It's part of your design. If you haven't experienced this already by yourselves, then surely you managed to touch it during our secret exercises."

"It's there where you can even drop this 'me – me – me' altogether, Erin," pointed the One with the raven. "Don't you remember? All those moments in your life when you found yourself simply floating on life's current? Those gracious states of flow, when 'you', 'you yourself' weren't in the way. When your life, your actions, your decisions simply came spontaneously, without the slightest resistance."

"Those moments, Erin," added the One with the daisy, "when you simply allowed your life to unfold serenely in the greater unfolding of the entire existence, like the spot on the petal. Remember?"

This got Erin thinking for a moment. Then her eyes briefly lit up, only to lose the light as fast again as it came. "All those moments, you say. Well, I can't recall that many of them."

"There's more of them than you think, Erin. Perhaps you fail to appreciate them? We all do have a tendency to focus on the bad, now don't we?"

Charles and a few other British fella's all went 'aye'.

The glowing One felt inclined to speak a bit louder now. "But surely we all have experienced these feelings of flow, now haven't we?"

"Hear! Hear!" That grew louder as well.

The glowing One really was on a roll now and spoke in a loud and convincing tone. "It kind of starts as a feeling which can be described as a feeling of space. Bit like a natural openness. And in this space, all identifications and attachments gradually start to evaporate, until, at some point, they are totally eradicated. The 'me – me – me' noise sort of gets turned down. Right?"

"Aye! Aye! Hear! Hear!" By now, even the non-British joined in.

"It is in this instance that we come in touch with a rare and precious form of spaciousness. One that exceeds the concept of space as we usually know it. And the more it manages to outshine the 'me – me – me', the more we come in touch with this spaciousness, right up to the point where all boundaries seem to fall away. Right?"

Feet stamped. "Hear! Hear! Aye! Hear! Hear!" The fishermen and -women had trouble keeping the boats steady as they were.

"Now, here's a thing I didn't know," remarked the One with the daisy.

"Didn't know what?" asked the One with the Viking horns.

"Those folks in parliament. I never realized that lot already knew about all this."

"Right," sighed the One with the dice while almost invisibly shaking his head. "So anyways, when all boundaries seem to fall away, then… …well, then we rather prefer to use the word 'boundlessness' instead of space or spaciousness. Now, we know, we know, it sounds a bit mumbo-jumbo-spiritualo. And it can be perceived as overly utopian in nature, certainly when you look at it strictly from a rational perspective. But on the other hand, the word effectively helps us to describe a feeling which seemingly – I repeat – seemingly, goes beyond the limitations of physical existence."

"Yes," remarked the One with Vanessa (she decided to return from the whirl above), "let's keep in mind here that we are referring to a rather subjective experience. It's experienced differently by each and every one of us. Some can only find a brief glimpse of spaciousness in the vastness of the open sea or a mountain range. Others will even succeed in experiencing boundlessness while locked in a box. Some… some simple will not succeed at all. The resistance of the identity can feel as enormous as the widest ocean. The struggles of the ego can fill any space, no matter how large it may be. There sometimes really is no limit to the physical, mental and emotional boundaries one must first surpass to experience this boundlessness."

"But that's just the problem," objected Erin. "You are talking about rare, brief moments at best. That just doesn't work for me. You want me to make a weekly appointment with boundlessness and bliss? Saturday morning, from 9 to 10? Something like that? And that's when I'm lucky. And what about all the other hours in a week? Then it's back to usual? Struggle and resistance? Can't I be permanently liberated from all that?"

Andrea nodded and backed Erin all the way. "She's right, you know! And it exists. People in the east call it 'Nirvāṇa', or 'Moksha' or something."

"Ah, liberation," mused the One with Vanessa at her butterfly. "Aren't humans funny, my dear? Ever split. Ever torn. Running around like headless chickens all the time. And then they take a small break and try to be all serene and meditative. Pretending to be liberated in their studios in front of their flock. While you love, you simply flap your way elegantly through the paradox of being and being not. No need to boast. No need to lead or guide or convert."

"I see what you are saying," admitted Andrea. "You are saying that many only think they are liberated, but in truth, they are not. Spiritual ego, that kind of stuff, right?"

"You nailed it," clapped the One with the Viking horns. "10 points for Andrea!"

"But how then?" asked Erin. "How can we do it for real?"

"Let's start with giving them the key," suggested the One with the nón lá.

"The key?" Olivia asked. "What key?"

"You are asking for a permanent state of liberation, right?" quizzed the One with the dice. "So, you need something to constantly remind you of this state. Something that guides you to it and keeps you in it. Now, what might that be? That something which is constantly with you? That little thing which is ever there?"

"Other than this old fart in his wheelchair?" Erin asked.

"Oi!" Ol' Cormac wanted to react. But when he saw the teasing smile on Erin's lips, he realized he had got his jolly old nurse back and decided to leave it.

Then Erin sighed once more. "Well, if it's not the old fart, I give up."

"Why, it's the breath!" revealed the One with the dice. "You see, the breath is our most profound physical access point to both confinement and space. When we are in anger, distress or plain simply unhappy, our breath tends to become confined as well. It becomes shallow and short. Our chest literally collapses by the emotional and mental weight upon it."

"And the trouble is," added the One with the daisy, "it's hard to break. It becomes a pattern which sticks on your back like those cleavers children throw on you."

The glowing One chuckled in her hands while she looked at the cleaver on the back of the One with the daisy (It was already there since chapter 1 of part 2).

"But here's the great part," continued the One with the daisy unaware. "You can turn it around and use the breath to rediscover this innate openness we all have inside. You can re-enter this realm of spaciousness."

"Let's try!" beamed the One with the nón lá. "Remember the exercises we did before? They allowed you to plunge into Beingness a bit, right? Now, 'allowing' is actually a good word to describe it because that's actually the main objective of these exercises. You see, basically, they are merely openers to a deeper experience. But they do have the capacity to break this emotional and mental rigidity that has penetrated your chest and shoulders."

"Exactly," confirmed the One with the bow and arrow (it floated straight back to her. Can you imagine that?). "Without these preparations, we can't explore the deeper inhale and exhale. You'd only meet more resistance and more confinement instead of spaciousness, let alone boundlessness for that matter. That's why many people give up on Yoga and other stuff after one single class."

"Tell me about it," Olivia rolled with her eyes. "Every time I join a breathing class, I totally freak out because it blocks me even more."

The One with the nón lá slowly stood up and tried to find his balance on the bamboo boat. "Let's remedy this then! Now, since all of us here have become pretty good at those exercises, we can dive straight into the next step. Everybody ready? Let's start very, very simple. Please, stand up.

Very good. Now, bring your left arm up. Shake your hip to the right. Put your left foot forward and slightly lift your right."

The bamboo boats all started to wiggle in the direction of an imminent catastrophe.

The One with the raven slapped himself against the forehead. "Not the dance, you silly! The breath!"

"Oh! I'm sorry. My bad. Right. Everybody, please sit down again.

Okay, take some moments to experience your breath as it is, in this moment, here and now.

Now, consciously start to deepen your breath. From the belly up to the chest – in. From the chest down into the belly – out. Try to even the inhale and the exhale and allow them to become deep. Take your time.

(Then there followed a couple of simple but very secret exercises, which can't be revealed here for the sake of secrecy.)

Very good, very good. Now, give us one final inhale. Not too deep. And hold your breath as long as you comfortably can.

Evaluate your experience of spaciousness. Is it confined? Or wide?

Okay, exhale. And relax."

A profound silence blanketed the world. Until:

"Chuyện gì đang xảy ra?" asked the fisherman.

"Tôi không có manh mối," answered the fisherwoman and shrugged her shoulders. "Tất cả họ đột nhiên có vẻ rất yên bình."

They all looked peaceful indeed. Some even had a particular glow on their faces.

"This is just the beginning," smiled the glowing One. "See, it doesn't take much practice to bring back openness and space."

The One with the nón lá looked around and studied all faces. "Surely, some of you will still meet a bit of resistance in this inhale. Give it time and practice. Gradually, you will be able to release your emotional rigidity, both from the diaphragm, as well as your intercostal muscles."

The glowing One allowed her chest to expand. "The beauty of it is that you will also release the rigidity within the s̲elf. And as such, the s̲elf will be less and less in the way of the S̄elf and all the benefits it radiantly showers down."

The One with the dice let out a sigh of deep contentment. "In time, you will be able to extend the holding of the breath to the point where the need to resume it no longer occupies your mind. Then you can really surrender to this physical spaciousness and allow it to infect your entire being."

"Likewise," added the One with Vanessa, "the inhale and exhale serve as intimate, loving guides, continually leading you back to the vast openness at the core of your being—even in moments when you still find yourself contracted."

"Here, one can experience how the simplicity of the breath can take us where even the wisest words cannot."

"You see now, Erin," queried the One with the dice, "with the help of the breath, with that which you ever carry with you, you are capable of touching true liberation. Not by brooding on it, but by experience."

"It's not just a liberation of the 'me – me – me'," elaborated the One with the raven softly. "It's way much more than that. This liberation, in all its profundity, arises from the realization that there is no 'I' to suffer the absence or lack of free will. And so as well, the silly idea of thinking free will is only an illusion evaporates in the Knowing that there is no one to have free will in the first place. There never was."

The One with the raven allowed this to sink in before he continued. "In this state of non-being Beingness, a sense of non-causality emerges. It is here that the discovery is made – the true liberation of what is commonly known as freedom. Once it is made in the realm of no-you-ness, it will inevitably penetrate into your daily existence as well."

"Liberation of freedom?" wondered Olivia.

"Yes, dear. It's when this desperate need for control makes way for life to happen the way it is compelled to. Without this obsession of it going a particular way. Without fear of whichever way it goes. You start to see the great play. You recognize you are simply part of it. And you simply flow along without preferences, without bias, and surely without judgment. All is good. All is perfect the way it is and the way it continues to unfold."

"Exactly," affirmed the One with the daisy. "It's this regained boundlessness, whether you achieved it by practice or simply by natural occurrence, which brings you back to the true experience of the $\overline{\text{S}}$elf. And as we carry the breath with us in every living moment given, we are as well offered a means by life itself to sustain this connection indefinitely."

"And no, your sense of still being able to make choices will not disappear. That féeling is real. It's not an illusion. But you'll see, you will feel, there comes a certain ease to making them. It's like you move into them and find joy in that. Because somewhere deep inside, at some level, you are at ease and relaxed. Somehow, you find yourself able to balance the causal existence of the self with the non-causal limitlessness of the $\overline{\text{S}}$elf."

"This rediscovered vastness of Beingness offers a soothing effect on the tyranny of choice we often face in our daily freedom. In this vastness, the situation is rather allowed to unfold serenely and in peace than that it is stuck in a struggle with stuff like doubt or regret."

"It's quite paradoxical, isn't it?" chuckled the One with Vanessa. "We can have choices, more than we'd like, and at the same time, we can linger in the space of this hardly describable freedom which transcends all choices. This openness which simply allows, without nihilism or apathy. It's not that you won't care. You will still be involved, perhaps more than ever before. And just as well, sadness will still be there. You will still feel annoyed or angry. Your need to change things will not disappear. But it will all happen in this serene field of awareness. In discontentment, still, you will be content. In turmoil, still, you will be peaceful. Your presence will remain intact without being hijacked by those feelings that always blocked you before."

"So, when it comes to words like 'boundlessness' or 'timelessness', you see, they no longer need to be those fluffy, spiritual concepts sold by the CSDCs for profit or fame. If you allow them to touch you on a deeper level, you will find them to be far from mere conceptual expressions."

"Indeed, from the perspective of a genuine experience, they will reveal themselves as real and tangible as can be. And as such, they can be thé answer to our psyches craving for limitless freedom."

"It's here you are allowed growth or joyful presence, deep contentment, love and wholeness, regardless of physical or mental confinements."

"Here, Erin, you can have my flower."

While the fishermen- and women steered the bamboo boats once more into movement, Erin stared at the daisy for some time. An ingrained habit from her childhood resurfaced out of the blue when she gently started to pull out petal by petal.

"I am – I am not – I am – I am not – I am – I…"

As her fingers extended toward the last petal, it unexpectedly detached on its own. This brought Erin to a sudden stop. It was not just her hand or gesture that froze. Everything did. It was like an inner nuclear explosion, which brought her entire psyche to a full stop. While the grace of oneness befell her, divinity was all that remained.

Ego

"That's odd," wondered the One with Vanessa's whirling high above her. "Why are we moving?"

"This spot was perfect!" protested the One with the dice. "Could have lingered here for hours."

"Don't look at me," deflected the One who is writing all this. "Haven't got a clue."

"Cô ấy sắp có em bé," cautioned the fisherwoman while she looked in the direction of Márcia.

Confused gazes went from Márcia to the fisherwoman and back again. Márcia could only stare back in utter denial of whatever was being said about her.

"Em bé!" insisted the fisherwoman. "Em bé! Chúng ta phải đến làng của chúng ta ngay lập tức!"

None of the looks did go unconfused after that explanation.

"Baby!" her husband translated in the briefest possible way.

The glowing One shrugged her shoulders. "Perhaps she thinks the baby is about to throw something overboard? No feeding the fishes, remember?"

Bram paid little attention to the sudden movements of the bamboo boats. His mind, lost in contemplation, was still lingering on the words exchanged in the previous sub-chapter.

"I'm still a bit confused," he dared while the boats lined up in rows of four or five. "You said we have to liberate ourselves from freedom, right?" (The Illustrious Sages of Infinite Zero politely shook their heads, but Bram chose to ignore it.) "Does that also mean we should liberate ourselves from the ego? I mean, all this needing and choosing it starts from the ego in the first place, doesn't it? And yes, I know, you said it before; it is just another need we have from within our_selves. But once we are past that, shouldn't we kill the ego, like many say we should?"

"True, Igor is a troublemaker," confirmed Mykhailo. "And you should not hang out with him. But killing Igor? That's not nice either."

"Not Igor, Mykhailo. E-go!"

"Oh, E-go. Don't know him. Still, killing is not what I would recommend."

"Now, we never said anything like that, Bram," corrected the One without a flower. "There is no directive to kill or destroy anything. We may be wearing silly masks, but we most certainly are not a cult telling you this or that."

"But why not eradicate the ego?" protested Bram while he looked left and right for the support of the crowd. "It's a burden, isn't it? I mean, djeez, the countless times we are in conflict with ourselves. The amount of times we sabotage ourselves. I know for myself that my ego surely isn't my best friend. And that's even without mentioning the many moments I comment about someone else's ego. If we would be able to get rid of our ego, it would solve all that stuff instantly."

"We've been here before, Bram," sighed Marwa. "It's 'you' trying to get rid of 'you'. No can do."

"Here's the thing," started the One with the magician's staff before Bram could defend himself. "It's always the same. When the ego enters the stage, most people immediately burden it with all biblical plagues possible."

" 'Slash it!' they say," spoke the One with the Viking horns firmly while waving an imaginary sword. "Or 'Eradicate it!', 'Overcome it!', 'Tame it!' Or what about this one: 'Destrooooy it!' " The imaginary sword moves that came with all that almost caused the boat to topple over.

"While it's basically plain silly," said the One without a flower. "Killing the ego would be a bit like chopping off your hand because it puts chocolate in your mouth."

"That's silly indeed," scoffed the One with the Viking horns. "Even without hands, I could still ask someone else to put chocolate in my mouth."

"Right, that's enlightening, indeed."

"Anyways," continued the One with the magician's staff. "Seems to me, Bram, you are rather persistent on getting rid of your ego because of the many troubles it appears to be giving you. Question is, how would you go about, all ego-less? Would that be practical? Would the world be a better place if all of humanity would get rid of their ego?"

"Err, I don't know," admitted Bram. "Haven't looked at it like that. I guess having a smaller ego would already make a huge difference, no?"

"That sounds a bit confusing if you ask me, Bram. So, you should have a small ego. But you also should stand up for yourself. Be more self-confident. Likewise, you should be your true self. Be more authentic. But that basically implies you should have a pretty solid ego."

The One with the raven intervened. "Small ego. Big ego. No ego. This is leading nowhere. We could circle around for decades here."

"I get it," exclaimed Bram. "It's an illusion, right?"

Suddenly, Imagination rang out loudly from out of nowhere. *"Could it be that…"*

"So sorry, so sorry" apologized one of the fishermen while picking up his phone. "Xin chào? Không, mẹ ơi, con không quên. Bây giờ tôi đang làm việc. Cần phải đi. Tạm biệt mẹ, tạm biệt"

"Putting me back… in all this confusion," the glowing One sang softly while snapping her fingers in rhythm with imaginary music.

At that point, the red admirals collectively decided to stop playing whirly-whirly up high. With the most gentle touchdowns, they landed in little clusters on the nón lá of the fishermen- and women. Only the original Vanessa loyally stayed with the One with Vanessa, which was much to her great relief.

"Look," spoke the One with the magician's staff. "From a certain perspective, it's an illusion, yes. But so is time. It doesn't really exist, but it still is a convenient tool nonetheless."

Again, background whispering and muttering. "Time doesn't exist? – That's what my wife always says about me. – I'm still wondering where fortune cookies are really from. – Does anyone know the time?"

The glowing One lifted her index finger. "Did I mention there's a great talk show about that?"

The One with the magician's staff sighed. "The problem is we are overly keen on dissecting things into oblivion. It's the same with the <u>s</u>elf. We cut and divide it up in many little bits, right up to the point where we end up with something that all seems to make sense… but no longer corresponds with reality. Mind, ego, intellect, intuition, … In reality, we sense and experience it as one unity, no?"

The One with the bow and arrow nodded while she examined the tip of her arrow. "Splitting it all up may give you a sense of empowerment, like a means to work on certain inner aspects and stuff like that. Question is, how is this working out for you?"

"Not really," admitted Olivia with a sigh.

"So we shouldn't talk any longer about ego or mind and stuff?" Bram wondered.

"Well, for the sake of habit, let us humour you just a little bit, okay?" proposed the One with the magician's staff, who seemed eager to elaborate a bit more. "Simply put, the ego is your capacity to form and uphold an identity. And that, my friends, is an absolute necessity in your daily existence. As one would not cut off one's own hand, nor would one start cutting into one's brain to remove the ego."

"Are you speaking about us now?" queried the One (get it?) without a flower, "or just referring to people in general? It's a bit confusing."

"Right. Where was I? So, like it or not, your identity is vital. It allows a certain degree of consistency, not only in your social interactions but also in your personal endeavours. Without ego, one – I mean, you – would buy a house today yet live in another the day after. You would go to university only to abandon all studies one week later. Even raising and loving children would be nothing but a reflex, now would it?"

"My love for my baby is absolutely genuine," objected Márcia. "I would never just raise it because of some reflex."

"Actually, that's not entirely true," reported a person with a thick beard. "There happen to be females who are no longer able to love their children after suffering brain trauma."

While Márcia's face instantly turned into agony, the One with the raven quickly intervened: "Yes, that's correct, Oliver. But the odds for that are about just as high as a man mistaking his wife for a hat, aren't they?"

Oliver shrugged in agreement while Márcia's face settled down a bit.

"So," continued the One with the magician's staff. "Without ego, you'd make a promise only to break it. You'd change opinion as fast as the wind would change direction. In short, without ego, it would be nearly impossible to have meaningful interactions with others. And likewise, it would be impossible to start something with a long-term perspective. Without the ego's consistency, not much would get accomplished."

In the other boat, Oliver became more uncomfortable by the second. "I am terribly sorry if I offended you in any way," he sincerely apologized when he noticed Márcia's face in renewed agony. Márcia gently waved him off, indicating they were good. She tried a long, deep exhale through puckered lips to calm down.

"So this self-identifying ego/mind stuff is a necessity, if I hear you right?" asked Bram with a frown in Oliver's direction.

"Of course it is, Bram," answered the One with the magician's staff gently. "Look, you can see it as this one app on your phone, which you need all the time. But, by Murphy's law, it happens to be exactly the app which tends to glitch more often than not."

"Hey," objected Murphy. "I have nothing to do with that! People always misunderstand me."

"Still, I can picture it clearly," laughed Olivia. "Mine tends to go on repeat, like forever! And if it doesn't do that, it simply doesn't know what to make of itself."

"Or it simply freezes when I need it most," fumed Georges out of the blue. "Mine does that all the time. Ça me rend fou!"

"Mine thinks it's the best app on the phone," sighed Bram.

Then Georges's legs suddenly unpretzled and made him tip over backwards in the boat. "Nom de Dieu de putain de bordel de merde de saloperies de connards d'enculé de ta mère!" he angrily exclaimed while getting upright again. "Been sitting like a pretzel for years, and still, this app doesn't work the way I want it." His heated rant seemed to address nobody but the air around him. Still, it seemed there was a lot of collateral damage amongst the crowd in the boats.

When he noticed the wrinkled looks in his direction, he blushed. "Excuse my French, please. That was years of frustration leaping out of my mouth."

"Err, okay, thank you for sharing, Georges," hushed the One with the dice in a pacifying tone. "So... this app we were talking about... The funny thing about it... It doesn't consider itself to be an app. It thinks itself to be the phone."

"The best phone!" added Bram with another sigh.

"Still, it's pretty profound if you think about it. From the moment it becomes active, from the moment you are born, the identification process kicks in. The app starts to shape and transform itself."

"Likecodewritingit'sowncode?" tried 방찬 from his ICT perspective.

"Exactly!" beamed the One with the dice. "And while it is active, it actually grows. It starts to consume more and more memory. It sucks up most of the processor. It basically takes over the phone."

"Over time, you develop a character, a personality. You even develop multiple variations of it, depending on where you are and who you are with. In no time, your closet is filled with masks, each for their very own specific occasion."

"During your ascent into adulthood, your identity gradually solidifies. And that happens with parts you like... and parts you don't like."

"My point entirely," intoned the One with the Viking horns wisely. "Some masks you like. Some masks you'd rather throw in the bin but..."

"... we can't," concluded Olivia. "They are forced on our face, if not by ourselves, then surely by others."

The One with the raven nodded. "And so, you slowly become prisoners of your own consistency. Most of you end up with five to ten different masks, but that's it. The sum of them becomes your identity. And this solidified identity can become a serious burden, surely when it is no longer adequate in new situations."

Olivia stared uncomfortably at the ground before her feet. "Or simply when you come to dislike your mask in existing situations, right up to the point where you want to break out and-"

"And so the battle begins," announced the One with the dice. "By nature, you start to revolt against yourself. You blame yourself. You dislike yourself. You're hard on yourself. You're disappointed in yourself."

The One with the Viking horns ferociously raised a fist. "And with the help of yoga teachers, health gurus and self-help books, you try to love yourself. Be kind to yourself. Forgive yourself. Engineer yourself."

"Gradually, it starts to dawn on you," said the One with the dice. "You basically never are your authentic you. You're nothing but a series of fictitious characters in multiple narratives. So you start to wonder: 'What is the real me underneath them?' You come to realize you're not who you think you are. But at the same time, you have no idea who you really are."

The One with the magician's staff prodded her staff against the floor of the bamboo boat. "And so, little by little, the revolt turns into an uprise."

"But an uprise against what?" questioned the glowing One with a most intriguing tone. Then she sang, *"ooh, ooh ooh ooh, aha."*

"I'm sorry, Misses Ser Nada," interrupted Oliver once again. "I really am."

Everybody looked rather annoyed in his direction. It felt like the glowing One was about to reveal something important. And just at that time, Oliver sacked the attention of the Illustrious Sages of Infinite Zero.

"What's up, Oliver?" asked the One with the Viking horns.

"Something's really wrong with Misses Ser Nada here."

All eyes turned to Márcia, whose face was back in agony.

"I don't know what's wrong with me," she puffed between breaths. "It feels like…"

"Em bé!" shouted the fisherwoman while she signalled all other fishermen and -women to row faster.

"Baby!" translated the fisherman once more.

"Baby?" the crowd gasped in unison.

"Twins!" cheered the glowing One. "It's twins!"

"Twins?" puffed Márcia. "OMG! Twins!"

Without losing their poise, the fishermen and -women kept rowing at a well-determined pace. Luckily enough, right around another bend in the maze of Fengcong and Fenglin karst, their destination suddenly became clear. A fishing village came into sight against a staggering mountain backdrop.

It turned out to be one of the more secluded villages in the area. Tourists were not allowed to come here. The whole village consisted of a seemingly chaotic hodgepodge of colourful houseboats, rafts and platforms securely tethered together in clusters. The houses all had different hues, going from green to pink, blue or brown.

There was a serene atmosphere without anyone taking selfies or reading their messages. Children were playing on the platforms. Men and women were checking their fishing nets. While the bamboo boat with Márcia was steered to one of the floating houses, the others docked a bit further. From there, they saw how Mykhailo gently lifted Márcia from the bamboo boat onto the platform of the doctor's house. The fisherwoman then led her inside.

Meanwhile, the crowd and the Illustrious Sages of Infinite Zero took a moment to marvel at the peculiar town they were in.

Merely ten minutes later, while some fishermen were teaching the crowd how to make knots, the fisherwoman came out of the house.

"Boy!" she shouted. The cheerfulness on her face told all that needed to be told. All was well.

Márcia's relieved face appeared from the window. "Easy peasy," she shouted. "I really wonder why all those actresses in the movies have to overact this beautiful part of life. What a fuss they always make of it."

All laughed and cheered while Márcia allowed herself to rest and enjoy the two beautiful creatures against her body.

"So, where were we?" queried the One with the Viking horns.

"The uprise!" hollered ol' Cormac from his floating wheelchair. "The bloody uprise!"

"An uprise?" wondered the glowing One. "Uprise against what exactly?"

Ol' Cormac turned all red. "You freakin' tell us now; you masked little gobshite! And can anyone lift me onto that platform, for God's sake!"

"There there," hushed Nurse Erin while unconsciously switching to Scottish. "Yer awfy crabbit now, aren't ye? Get a grip of yourself, will ya."

"That's it!" exclaimed the glowing One in delight. "The uprise against yourself. Can you believe that? Hilarious, isn't it? Imagine Chuck Norris challenging himself to a fight. High kick in the face. Wack! Punch in the stomach. Bam!"

"That's stupid," said Jimmy. "Who'd wanna see that?"

"But that's exactly what you all do!"

"And along the way," divulged the One without a flower, "there will be plenty of CSDCs offering assistance to help you with this silliness. They will offer hacks and tools, methods and rituals, all to lure you into this impossible fight which cannot be won."

The One with the dice shook his head in disapproval. "Gurus on stages, YouTube videos or podcasts thrive on this. 'Your mind this,' they say. 'Your intuition that. Your heart such. Your ego so.' It basically is a self-sustaining success formula. The division of the self is the perfect means to fill hours and hours of useful-sounding nonsense. A little insight here. A little light there. But the whole house never gets lit up in its entirety."

For a minute, all became silent.

It was Kalle who broke it by playfully prodding Sven in the ribs. "By the way, Chuck Norris would certainly win that fight!"

"But why is it a fight which can't be won?" asked Olivia.

"Because, contrary to what you like to believe, there is no authentic, maskless 'you' to win this fight. As a person, engaging with others, as well as yourself, you always wear a mask." The glowing One then pointed at her mask. "You simply can't not wear one. Would be silly, wouldn't it?"

"But..." Olivia hesitated.

Ol' Cormac didn't. "Get to the freakin' point, ye lavvy heid! How do we win?"

"You don't need to, my friend," answered the One with the dice. "And you know this already. You see, how easily you forget?"

Ol' Cormac looked up at his nurse through one eye only. "Is the laddy saying I'm a bloody eejit?"

"What I'm trying to say, ol' chap. All this bickering and fighting... all this self-contempt and self-loathing... all this inner and outer fretting... this mask vs mask... it totally alienates you from your primal essence, even when you have realized it before."

"Now, now, that's a bit of a negative tone there," said the One with the buckwheat flower (he just got it from a sweet little girl with the most radiant smile ever). "I'd say, even when you're jolly great, fit as a fiddle or walking on sunshine, still, it wouldn't be bad to be aware of your primal essence."

"Would give it a nitro-injection boost," said the One with the Viking horns while mimicking speeding up ridiculously fast in an imaginary car.

"With primal essence, you mean the $\overline{S}$elf, right?" asked Nurse Erin.

"Of course. And that's the thing. Even when you know the Truth, even when you've realized and experienced it, the $\overline{S}$elf somehow ever becomes obfuscated by the $\underline{s}$elf."

"And that's rather unfortunate," said the One with the bow and arrow. "Because in the experience of the $\overline{S}$elf, the state of pure Beingness, not only can you find a moment of solace and revitalization, you might as well find the start of inner peace treaties that can last for the rest of your life."

"There we go again," mocked Jimmy. "The $\overline{S}$elf this, the $\overline{S}$elf that. I still fail to see how all this mumbo jumbo about this $\overline{S}$elf practically benefits me."

"Perhaps true," started the One with the dice, "this maskless state will not be of much service while you are in interaction with oth-"

"I think ur Jimmy boy is more afraid of dropping his Jimmy-ness than he likes to admit." It was none other than ol' Cormac who threw this line in. And he said it with narrow eyelids which eyed Jimmy from the corner of his… eyes.

"I… What… No…" blurted Jimmy, who felt caught in the act.

"There's nothing to be scared about, Jimmy," comforted the One with Vanessa. "Rationally, you may conclude that this state of Beingness results in losing your Jimmy-ness. But here's the thing. When your sense of $\overline{S}$elf gradually continues to expand, right up to the extent that all boundaries seem to fade away, nevertheless, it will not result in a loss of $\underline{s}$elf."

"It won't?"

"On the contrary, Jimmy, you will grow to feel much more yourself. More real. More present. More solid and self-confident."

"And you'll feel less lost or in conflict," added the glowing One. "It doesn't have to be a permanent state you are looking for. Still, when the boundaries of your individuality are lifted, even if only from time to time, you will discover a lasting effect nonetheless."

"And thus, there's nothing wrong with wearing a mask."

Imaginary drum roll by the One with the Viking horns. "Paradoxically…"

"Ah," beamed the glowing One. "There's the paradox we were waiting for."

"… behind the mask, we still can be maskless, like all the time."

"From the experience of Truth," started the One mimicking master Yoda, "impersonal presence one can be, while ever personally present. Nameless one can be, while ever upholding an identity. Timeless one can be, and ever on time."

Bram scratched himself on the head. "You may wanna repeat that one."

All laughed while they secretly turned the book to this page and reread what the One with no particular characteristics (except mimicking Master Yoda) just uttered.

"It simply is a thing of beauty," said the One with Vanessa. "We all have this peculiar, near-impossible capacity to consciously be aware of our non-existence. While simultaneously, we nonetheless exist, unseparated from existence as a whole. It's this realization that results in this mysterious, wordless Knowing that is typically attributed to the sages and the wise."

"It's the ultimate paradox," whispered Nurse Erin. "We can be present and absent at the very same time. A paradoxical existence indeed. I am – not!"

For some reason, the crowd went silent. And so, the Illustrious Sages of Infinite Zero went silent as well.

All stared at everything that passed by in their line of sight. At first, they saw the villagers as simple, good-hearted folk, yet ignorant of their true, non-existent-existent nature. This made them feel like gods, thinking themselves to be the only ones who Knew, the only ones aware of Truth, observing every word and action unfold like leaves on a tree. But soon, they recognized the folly in this rather condescending attitude and dropped all judgement or separation.

And then, they even dropped themselves, and only unfolding remained. It was a moment of bliss. Many simply were unaware of the tears rolling down their cheeks.

Soul

"Blimey freakin' frack!" It was ol' Cormac who broke the spell.

"What's the matter?" asked Nurse Erin genuinely concerned.

"There's tears rolling down me cheeks. Where the frack did they come from?"

"From your eyes, you dimwit!"

All laughed. Even ol' Cormac did.

"Hang on, hang on," spoke Andrea all of a sudden. "That's all nice. But, what about the soul? What about that?"

"Ah, the soul," answered the One with the dice. "That's a special kind of ego."

"A what?" Andrea felt misunderstood. "No, no, no, not the ego. I mean the soul," she said while extending the vowels of the last word across multiple seconds.

"Yes, yes, yes, we know, the sooouuuuul: a special kind of ego."

"How can the soul be a special kind of ego?" protested Andrea. "That makes no sense at all!"

"But it does."

"Does not!"

"Does."

"Does not!"

"D…"

"I wish I could zap you all into Beingness," waved the One with the magician's staff with her… magician's staff.

"Don't look at me," declined the One who is writing all this. "I've broken enough rules as it is."

"Right, Andrea and all, indulge us for a moment, please. So, the soul, you say. Tricky thing, the soul. The soul, if you ask me, is perhaps the most confusing, intriguing and satisfying aspect you use when referring to yourselves."

"Satisfying?" wondered Andrea. "How can it be satisfying."

"Well, you do tend to refer to yourselves with 'my ego' and 'my soul', now don't you? Silly thing is, it appears you all mostly use 'my ego' to refer to the darker, less likable aspects of yourselves. While you rather use 'my soul' for the more positive vibes, so to speak."

"They like to see their soul as the best of themselves, don't they, my sweet little Vanessa? It's this little thingy that really knows what's best. What course to follow? Who to be with? What to accomplish in this life? And they also firmly believe everyone has one. And they all are radiantly equals there, filled with respect, love, understanding, compassion, etc."

"While it's only their naughty, little ego that makes them shout at one another when they are driving in their cars," chuckled the glowing One.

The One with the dice spread out his arms while holding a die in each hand. "If you'd put it on a timeline, you all prefer to see the ego somewhere in the past. It's still chasing you in the present, of course, but generally speaking, it's something you'd like to leave behind. The soul, on the other hand, is more like an ideal in the future. A better version of yourself, with more clarity, meaning and purpose, only waiting to be revealed when the veil of the ego is lifted. It may not be today, but the promise of tomorrow offers relief. So yes, satisfying, I'd say."

"And confusing?" asked Bram, who didn't feel satisfied at all with that answer.

"Well, yes, my sweet little Vanessa. They will not like to hear this, but this 'soul' thingy of theirs does have the knack of being a bit of an overidealized fantasy, don't you think? People aim to be all soul and no ego, but they practically have no idea what this really means. How'd you be when you are nothing but soul? How do you communicate with other souls on that level? What's left to say or talk about when you are all soul-state?"

"Well," remarked the One with the buckwheat flower. "There's many folks out there claiming a bunch of souls first have a meeting before you enter a new body. You decide with them where to land, what to accomplish… But, if you'd ask me, it all seems like a bunch of light sparks displaying a lot of typical human characteristics. It's all still 'I', only on some vague, higher level."

"So it's all useless?" sulked Bram.

"Not necessarily. When you scrape the fantasy layer away, there are practicalities still to be found."

"One can pour one's heart and soul into something."

"One can have a soul sister."

"Or a soul mate."

"You could sell your soul!"

"But you can never tell a soul about that."

"You could lose it."

"You can even listen to soul. I'm more into disco myself, but who's judging, right?"

"It's also a movie! Remember that great scene when-"

It was the One with the raven who cut them short. "It simply is most intriguing how our inner monologue spontaneously drives us to divide ourselves up in the best and worst of ourselves. You see, the soul is about our inner qualities when they are not covered by more egoistical or selfish endeavours. The word refers to these deeper levels where we are able to serenely interact with each other without an agenda, or at least less of an agenda than usual. It's on this level where a more authentic connection is able to flourish, both through the inner monologue, as well as with others."

"Everything around the soul radiates beauty," sang the glowing One. "As a thingy, it may not be a reality the way most people think it is, but as an inner, human quality, it is as real as it gets. And it has this genuine purity about it which we like to deem as timeless in nature."

"But of course, the concept of timelessness can only be understood by those who experienced it. Others will turn it into 'everlasting', and 'everlasting' becomes 'immortal', and 'immortality' is the source of many narratives, ranging from Tom and Brad as vampires to Patrick and Whoopi as channel-buddies."

"So," wondered Marwa, "it seems to me you are saying the $\overline{S}$elf is the same as the soul, no?"

"We'd rather choose not to pollute $\overline{S}$elf or Beingness with words like soul, Marwa. To those who approach this only mentally, without an actual experience, it will still lead to nothing but daydreaming."

"Even if they'd abandon the soul for its many confusing aspects, they'd soon be seeking refuge in other words like instinct, sixth sense or intuition."

"Intuitions are not to be ignored, John," said the One with no characteristics except for exactly copying the Benedict Sherlock. "They represent data processed too fast for the conscious mind to comprehend."

"Yes, Sherlock," said the One with the buckwheat flower, "but intuition is not as flawless as most people make of it. There's still a lot of unconscious bias and misinterpretation going on there as well."

With a deep breath, Marwa drew all attention in her direction. Then she faltered… Then she found her words. "I think I get it now. At first, I couldn't make sense of it because of this overly conceptual approach. It's all definitions, liked or disliked. But when I innerly reach back to those experiences you already helped us have, it becomes clearer. Being self-aware, or self-conscious, implies we are capable of interacting not only with others but also with ourselves. That inner monologue you referred to, right? And that interaction doesn't need to be strictly… err…"

"…mental…" helped the One with the raven.

"Yes, mental! Right. And I see now this happens on many levels. Dividing our better selves up in soul, or heart, or intuition or whatever, it's all about connecting with those inner qualities which operate outside the mental realm. It's also about connecting with others on that very same sensory level. And I know now it's not that these qualities are of a supernatural nature, as we often hope they are. In reality, they are super natural, defining us as the human beings we all are. They are far from flawless, although we don't like admitting that, but nonetheless, we can allow them to grow. We can nurture them. And I felt that already. Even when I myself just briefly touch this… this radiance of Beingness, whatever, it… I mean, I find connection, impartial and candid, with both myself and others. I feel content. Really."

Then Marwa flapped her hands in front of her face. She got all emotional, but still, despite some wetness in her eyes, she genuinely smiled.

"Amen to that," croaked ol' Cormac. For the first time in his life, he felt the soft hand of Erin on his shoulder.

Then all heads turned to the house where Márcia was resting. She appeared from the door with the newborn close to her chest while Oliver was making faces at the firstborn in his arms.

"Everything all right, Márcia?" yelled Olivia.

"Oh yes, absolutely. The elder was so good to me. She is such a good soul."

All laughed. Márcia and Oliver exchanged a puzzled look but then shrugged their shoulders and joined the laughter.

Purpose

Márcia was eager to rejoin the crowd. While she held the twins safely to her chest, Mykhailo gently lifted her from the platform back into the bamboo boat. And despite Oliver's protest, Mykhailo lifted him and the fisherwoman in the boat as well. The One with the Viking horns, who got stranded on the maternity isle too, stared in awe at Mikhailo's strength. Then, before he even realized it, he got picked up, too.

As this One was lighter than expected, Mykhailo instantly lifted him high above him. While the One with the Viking horns went 'hey' and 'ho', Mykhailo had a short, involuntary peak underneath his cloak.

Mykhailo's face went pale.

The fisherwoman rowed the bamboo boat to the larger platform, where they all rejoined. All marvelled at the twins with the widest smiles.

"What happened, Mykhailo," Kalle softly asked. "What did you see?"

"Nothing," Mykhailo declined and looked away. "And I don't want to talk about it."

"What was that all about?" queried Sven. They both shrugged their shoulders and turned their attention to the firstborn, who was just about to be handed into Kalle's arms.

"You talked about the soul?" Márcia asked.

"That we did," replied Andrea. "Case closed on that one."

"Oh. Ok. I'll read about it later."

"Case closed indeed," sighed Olivia. "There goes my soul's purpose as well, I reckon."

And with that, the sun set without anyone noticing it. It was the most beautiful sunset one could imagine. Since ages. Ever. – Too bad.

Correction, not too bad, it seems. While everybody was chatting amongst each other and cuddling the babies, the Elder secretively passed around instructions throughout the village. And so, as if out of nowhere, all around them, a myriad of the most colourful sky lanterns were lit and released into the air. It was like the scene in Tangled, except for the song.

A collective cheer and gasps of awe erupted as everyone marvelled at the breathtaking display. It was an evening of celebration. Drinks and food were passed around, and there was laughter and joy.

"Pssst!" A sound came from behind a set of clothes hanging to dry.

"Pssst!" Again. It was Olivia who stood closest. Intrigued as she was, she cautiously walked towards the sound. A slender, most elegant woman appeared from behind the laundry line. She wore the most beautiful dress, rich in colours, with a deep V-neck from the top while revealing her belly from below. Her long, chestnut hair was freshly washed and styled. The makeup on her face was all but subtle, revealing a woman who wanted to look her very best.

"Can I help you?" asked Olivia while dropping all suspicion at the sight of this graceful appearance.

"Hi, yes. My name is Desert Tulip. How do you do? I couldn't help overhear you talking about your soul's purpose. I hope you can forgive me."

"No worries. It's not like there's a lot of room for privacy on these platforms here, is there?"

Both women chuckled. "So you are also familiar with the concept?" Olivia asked.

"Why, of course I am. Actually, this is such a great coincidence. I happen to be an expert on the topic. And I totally understand your longing for your soul's purpose. Of course you do. We all do. That is the big reason why we are here, isn't it? To achieve our fullest expression. We were all born on this planet with this one specific, sacred purpose. And I am here to remind you of what that is."

"Oh really?"

"Absolutely," Desert answered while she popped out a book from behind her back. "See, I have written a book about it. It will remind you of the wisdom that lives inside your soul. It will help your outer reality reflect your inner radiance. I offer it to you at a special discount. And if you buy it now you can submit your receipt to receive exclusive bonuses in the masterclass I am offering. Don't worry; I will help you unblock all your limitations so you can reclaim your truth and overcome fear, disapproval, or limiting beliefs. You see, it is time for people to decondition their minds, remember their essence and step into the purpose... Oh, think I already said that part. Anyways, there is this pivotal shift going on with..."

"Hey! Raven-dude! I think I got one."

The raven flew up, croaking loudly. Desert Tulip had disappeared in the blink of an eye. Olivia held out empty hands with shrugged shoulders. "I swear, one minute she was here, and now she's gone."

With continuous croaking, the raven navigated between the air lanterns until it landed back once more on the One with the raven's shoulder.

"Really?" uttered the One with the buckwheat flower, surprised. "They even manage to pop up here?"

"I can't believe she expected me to fall for that," hissed Olivia.

"Oh, that happens easier than you think, Olivia," said the One with the confused Vanessa (the poor butterfly was in such awe of the air lanterns, thinking them to be extraterrestrial butterflies coming to save her from mankind's destructive nature). "This lady clearly had to rush things and overstepped. Usually, you get mellowed into this stuff. Once they trick you into believing the masses are wrong, and 'right' is only accessible to those embracing a new 'paradigm' and stuff like that, they own you."

"Well, you must admit," spoke Sven, "the idea of fulfilling your highest and truest expression can sound rather appealing, certainly when you are tricked into thinking being an accountant is the most boring way to live."

"Hey," protested Kalle, who ran an adventure store back in Finland, "if all accountants were to become yoga teachers, I'd most certainly have a problem."

"I'm an accountant," said Sven while raising his eyebrows multiple times.

"Really?"

"But come to think of it seriously," mused Olivia, "can you imagine the pressure? I mean, there you are, assigned to succeed in something some divine entity designed you to accomplish since birth. The whole idea alone stresses me out completely."

"Anyways," continued the One with Vanessa more softly as Vanessa had fallen asleep, "whatever method the CSDCs sell us to find our purpose or divine destiny, in reality, it will most likely remain veiled or obscured. There will ever continue to be this frustrating uncertainty that requires sweetness upon sweetness to obfuscate it from your daily perception. It may lull you into hoping it soon will become clear, but you will only find your purpose stolen by CSDCs."

"Thiefsess they are of our precious purpose," said the One with no characteristics with the voice of Gollum.

"Hang on, hang on," protested Andrea "True as it may be, all that ranting of yours does sound a little patronizing, if you ask me. Surely we shouldn't abandon purpose altogether? In my honest opinion, it remains an important aspect, if not a strength."

"Why of course it is, Andrea, of course it is. You see, where true freedom, the freedom we discussed earlier, is a deep, inner feeling serving us in the now, it is purpose which guides and propels us from one moment into the next."

"Ah! See! I knew it wasn't to be thrown out with the garbage."

"'course it isn't," whispered the One with the sleeping Vanessa. "And make no mistake, when you look at purpose in its pure energy, purpose allows your actions to align with what truly matters to you."

"With 'purpose', you are not guided by some divine force, not at all. You are guided by meaningful values and honest goals. It is a motivating and engaging energy which allows an expression of your talents, no matter what they are or what you thought them to be."

"That's easy said," complained Andrea. "But it can be such a struggle to find purpose."

"Is it really a struggle?" wondered the One with the magician's staff out loud. "Or is it some idea of purpose that got injected into your mind that causes the real struggle? 'Everybody is falling in love, so should I.' – 'Everybody is finding their purpose, so should I.' – 'Everybody is quitting their office jobs and becoming yoga teachers, burnout coaches, spirit guides or healers, so… so should I.' – Shouldn't I?"

"There's nothing more frustrating than the idea of an ideal which needs to be reached or accomplished," said the One with the bow and arrow. "This way, purpose will only become rigid or compulsive in nature. You can shoot all the arrows you want, but if the target is beyond reach or even not existing, it'll be nothing but a wild-goose chase. Hmm… Hang on… What's so impossible about chasing wild geese?"

"So," summarized Marwa while rolling her eyes, "if I hear you correctly, you're saying purpose can be a virtue, as long as… we don't turn it into a vice. Something like that, right? So, how do we tackle this?"

"Hey, I know," said the One with the Viking horns excited. "This is where the $\overline{S}$elf comes in the picture, doesn't it?"

"Sort of," was the short answer of the One with the magician's staff.

"Not entirely," added the One with Vanessa. "See, from the perspective of the non-identity – Beingness, the $\overline{S}$elf, all same same – the idea of 'purpose' may at first sight seem meaningless or pointless. After all, what purpose would there be in a timeless and boundless existence? There is no 'next'. All is One."

"So," concluded Charles, who was now holding one of the twins, "our abiding in Beingness – which I have become rather fond of, if I may say – seems to declare all sense of purpose void. It's simply rendered absolute otiose in favour of an all pervading, radiant emptiness in which contentment, love and gratitude are abundantly present in the moment itself. All is perfect; all is achieved, all is obtained, and all is fulfilled."

"Merde, Charles!" exclaimed Georges. "You are way ahead of me on this one."

Charles couldn't suppress a grin while he secretively handed the little paper he read out loud back to the One who is writing all this.

"That's all nice," remarked the One with the magician's staff, "but not really practical, is it Charles?"

Charles threw a not-that-secretive glance in the direction of the One who is writing all this. His body language was like, 'What the hell, dude?'

"Not to worry, Charles," laughed the One with the magician's staff. "Look, the importance of the $\overline{S}$elf, and our capacity to abide in it, can still prove to be extremely helpful when it comes to our sense and need for purpose. We should not forget being in a state of pure presence does not annihilate the self at all. The identity, and all its needs and problems, will continue to exist. And while we most certainly will come across moments of despair, or moments when all clarity seems lost…"

"…the radiant light of Beingness is capable of spreading its clarity all over the self," cheered the glowing One. "It can engulf it entirely. And in this light, any vague or unfound sense of purpose will find itself enveloped in a serene calmness. Isn't that great? To begin with, it can offer relief from the pressure of this imagined urgency, which we think is in need of resolution. And secondly, it can offer a serene form of patience. It can allow the clenched fist of the ego to loosen up into an open hand. And there, your identity-self will find itself in a relaxed, energetic stillness where everything is allowed."

"Mind you," tempered the One with the bow and arrow, "we don't want you to be all overexcited about this Beingness-stuff. To many people, the sense of purpose can come as natural as breath. They simply experience it at the moment as an unbound energy which rises without the slightest consideration, whether that is normal or required or whatever. They don't even consider giving it a thought."

"Exactly," added the One with the magician's staff. "For these people, no matter if the trodden path is ideal or not, it's clear at the moment, and every footstep is set firmly and with confidence. Ups and downs are met as they present themselves, handled on the spot, for the best possible outcome."

"Either way, whether it comes to you spontaneously or by a little abiding in Beingness, this state of ease can bring clarity where everything seemed hidden in a mist before. Fears and worries, which usually confuse or limit us, are traded for courage and confidence, for tenacity and perseverance."

"Also, this clarity will lift the veil of this judgement that typically makes us classify all doing in either dull or meaningful baskets."

"Filled with the pulse of life itself, every action possible, from doing the dishes to completing a vital task, becomes an action filled with passion and gratitude. And gradually, or all of a sudden – who knows? – these little acts of passion will naturally converge with a more purposeful path revealing a clear goal in the longer term."

"And even if there'd be no clear direction still, now, or ever," said the One with the raven gently, "being alive itself, and being utterly connected with this aliveness, is a path on its own. A conscious connection with this aliveness can offer all the satisfaction, as well as all the direction one may need."

"Soooo," started Andrea, "I was right all along; purpose isn't such a bad thing!"

"Of course not," acknowledged the One with the nón lá in his hands. He just got back from collecting the red admirals from all the nón lá in the village. They were now all safe asleep in the hat he gently held upside down.

Wait, let's do that again:

"Of course not," acknowledge the One with his nón lá filled with Vanessa's. "Purpose makes life meaningful. It remains a vital necessity as long as it is allowed to flow freely from a passionate way of living life without this 'purpose' becoming an objective on its own."

"Precisely," agreed the One with the buckwheat flower. "After all, it is fair to say, sometimes 'purpose' can take a volatile curve to the extent of taking all meaning from life."

"That happens when you live strictly from a collapse into the s̲elf," said the One with Vanessa. "When you are unaware of your essence, disconnected. This can make you cling to a purposeful life in such a way that its apparent absence can drive one to abandon life altogether."

The glowing One danced and hovered between the crowd with slow, graceful swings of her arms. "It is the $\overline{S}$elf which allows us to see beauty, purpose and meaning, regardless of the state in which the identity-self finds itself."

She became all lyrical in a mesmerizing way:

"Be mindful.

Listen. Feel.

Watch and smell.

Allow your senses to reveal the present underneath the past and future.

Whatever purpose the s̲elf may find on its way, the purpose of the $\overline{S}$elf is ever accessible here and now,

fulfilled already,

complete,

perfect."

"You see," smiled the One with Vanessa. "When one is present in the moment itself, living in the moment, hearing the calling of aliveness and Beingness, one is a present to oneself. In this radiant presence, the moment is allowed to open like a flower without any predilection about where each petal should end or what colour it should have. No judgement, no opinions, all is simply good."

"Wonder how that works when a lion attacks ya," joked ol' Cormac. But he immediately got reprimanded by the person who had just finished replacing his IV. "They refer to a more or less serene moment, you dimwit. Nobody said you should start meditating while a person near ya is in distress or in need of help."

"Thank you, Erin. When calamity is immanent, of course, action is required. Yet even then, when there's trouble behind life's next curve, those who are deeply connected with presence will find ill consequences no longer to be a terminus. Indeed, I'd dare say, a frequent abiding in presence and in Beingness rather allows the perspective to see ill fate or poor choices as an open path with new possibilities."

The One with his nón lá filled with Vanessa's nodded. "And this path is one where you are allowed to either gradually shed your baggage of blame and regret, or you find the strength and courage to carry them along, transforming them into the meaningful life lessons they can be."

"That's all just too sweet," remarked Jimmy. "A little less sugar, please."

"He may be right," said One to another One. "Perhaps we should take it down a notch."

"Nah," corrected Jimmy. "I didn't mean you folk. I meant the coffee they just gave me."

All gazes turned towards a bamboo boat floating by in front of their platform. On board it had Annie, who had decided to revisit her seventh sea. Together with some local fishermen, she performed a beautiful cappella version of Sweet Dreams.

At the end the crowd applauded. And then, all realized how fatigued they were. It was way past midnight already. While the crowd decided to tuck in, the Illustrious Sages of Infinite Zero couldn't resist queuing for a selfie with Annie. Wouldn't that look great on their Instagram?

Faith or fate? Wait, what about trust?

The next morning came with breakfast for all. The twins were great, the jokes about triplets rather poor. Then, all got back in the bamboo boats for the next destination.

The boats went straight in the direction of the South China Sea. Once in open water, they headed east. There was a bright and merry atmosphere among all the passengers. The need for Truth or Beingness seemed all forgotten in a moment of genuine happiness. It was Kate who briefly broke the spell: "Oh dear, I think I forgot to turn off my iron back home."

After following the coastline for about an hour, something weird happened. While land was ever in sight to their north, they now also saw a coastline on their south flank. As if that was not confusing enough, a large boat suddenly crossed their path from out of the blue. It was filled with people standing on two decks. The lower deck had a green colour. The upper one was painted in white.

"Was that the Star Ferry we just crossed?" wondered Paul Ruz, a guy from a country that was so hemmed in by France, Germany, Holland, Luxembourg and the UK that it split in two from the moment it got created.

"Impressive rowing," concluded Charles while staring at the skyscrapers on both the mainland and Hong Kong Island. They all were short on eyes, with Tsim Sha Tsui passing to their left and Causeway Bay to their right. The fishermen- and women kept rowing until they reached the Shau Kei Wan Typhoon Shelter. There, it became clear they were about to dock.

"Why'd ya freakin' row all the way up here?" demanded Ol' Cormac.

"Visiting family," replied the fisherman briefly while gesturing for everybody to step out of the boats up on Aldrich Bay Promenade. While waving and exchanging goodbyes and good lucks, the fishermen- and women steered their bamboo boats towards slightly bigger boats, which seemed to be both boats and tiny houses at the same time. The Vanessa's briefly whirled around as if they couldn't decide between the boats and the shoreline. Luckily for them, one of the fishermen turned out to be a butterfly whisperer. With an inaudible whistle, he lured the butterflies towards the boats, where they all came to rest once more. Only Vanessa decided to stay with the One still with Vanessa.

Behind the crowd, there was a semi-circled, open space on the promenade. Near the curved wall were five metal benches, all flanked by some sort of palm trees. The Time-worn Venerables of Endless Nothingness all got seated. So did the crowd in front of them.

"I just can't get over it," exclaimed Charles, still baffled. "Really impressive rowing. They should join the Thames Rowing Club. I'm serious."

"The Thames Rowing Club!" spat ol' Cormac. "Not much purpose with those lot, if you ask me! Now, on the other hand, the St Andrew Boat Club might consider taking those nón lá lot in."

"I beg your pardon!"

"There there," hushed Nurse Erin. "Let's stick to the subject before Mr Wheelchair-man here starts taking out his medals from back in the day."

"Right," started Ayush with his thick Indian accent. "Well, it seems we are all clear on purpose. But what about fate? Or is it fate? I can't seem to keep them apart."

"Well, the way you pronounced it, it's fate twice," mocked Charles. "You mean faith or fate? You need to put in your tongue for the first one."

Ayush wobbled his head for a moment before making up his mind. "Okay then, it's fate I mean."

"It's tricky," laughed Jimmy. "I'm still not sure which one he's referring to. All laughed while Ayush smiled and wobbled his head once more.

"No problem," started the One with no characteristics, leaving Yoda out of the picture this time. "When it comes to fate, we can keep it short, can't we? I mean, it's the free will theme all over again. You all want to be free to decide your fate, yet you wouldn't mind a supernatural power to decide it for you. Been there, done that, haven't we?"

"They should not forget, my dear Vanessa, just like there is no one to have free will in the first place, neither is there anybody being 'fated' into stuff."

"So fate goes in the bin?" concluded Charles.

"Not necessarily, Charles. If you like to stick to it, you can. The idea of fate needn't be all negative or supernatural. It can bring comfort, too, at times when you feel you can no longer hold on."

"And it's not even in conflict with your realization of Truth!" exclaimed the One with the Viking horns while slapping himself on the thigh.

"The horned One is right, for once. From the perspective of Truth, fate is ever available if you need it."

"But for the sake of clarity, your fate is not written down by some almighty intelligence. It's not coming forth from some grand design with you as the antagonist. It's not even personal at all. These would all be rather self-centred ideas anyways."

"Fate, in Truth, simply finds expression in the continuous unfolding of existence, where every next is decided by the previous. Call it instantaneous fate, which never ceases to persist in its consistency. Nothing escapes it. And neither is it specifically tailored for Bert or Ernie. Where's the oneness in such personalised catering anyways? Fate covers everything in its totality, in one single, continuous sweep."

"I think I understand my mother better now," realized Marwa out loud. "She calls everything the will of Allah. And she abides by that. It gives her comfort like nothing else can. I never really understood. But now I realize she was much closer to Truth than I ever was back then."

"We can be all 'do' and 'need' as much as we want," said Erin. "But at times when it's all too much, it's good to realize it's all God's will. Can you imagine the idea alone brings peace to my heart?"

"Hmmm," doubted Charles, "I'm not sure it brings peace to my mind, which is usually in contr-"

"Screw yer mind for once, laddie!" huffed ol' Cormac in defence of his nurse. "Live a little from yer heart, will ya!"

The crowd went silent for a moment. Then Ayush's head wobbled more than it usually did. When all were about to get dizzy in his stead, his head came to a stop. "But what about fate?"

"Faith!" the crowd corrected in harmony, causing a big smile on a wobbling head.

"Ditch that too?" asked Charles with a ton of irony in his voice.

"Absolutely not," responded the glowing One. "Faith is a powerful ally if not one of the most powerful the human psyche is equipped with."

"How so?" wondered the One with the Viking horns.

"Hey, that was my line," objected Andrea.

"Sorry, my bad," excused the One who is writing all this. "Lost my focus there for a bit."

"Bear with me for a moment," said the One with the bow and arrow while retrieving a note from her pocket. Then she read it out loud: "Deprived of all paraphernalia, faith in its essence is a powerful capacity of the psyche, allowing humans to reach beyond rationality, where the seemingly impossible may yet have a chance to manifest."

"Voila," she said at the end while she crumpled up the paper and threw it straight into a bin a few meters further away."

"Voila?" Andrea exclaimed. "That's not voila! Could you repeat that in English?"

"Look there!"

"Not that! The bit you read from the paper."

"I can't! I just threw it in the bin. Probably covered with all sorts of sticky stuff by now."

"Aaaargh!"

"You see, Andrea," came the One with Vanessa to the rescue. "From the perspective of the self, we happen to have a sense of continuity in life. It's this sense of continuity that allows us to set goals, targets or objectives.

Now you all know the biggies amongst them usually take some time and effort to accomplish, right?"

"And that's where faith comes in," explained the glowing One. "You see, most of these goals require patience, endurance... willpower. But willpower is a rather short-term strength. You can use all the willpower you have to deny yourself a second piece of that delicious pie. But two minutes later, the pie is on your plate saying 'Hah!' at your willpower."

"It's not all pie and chocolate, Andrea. There's so many blocking factors obscuring the bigger goals from sight. Doubt, fatigue, fear, distraction – they are all pretty strong elements where willpower alone will rarely cut it."

"Yes, that's the thing. Our built-in negativity has this tendency to take any limitation, no matter how small or remote, as a blocking factor. Our psyche simply turns the slightest indication of resistance or difficulty into an obstacle impossible to overcome. It's in our nature!"

"Indeed. During our lives, the possible often becomes overly limited due to anxiety, pessimism or a string of events which seem to be deprived of luck or positivity. Where these negative aspects can operate as irrational villains, faith, belief, or hope can equally be the countering superheroes."

"Hence, faith itself is not allowed to calculate what is really possible and what is not. Boundlessness is the key ingredient for it to take root and flourish in our inner psyche."

"And that's exactly why the arms of faith can reach further than those of patience or endurance. It allows us to keep up, to hold on, despite resistance or setbacks. Moreover, faith allows us to envision the set task as accomplished already. And this feeling of success helps us to gradually gravitate towards it."

"On top of that, not only can we have faith in ourselves, we can have faith in others as well. And by sharing this confidence, as a collective, we can succeed in things deemed impossible before."

"Hrrrmmmm, still," started the One with no characteristics, mimicking master Yoda once more, "tricky faith can be."

"You mean faith can become too irrational, making us believe in stuff that isn't there?" tried Ann (really must look up which country she's from).

"Hrrummpphh, too irrational? Irrational not the problem is! Pure, faith is."

"So what's the tricky thing then?" wondered Ann.

The raven croaked. "What? Who? Oh. Tricky thing? Well, the greatest weakness of faith is not its irrationality, Ann. It's our very own rational self which is the problem. It will claim faith for its own."

"I don't understand," shook Ann with her head while Ayush's wobbling didn't provide any indication whether he did or didn't.

"Okay, listen," replied the One with no characteristics with an uncharacteristic tone. "Faith's formidable might stems from its limitlessness. It doesn't care what's possible and what's not. But when wielded by the human mind, it gets torn or bent in multiple ways to fit our personal agenda."

"How's that?"

"Well, to overcome things which seem greater than ourselves, our mind is overly keen to believe in something equally greater as well. Fear of dying? Bad luck or adversity? An incurable illness? Soon enough, we will abuse faith to push natural and unavoidable boundaries or limitations into the realm of the miraculous."

"So, we invoke God or gods. And we think up ways to please them. That's not irrational behaviour," concluded Ann. "It's actually rational thinking!"

"But of course it is. It's all mental fabrications to begin with. Then, it gets interwoven with feeling and emotion. And when it's done by CSDCs, who are no more or no less human beings themselves, searching for wealth or meaning to their own existence, it will catch fire and light up whole communities."

"You see, that's the tragedy. Faith's prime quality is that it can act as a countermeasure to our overly protective negativity. While faith requires boundlessness, it will, in reality, restore shrunken boundaries to their natural position. But humanity is a greedy lot. They will always seek ways to stretch those natural boundaries into a realm where they will only find seduction accompanied by abuse."

"So, to round things up, faith is not about making room for the supernatural to bypass the laws of existence. It rather is an intricate countermeasure within ourselves, like antibodies, but on a psychological level. It helps us to overcome aspects of our human nature which tend to block us or hold us back."

"It's really remarkable, isn't it, Vanessa? One could say it is perfectly rational to see the strength of the irrational, while it is overly irrational to shun the benefits of the rational."

"Have faith in yourself, Ann. Accept the limitations of the possible. There is no need to levitate, read minds or materialize yourself thousands of miles away in a flash. What you áre truly capable of is that you cán dissolve impossibilities which are unreal. And that's pretty remarkable on its own, wouldn't you agree?"

A moment of silence decided to drop in. Less than a minute later, it got kicked out by the twins' need for nourishment.

"Hmm," started Ayush, "I think it's correct to conclude faith is a quality which operates in the realm of the s̲elf, right? So, I can't help wondering, how do faith and the S̄elf interact?"

"Ah, good question!" said the One with Vanessa. "Indeed, Ayush, the s̲elf can use a little faith now and then, surely when the natural flow of healing and wholeness is inhibited by all things that tighten us up. But the non-identity requires no such thing. If any name would be given to a similar state in the S̄elf, it would be Trust."

"Trust?" rasped ol' Cormack. "Don't get me started on trust. Shall I show you my underwear? It's from that X-files-couple. It says 'Trust no one'!"

"Fair enough," chuckled the glowing One. "But we don't mean that kind of trust, my friend. And rest assured, we don't aim for your trust. That would turn our relationship into a CSDC-bond. Trust amongst people is earned, not given blindly. Yet even then, it remains both a bold and fragile thing."

"Exactly," continued the One with the lantana (this one is rather neat; from a distance, it looks like one flower, but actually, it turns out to be an explosion of multiple little flowers in different colours). "The Trust we speak of is not the typical trust one can have amongst humans. We actually refer to the relationship you can have with life itself and with existence in its entirety."

"You mean you trust everything will eventually always turn out alright," asked Charles with a bit of a cynical tone, "no matter how bad things are going for you?"

"That's the perspective of the self again," answered the One with the lantana. "From that perspective, this kind of trust is rather a form of oversized fate. Believing the outcome of things will turn out to your benefit is the typical situation where the self goes for a win. Personal gain or loss is not part of the realm of the $\overline{\text{S}}$elf, you know that by now, Charles."

"This trust we speak of is not about expectations for a certain outcome," explained the One without Vanessa. (She was off examining the lantana). "It rather flows from a deep recognition of Truth. The $\overline{\text{S}}$elf has this sort of non-mental Knowing that all is exactly as it should be, despite whatever judgment the identity may have about any situation possible. It simply realizes that everything as it is couldn't be any other way. All is perfect as it is, because…"

"… it couldn't be any other way," ended Charles.

"Hence, there is no longing to change anything. The Trust of the $\overline{\text{S}}$elf radiates a deep form of being relaxed and at ease. And as such it has a soothing effect on the self. It brings a sense of peace. And paradoxically enough, it brings vitality along as well."

"It doesn't bring apathy?" asked Charles. "I mean, a-"

"You overthink it, Charles. This Trust brings aliveness. It brings eagerness to life. Take a deep breath, Charles. Let's all take a deep breath. Feel it. Allow yourself to sink into this Beingness. Let it engulf you."

"I want to do something fun!" Ann exulted.

Acceptance

"Ding Ding!" the glowing One whooped.

"Ding Ding?" the crowd collectively asked.

"Come," gestured the One with the raven while he rose. "Follow us. We've booked fun."

"Actually, I did," grumbled the One who is writing all this silently between clenched teeth. "Made the impossible possible again, but who'd mention that, right?"

"Yes, yes, follow us," said the glowing One thrilled. "You can trust us."

"Right!" said Sven. "Is this a trick or something? After all that talk about trust, now you want us to trust you?"

"It's a joke," jested the glowing One. "Still, if you want fun, 'Ding Ding' it is."

In the centre of the semi-circled wall, there was an opening towards a wide, paved path leading into a garden of trees. The path ended with a view of many apartment buildings that didn't look that appealing to live in. Air conditioning units were mounted everywhere. The colours of the walls were supposed to be jolly, but poor quality of paint or decay decided otherwise. From there, the crowd found themselves guided further through another few streets which equally reflected anything but fun.

Then, they reached the Shau Kei Wan Tram Terminus. They couldn't be less amazed by what they saw. For one, this seemed like a roundabout for trams, which looked kind of funny. On top of that, there were two trams waiting to be boarded by the Ancient Mystics of Infinite Zero. The cloaked and masked figures waved the crowd to follow them along.

It seemed the Ancient Mystics of Infinite Zero had chartered both trams. One was a red antique double-deck tram with the number 128. The other was a green, equally antique tram with the number 28. The crowd fanned out on both trams. Some preferred the lower deck, while others preferred to sit on top.

"This is exciting," beamed Bram. He felt like the little boy he was only just a few years ago. "Still, I wonder what she meant with that Ding Ding stuff."

"Ding Ding!" a bell rang while the trams came into movement with a slight jolt. It took about two seconds for the same jolt to kick in in ol' Cormac's wheelchair which got tied on a rope behind the second tram.

"Everybody comfortable?" The sound of the glowing One came from well-hidden loudspeakers for all to hear. It seemed there were hidden microphones as well, for they soon realized they could all hear each other despite being separated over two trams and four decks.

"Well, this is fun," repeated Bram while ol' Cormac's knuckles went all white from keeping a firm grip on his wheelchair.

"Still, I find this trust-thing a tough nut to crack," complained Olivia, who got bored soon enough.

"You ought to relinquish control over to the Lord," advised an old lady next to her on the lower deck. She was a tiny thing, with her back bent into a remarkable kyphosis. Despite clearly looking like a local, she spoke eloquently with a British accent.

"See," she continued. "I handed control over to the Lord many years ago. Nothing really changed much. So, one day, I decided to take this tram and said to the Lord I'd only get off if He'd give me a clear sign. I mean, not a sign like hearing a tune from my youth, or seeing a man I loved many years ago on another continent, or … Well, certainly not a silly conductor telling me to step out. A 'clear' sign, you understand? Something that would change my life permanently if I were to follow its lead."

"But how long have you been on this tram?" Marwa asked.

"Must be twenty years now, lass. Twenty seven, if I recall correctly. People give me food. I am actually quite famous. Saw myself in the newspaper of a person next to me once."

"Twenty-seven!"

"As the Lord asks tenacity of me, I shall ask no less of Him," she chuckled.

"Relinquish control over to the Lord?" Jimmy scoffed. "And what about all these millions of people meeting ill fate and terrible endings despite all that?"

"Well, they didn't really relinquish control over to the Lord, now did they? Pretty obvious if you ask me."

"Sounds like the Lord is a pretty pompous and vindictive fella, if you ask me," Jimmy concluded. But the old lady seemed to have dozed off.

"My yoga teacher often speaks about acceptance," said Andrea. "I think the old lady means the same, sort of."

"Aren't yoga teachers supposed to teach yoga instead of giving lectures of all sorts?" Bram wondered.

Andrea totally ignored Bram. "No, really, she said that acceptance is the way to leave the important things in your life to a divine source. She advised us to practice acceptance as much as possible because 'it' has the best intentions for us."

"Acceptance," the voice of the glowing One rang through the sound system of four decks (Remember? Two trams, two decks each). "Such a beautiful thing."

"Really? That sounds even worse than trust," sneered Charles from the upper deck of the Green Tram. "How can you promote a thing like acceptance? Do we need to give up now? Do you want us to avoid struggle, or not be assertive, and let it all just happen to us? I take it you eventually want us to give up on just about everything, no?"

"Of course not, you silly. Don't be such a drama queen, Charles."

Charles looked up and around, baffled by the quality of the sound system. He even could feel the warm pun in the words spoken. Then he realized the words came from the One with the lantana who was sitting right next to him.

"Acceptance is not about giving up or any stuff like that. What a depressing idea! And it surely isn't about blindly accepting the words of some yoga teacher, guru or any other CSDC."

"Most certainly not," started the One with the magician's staff. "Why don't we first take a look at acceptance from the perspective of the self."

"Yes! Let's do that!" the One with the Viking horns agreed firmly from the deck below while stamping one foot on the floor.

A man next to him, wearing an impeccable 1920s suit and a Homburg fedora, kept his poise despite the trembling action next to him. He inaudibly kept muttering the same line over and over again.

"So from the position of the self, acceptance surely is not about meekly going into submission or avoiding struggle. What good would that do?"

"Indeed," said the One with the bow and arrow while pointing from the upper deck of the red tram at Sven on top of the green tram. "Imagine me shooting an arrow in Sven's heart. Would you all accept that?"

"The thought sounds appealing," joked Kalle. But then he added he'd shove that bow into One's particular place in a very precise way, which sounded far from comfortable and rather lethal as well.

"Of course, you wouldn't," muttered the One with the bow and arrow with a loud swallowing sound. "When you clearly feel you can or must change the outcome of things, you will. Why wouldn't you? It's a thing which rises as natural as… the sun?"

"Then again," raised the One with the magician's staff, "this need to intervene or resist can also be overly adamant at times. While perhaps, when there is no possibility of change, acceptance could bring more relief than continuing a pointless fight."

"When will you fight against cancer, and when will you accept it is time to let go? When will you keep resisting against growing older, and when will you accept the wrinkles of time as they come?"

"When will you curse the wheelchair," mused ol' Cormac demurely, "and when will you learn to accept it?" Of course, nobody heard him except for Erin, who could read it in his posture as clear as if it was written out.

"I'd say," added the One with the lantana, "even when you are only able to change the outcome of things in the future, the feeling of acceptance needn't be out of reach in the present. You see, even in struggle, while not accepting the situation itself, one can still accept the struggle or the dealing with continuous hardship. It can be a way to loosen an all too tight grip which counteracts any chance of reevaluating things and taking a different approach."

"Countless, aren't they, my dear Vanessa? The struggles they find themselves in without a healthy form of acceptance. Just look around at how many people can't accept some questions that have no answer, now or ever. They rather create their own false truth, readily available here and now, instead of putting in the hard work and patience which might even span generations."

"I totally agree with you and your butterfly there," said Marwa. "You can't believe how many Westerners come to my country to look at our ancient buildings. They can't figure out how they are made or what they are for, so it's always the same shortsighted conclusion: it must be extra-terrestrials who did it. I myself am proud of my ancestors. And I'm sure we will figure it out one day, how and why they did it."

Georges, who was sitting on the other side of the man with the Homburg fedora, somehow was drawn into the old man's muttering and decided to understand what he was saying.

"Sacrebleu!" Georges exclaimed. "I understand what he's saying!"

"Who's saying…?"

"…what?"

"This man here on the tram. He is repeating the same thing over and over again."

"So what is he saying, man? Out with it!"

Georges listened again to make sure he got it right. Then he repeated out loud: "Dear Lord, grant me the serenity to accept the things I cannot change… the courage to change the things I can… and the wisdom to know the difference."

"Not bad," commented the One with the Viking horns. "Couldn't have come up with that one myself."

"Not bad, indeed," agreed the One with the lantana. "Sums it up nicely, I'd say."

"That must take a lot of practice to accomplish, no?" wondered Andrea.

"Oh, you can go all mindfulness on a regular basis, sure," said the One with Vanessa. "But the wisdom this man speaks of actually takes no practice at all. This wisdom is directly accessible in the realization of Truth. It's not the wisdom of a mental kind. 'Practicing' acceptance may be practical, but it will rarely lead you to the deeper experience of Truth. It will not tell you who you really are and how you relate to the universe."

The One with the dice kindly put his hand on the shoulder of the person with the Homburg fedora. "Like this humble person here with us. Despite all his wisdom, he couldn't shed the last duality of him and the Lord being two separate things."

"So?" countered Andrea. "He seems content. Isn't that what matters most?"

"You are absolutely right about that, Andrea," answered the One with the raven. "But please, do not mistake our sharing of the Truth with being judgemental of those not having realized it. All is good. And we wouldn't have the slightest need to convert this content person here. It is you who asked us for Truth, and we merely comply."

"And that's the thing with our current topic," continued the One with the dice. "When you 'know' the Truth, when you 'know' all is moving as one, when you 'know' you-are-not, when you have 'realized' this to the fullest – I know you may not believe me now – acceptance is the only possible outcome."

"This knowingness is beyond words or feelings. It is more of an intuitive nature. In the experience of Beingness lies the realization of nothingness. In this realization one couldn't find more humbleness possible. It's not the humbleness of bowing down to some supreme being. It's humbleness in its purest, most essential form. Simply 'it' as it is, not as it usually manifests from one to another. And this purity, in turn, evokes the most pure and serene acceptance there can be."

"Within the $\overline{S}$elf existence unfolds in an ever now. Not even the slightest crack or bend could make it be any other way than it is. Now, for the self, when you approach this strictly mentally, such a view may seem a depressing or nihilistic idea which is utterly useless. But the $\overline{S}$elf is beyond all this. It simply is."

"And once more, the beauty is how this serene state of acceptance reflects upon the self. This state of humbleness, this state of acceptance, it can be more practical in your daily existence than you could ever imagine."

"Oi," shouted ol' Cormac. "I would really accept you lot pulling me in now."

Surrender

Nurse Erin stood at the rear end of the green tram's balcony. She looked down at ol' Cormac and smiled.

"Quit smirking ye wench, and pull me in!"

"You haven't had this much fun in your life, like ever, you ol' complainer!"

"If I may," Kalle started. "We've been talking about acceptance just now. But how does that rhyme with surrender?"

"It doesn't," the glowing One chuckled. "Acceptance – surrender, Accender – surreptance? Nope, it doesn't."

"Very funny," Kalle rolled his eyes. "But seriously. Is it the same thing? Or is it different?"

"It's not the same thing," the One with the Viking horns guessed, "is it?"

"It surely is not," the One with the magician's staff replied. "See, perhaps you haven't noticed, but this exploration of words is leading us deeper into the realm of the $\overline{S}$elf while we progress. At first, there was a balance, but with concepts like Acceptance and Trust, it had already started to shift. Surrender surely tips the scale to the other side."

"What do you mean," Sven queried. "So far, we've been looking at things from the point of view of both s̲elf and S̄elf, didn't we? So you're saying surrender cannot be applied to this approach?"

"Definitely not. You see, surrender is the most beautiful thing. It's the pinnacle of knowingness. But it's also… how to say it?"

"Dangerous, surrender is," said the One with no characteristics in Yoda's voice. "Applied to the s̲elf, only abuse and deception found can be."

"Someone really ought to take this fella to a doctor," Erin commented while ever keeping one eye on ol' Cormac.

"Andrea," asked the One with the lantana casually. "Did your yoga teacher ever mention surrender?"

"Did she mention surrender?" Andrea repeated. "Like all the time she did! Surrender this. Surrender that. If it's not surrender to a freakin' difficult pose, it's surrender to a situation, or surrender to God or some other deity. Or surrender to the community. Or surrender to her guru. Supposed to gain this and that when you'd do that. Mostly lost some money and gained a lot of books I can't get rid of."

"Well, that clearly needed to get out," Kevin joshed (who's Kevin?).

Andrea clearly looked relieved. Then she started crying. "Can't believe I ever fell for all that stuff. And would you believe it? The moment I met your masked lot, the first thing that popped up in my mind was, 'Maybe I should surrender to them'. Like it's some disease that makes me wanna trip over and over again over the same stupid branch on my path."

"It's like when you realize one particular kind of candy is bad for your teeth, and you switch to another until you realize that one's bad too. So you basically keep switching as long as you don't realize where this urge for candy is coming from."

"Wow, Sven," remarked Kalle surprised. "You must definitely become the candy guru."

"Blimey," gasped Jimmy. "We all are CSDCs. It's not just those ever lovingly smiling people on stages or TV, it's all of us."

"Hang on, Jimmy," said Charles. "Hate to pop your bubble, but charismatic is not particularly your main quality. I'd agree we're all SDs. We trick ourselves, and in doing so, we allow them to trick us twice over."

The Ancient Mystics of Infinite Zero seemed content at hearing this conversation without involving them. (Well, they always seemed to be content, given their smiling masks and flair for silliness.)

"In the realm of the identity," said the One with Vanessa, "surrender is never ever a good idea. It will always turn into submission, deception or abuse. And if it's not that, then it's all promises never kept or fulfilled. The reason is simple. In the realm of the self, it's always about a relationship with 'another'. Hence, surrender is always about you surrendering to someone or something. Nothing good can come from this duality. There's always something to gain and much to lose."

"My yoga teacher, back in Aurora," Olivia began, "says we need to surrender by bowing down. Because when you bow down, grace can stream down upon you, while when you are insistent on standing up…"

"Really?!"

"Oh my," she gasped. "I'm doing it again! But they make it sound so logical, like it truly makes sense and all."

Olivia blushed and started sulking a bit. It was Andrea who comforted her while the eyes of all others betrayed the same feelings.

"Surrender is that what happens when the ego spontaneously gives way. When it dissolves." The One with the raven looked up at the raven and gave it a gentle caress on the chest. "We have told you before. The ego cannot decide to remove itself. It will only think it to be a cool idea and swell at the thought of shrinking. That's why the Seekers will never find what they are looking for, for they look for the wrong reasons.

When the realization of Truth dawns, when knowingness infiltrates every part of your being; only then clarity emerges like the sun rising at the horizon at dawn."

"Oh, there's the sun again."

"It's an experience which brings tears to the eyes and a smile to the lips.

All is complete. All is accomplished. There is no need to gain a thing. What need would there be?"

"You will start to spot all the folks deluding themselves and trying to pull you along in the gravity of their delusion. 'Surrender,' they say, 'and the world will serve you. Surrender,' they say, 'and you will be guided.' But how strange is this surrender when we decide to surrender only to gain from it. Do you see the great folly in this?"

"You see, you cannot practice surrender. It will ever be self-trickery in which the ego rolls itself like a pig in mud. Surrender happens in the form of grace. You cannot invoke it; it simply happens. And this surrender invokes a deep humility beyond anything to compare with. Such a person will not display it. Every display of humility is a display of the ego. No, such a person might even seem to be the most obnoxious living being in the world. But deep inside, there nonetheless is this hidden, ever-present surrender."

"Creates an entirely different view on obnoxious people, doesn't it?" Kalle joked.

"But?" It didn't seem to sink in with Sven. "It's... I can't relate to it. Sorry, I really can't. So, how..."

"Ok, let's breathe," tried the One with the nón lá.

Ding Ding!!! – "Whooaaa!!"

That was the next stop.

The One with the nón lá threw a can-you-guys-keep-it-steady glance at the One conducting the tram.

"Ok, let's try that again. Breathe in... Breathe out...

Imagine the universe.

Imagine how this universe sprang into existence. Imagine it from the very first few seconds.

There was not a soul present to witness it. It simply did, unseen, unaware, yet as present as can be. Imagine this vastness, spanning lightyears in all possible directions. Planets, suns, supernovae, black holes, clusters of galaxies, most unseen, most unaware, yet all present, present as can be.

We think ourselves special in being aware of all this. We almost think ourselves to be gods, immortal and capable of shaping and bending the flow of the universe to our will by ritual or prayer.

See how we, in reality, merely are a tiny speck of dust, present only in a blink of an eye. Feel how humility and surrender spontaneously rise in this honest recognition. And realize, truly realize, how we nonetheless have this most beautiful capacity to not only be aware of our non-existence but we also are gifted with the capacity to dive straight into existence in its totality, through the purest state of Beingness, giving rise to the mystical experience of timelessness and boundlessness."

The One with the raven nodded. "True surrender rises from the realization you are nothing. Nothing at all. Yet hidden in this nothingness, there is this boundless vastness available to be touched. You are infinite and zero at the same time. The ultimate paradox. You are a self-identified, sentient living being, and you are nothing but a part of the great unfolding. You are a paradox living a paradoxical existence. That realization is everything. And it is enough. You are fulfilled."

"In this radiant contentment," added the One with Vanessa, "with nothing more to gain, nothing more to need, the self can find peace and rejuvenation. And once you recognize this house, you can always come home to it, be it during your greatest struggle or your deepest despair. Be it when you are in need of comfort or when you are overcome with sadness or grief, it is there."

"And when you are happy as a fiddle with no one around to hear your tunes, you can go crazy there as well and have a jolly good time."

Ding Ding!!! – "Whooaaa!!!"

Gratitude

"Is anyone else hearing this?" asked Marwa.

Bram looked left and right, up and down. "Hear what?"

"Oui, I hear it too," said Georges who was habitually sitting like a pretzel again. "Every time there is Ding Ding, there also is this Whooaaa."

"Exactly!" exclaimed Marwa.

"Oh that," sounded Erin's voice through the speakers. "That's me ol' Cormac, out there. Every time the tram stops, his wheelchair heads to collide with it. But nothing to be worried about. I just recently checked his breaks. It'll be fine. Keeps the ol' bugger awake, doesn't it?"

All at the upper deck of the green tram laughed. The reason was not ol' Cormac hanging behind the tram on a rope. It was the delightful grin on Erin's face when she spoke of him.

"He must be very grateful to have you," said Márcia.

"Haven't seen much of that coming from him," snorted Marwa from the lower deck of the red tram.

"He has his own way of showing it," Erin confidently replied. "He's a proud and stubborn man, I know. And yes, he has many a moment of being obnoxious and all. Still, he knows gratitude. He really does."

"Ah, gratitude," sighed the glowing One as if recalling a distant but happy memory. "More than love, gratitude is most likely the pinnacle of humanity's continuous evolution."

"Say what?" said Jimmy. "Did she say pinnacle, or was it pin-apple?"

"Either way," added Charles, "that sentence just didn't make any sense."

"Are you kidding me?" gasped the glowing One. "Gratitude! It most surely is that aspect within all of you in which all your diverse properties as human beings converge into a deeper quality. A quality, mind you, which abundantly radiates health, happiness and contentment, and that's only mentioning a few."

"Whaaat???" piped Jimmy.

"I'm confused as well," said Bram. "Isn't gratitude more like a form of politeness? You know, when someone helps you out, you ought to say: thanks."

"Just thanks!" protested Hoshiko Hikari, an elderly woman from Okinawa. "In Japan we have many ways of saying a lot more than just thanks."

"Domo arigato gozaimas', Hoshiko-sama," bowed the glowing One while receiving a humble bow in return.

Bram blushed. He had the feeling he should have known this about the Japanese. "Well, yes. But still, polite or super-polite, it's just a token of appreciation, no?"

"Is anyone else noticing all misunderstanding about gratitude is coming from the boys only?" chuckled Márcia.

"Men," snorted Andrea. "They haven't got a clue. Things I've done for men. Well, actually, for my mother too. Things I've done. And never not even a simple thanks, let alone your domo-gazi-I-don't-know."

"And if they're not forgetting to show even a little appreciation," ranted Olivia, "then there's this other lot going 'thank you this' and 'thank you that' for all to hear. 'I'm so grateful to be here.' – 'I'm so grateful you are here.' – 'I'm so grateful my house burned down.' All nothing but a bunch 'a humblebraggers, if you ask me!"

"Well, ladies," remarked Jimmy, "seems like you lot as well have a particular angle on gratitude, don't you?"

"Hang on, hang on," interrupted the glowing One. "I'm afraid you are all missing my point."

"Hey guys, look!" shouted Paul. "We're in a tram jam. There's like six trams right in front of us, all standing still."

Olivia rolled her eyes up and around. "Well, that's informative, Paul. Thank you very much."

The glowing One quickly stepped in before all went into another rant. "It seems you all only know gratitude as a relational exchange. Like where you need to satisfy an expectation of appreciation..."

"… or, you know it as a feeling of frustration when there is a lack of it," added the One with the Viking horns.

"But that's not the gratitude I was referring to with my pineapple… pinnacle-phrase," wailed the glowing One. She really became more and more upset about how her words all got misunderstood.

"There there," hushed the One with Vanessa. "Let's all settle down a bit. Seems like you are all approaching this gratitude thing from the perspective of the self only, aren't you? But self and gratitude, they are rarely a good match. One expects it, one demands it. One brags about it, one abuses it. One unexpectedly gives it, one doesn't know how to express it, etcetera, etcetera."

"And the common denominator in this story is?" quizzed the One with the soft brome (to be honest, the lantana got a bit heavy).

"One?" guessed Bram, who got lost in one doing this and one doing that.

"One?? Not one! Two!"

"Two?"

"Yes, Bram, two. But here's the thing. It should be one. It's only effective in case of one."

"Ha!" Bram felt he was right all along. Then he looked at Marwa's face and realized he wasn't. "You lost me," he sighed.

"It's two, because there's the one being grateful, and there's the one being appreciated. Or also, there's the one not being appreciative and the one in need of a little appreciation, right?"

Olivia confessed: "Most of us are pretty good in needing a little appreciation, but…"

And Andrea was remarkably fast to finish this sentence: "… most of us pretty much suck in giving it."

"Girls! That's deep," said the YOLO-jester (ha, remember him?). "But… why are we so bad at it?"

"Space," replied the One with the soft brome in the shortest way possible.

"Space?"

"Gratitude requires space," explained the One with the magician's staff. "Remember the feeling of space? When there is anger, fear, or feelings of being oppressed, abused, wronged or stressed, there is no feeling of space. Gratefulness cannot take root there, not spontaneously."

"And then you're in a pickle," said the One with Vanessa. "You either become sort of a grinch-character, ever consumed with your own feelings and your own perspective."

"Or, you come to realize this pickle-thingy, and you want it solved. So soon enough, you'll be collecting advice left and right from people who somehow inspire you and seem to have all the advice you need."

"They might suggest you practice gratitude. Try to be grateful for small things first. Hug a tree. Stuff like that. Nothing wrong with that. But it won't help much when the lack of space remains."

"So instead of enforcing gratitude upon yourself, one would rather reconnect with that inner space in which gratitude genuinely can flourish."

"Let's try it!" cheered the glowing One.

"Ding ding!" agreed both trams.

"Whooaaaaa!!"

"Very well," started the One with the nón lá. "Let us bring our attention to the breath.

Become aware of each exhale and each inhale.

Now, gently start to breathe a little slower… and a little deeper.

Feel the growing space on the inhale. On the exhale, let go of anger. Let go of fear, sadness, despair, or frustration.

With each inhale and exhale, allow yourself to submerge in both spaciousness and contentment.

Feel… how gratitude itself starts to fill the boundless space of the $\overline{\text{S}}$elf. Notice how there is no need to be grateful to someone or to be grateful for something. Simply abide in gratefulness itself while it gently starts to overwhelm the s̲elf as well."

The glowing One looked around and found many with tears in their eyes. "So you see, the mere ability of being genuinely appreciative, automatically comes accompanied by contentment and inner peace. You'll find yourself to be more relaxed, even when in a stressful situation."

"The presence of gratitude is vital to your wellbeing in the now, as well as how your character develops over time."

"Gratitude simply is a profound healing mechanism which is available to us all," said the One with Vanessa. "A state of gratefulness appeals to a healthy kind of humility while simultaneously nourishing our self-esteem. See, another paradox!"

"Gratefulness invokes deep presence, a mindful state of being which is like ever on."

"In this recognition of spaciousness, you will find yourself able to treasure life itself. You'll be appreciative of every new breath you can take. Soon enough, you will discover yourself to be gratefulness itself, without there being anything or anyone specific to be grateful for. More than any fancy method or technique, this is the main key to happiness and wholeness. And its effect on your mental and physical health will be significant, to say the least. No need for the supernatural once you realize the magic of gratefulness."

"Allow yourself to stay in touch with this feeling by frequently reconnecting to spaciousness," advised the One with the raven. "For the potential of gratitude stretches far beyond the identity-self. Genuine gratitude has a transcendental aspect to it. And submerged in this gratefulness, life becomes less about persistently having control over things."

"See, my sweet little Vanessa, the value of presence itself, something which they deemed trivial or pointless before, will become more and more understood and cherished even. And they themselves are the only ones in the world able to take this away from them. Isn't that silly, my dear?"

Abundance, abundantly available – really!

Ding Ding!!! – "Whoaaaa! – Pleeeeease, enough!"

While all were talking or explaining, the two trams ding-dinged through Causeway Bay and Wan Chai. Then the airco-appartements suddenly made way for tall buildings of glass. They had reached Admirality.

"This is our stop, ladies and gentlemen!" shouted the One with the bow and arrow.

All disembarked the trams. None of them could help themselves staring up with open mouths. The buildings in this area were much taller than the ones they saw up until now. Some simply went straight up. One looked like it was made of Lego blocks. A little further along was a building that resembled a praying mantis.

"Could you all stop gaping around and help me from these bloody rails!" barked ol' Cormac. There were about 9 trams behind him, all with barely an inch between them, all eagerly dingdinging ol' Cormac to clear the rails.

"Admit you had fun," honey-voiced Erin while she rejoined him with the rest of the crowd and the Surrealistic Shamans of Infinite Zero. Despite his ever-grunting response, the Irish Scotsman simply couldn't suppress his eyes from radiantly sparkling like they never did before.

"Here, we need to go up the stairs so we can go down and head for the MTR," signalled the One with the bow and arrow.

"Paradoxes, paradoxes," said Sven while shaking his head. "They just keep falling out their sleeves, don't they?"

And so, the crowd went up on the walkway over Queensbay. And then they went down again to board the MTR which arrived shortly after they had done so.

"Wonder where we're heading this time," said Kalle while the MTR continued its journey. All grabbed anything with a red colour, although that didn't seem necessary as they were packed upon each other like sardines in a can.

Suddenly, Marciá seemed to suffer a severe cramp. She started breathing with puckered lips. "Oh no," she gasped. "I think another one is coming."

"Triplets!" cheered the glowing One.

Oliver's face went completely white. For a split second, there was not a single trace of blood present above the region of his shoulders.

"In the MTR?" feared Olivia. "How are we going to pull this one off?"

"I just did," chuckled Marciá. "I pulled your leg, didn't I?"

All laughed. Some faked to be angry. And the MTR seemed to keep increasing speed as if there was nothing holding it back. Through the windows, they all could see nothing but a blurry greyness passing by. Then, all of a sudden, the MTR started slowing down again and came to a stop. Somehow, the red interior had switched to a more blueish palette.

The doors opened, and the crowd dripped out like pudding from a crack in its jar.

"What you all lying on the floor like that for?" asked the One with Vanessa while the Surrealistic Shamans of Infinite Zero all disembarked. "Come on. We need to go up! So up yourselves, pretty please."

"Indeed," affirmed the One with the magician's staff. "Up it's definitely going to be. Follow us."

The One with the magician's staff led all of them further in the subway system. There, they arrived at three shiny white doors, each framed in the best-polished silver metal. The most amazing part of it all was that each door somehow had a large number projected on it. And underneath the large number, which happened to be counting down really fast, were smaller numbers, giving a somehow ominous indication of height and speed.

"Are we gonna go in space?" wondered ol' Cormac when the doors slid open simultaneously. The One with the magician's staff, the One with the bow and arrow and the One with the Viking horns stood each at a door and gestured everybody to step into the dark rooms.

Once all were inside, the doors closed. A flowerlike symbol appeared on the walls and roof of the elevator, which seemed to consist entirely of glass. Then, stars and planets appeared all around them.

"We àre going into space! – Erin! What did ya put in me IV?"

The stars and planets turned into fireworks. After the fireworks, the glass turned into regular glass again. They were in the clouds. A tall tower appeared on one side while a number on a screen kept going up and up. When it went over 120 many started to worry.

"My God," Charles realized. "I know where we are. We are in the Burj Khalifa!"

The number came to a stop at 148. The doors slid open. All stepped into a fancy lounge where they were welcomed by waiters offering them colourful drinks and sweets.

Ol' Cormac was the first to roll his way to a window. "We are in an aeroplane!" he croaked. "We are in a freakin' aeroplane! Just look at those skyscrapers below us."

"I'm afraid we're not in an aeroplane, ol' chum," said Charles. "We are still very much inside a building."

Olivia's face went white while she crawled on all fours to the centre of the room. There she looked up at the smiling masks of the Surrealistic Shamans of Infinite Zero, who were all comfortably seated in curvy sofas.

Somehow, their smiles eased her anxiety. She managed to get up and took a seat in a cross-legged position on the carpet. Others followed her example, except Georges who decided to show he could still do his pretzel thing. The more elderly amongst the crowd sat down with their back against the white walls around the sofas.

Only ol' Cormac remained near the window. "What? You can nearly see Australia from up here! And you lot decide to sit on the floor?"

Nurse Erin decided it was time to change his IV and rolled him towards the wall, where they joined the rest.

"Dude," started the FOMO-jester (yeh, he was that too). "You guys really know the secret to how to manifest. How did you pull up those elevators and this entire floor just for us? Incredible!"

"Mind you, my manifestations have nothing to do with that stuff you are referring to," remarked the One who is writing all this.

"What's this manifesting stuff anyways?" asked Mykhailo. "Is it when you visualize you are doing your exercise on the rings better than before, and then you actually do?"

"Exactly, dude! You visualize it, and then it happens! Works exactly the same way with money, success, a house, a wife, you name it."

"I manifested myself gold metal on Olympics," replied Mykhailo sceptically. "I didn't make it to last round." Then he burst out in laughter. "And I visualize different woman every day. Still, no wife for Mykhailo."

All laughed. Then the One with the raven commented on the conversation: "What Mykhailo describes with the rings is actually something that works. However, the margins are pretty narrow. Ol' Cormac can visualize himself as a champion on the rings as much as he likes. Without putting in the hard work, nothing will happen."

"Oi," protested the Irish Scotsman. "You haven't seen me rowing, now have ya! I challenge ya anytime, even at me old age."

"I wouldn't dare, my friend. I'm just saying there's that what is possible, and there's that the CSDCs shamelessly sell you at a good price."

"Now you are talking about abundance, aren't you?" asked Andrea.

"A bunny dance?" chuckled the glowing One. "Love your German accent, Andrea."

"A beautiful concept," said the One with the soft brome. "Abundance, I mean. Sadly, yes, the CSDCs indeed turn it into a bunny dance. If there is one word in all the words we've been looking at, this one is definitely the least achievable of all."

"Really?" said Erin, disappointed. "And here I was, just waiting for this ol' bugger to bite the dust, hoping I'd be in his will."

"Ya wish, ya evil, wicked wench!"

"Why is that?" asked Márcia sincerely when all stopped laughing. "Least achievable, I mean."

"Simple," answered the One with Vanessa, "although I must add, we are now strictly referring to the identity, to the self. From this perspective there can't ever be enough. If there'd be one thing abundantly present, there'd be ten others where there is still lack."

"Exactly," added the One with the soft brome. "Our ego is never satisfied. Even if it would be, it would only be for a brief moment. The itch of need and want would soon enough pop up again."

"And that's a good thing, too," commented the One with the raven. "This continuous itch of dissatisfaction is not necessarily a negative aspect. See, if everything would be abundantly present, all motivation would disappear. There'd be no growth, no goals, no efforts, no accomplishments. We'd slowly head into a lethargic state or some form of mental crash."

"Still," dared Kalle. "A little abundance wouldn't do any harm, now would it?"

"There's no little when it comes to abundance, Kalle," said the One with the soft brome. "Abundance is rather of an infinite nature. And there is no amount of money, luxury, commodity or status which can measure up to infinity."

"But that sounds totally unachievable!"

"Not at all," said the glowing One. "It's right within arm's reach."

Kalle scratched his head. Sven noticed it and started scratching Kalle's head, too. "Flee?"

"Look at abundance in its depth," continued the glowing One. "It's not a measurable artefact of any kind. It's a feeeeeling. And it rises in moments where there is enoughness, where there is wholeness, or completeness."

"This feeling can be discovered by chance," said the One with the raven. "Call it grace if you like. And whenever you encounter this feeling, you will notice, your identity diminishes. And however briefly it does, it opens a portal to an experience of the $\overline{\text{S}}$elf.

You see, my friends, whether it is Love, Trust, Surrender, Gratitude or Abundance, all of these feelings allow you to fall into the $\overline{\text{S}}$elf. They allow you to fall out of your limited identity. It's precisely these brief moments that drive you to seek for Truth. Because whenever you drop back into the $\underline{\text{s}}$elf, you experience this lack, this incompleteness or this idea of not being good enough once more.

You can choose to wait for these rare moments to happen by themselves. You can also try to induce them. But we have taught you already how you can approach them from the other side, from the deep experience of the $\overline{\text{S}}$elf. For it is within the $\overline{\text{S}}$elf where you can find true abundance, simply because abundance and boundlessness are quite the same."

"Within the $\overline{\text{S}}$elf," said the One with the magician's staff, "there is nothing but enoughness, nothing but wholeness, nothing but completeness. As we keep repeating over and over, a touch of the $\overline{\text{S}}$elf unavoidably showers the $\underline{\text{s}}$elf with similar feelings in its own realm. And hence, gradually, you will come to realize, even in the realm of the $\underline{\text{s}}$elf, you are enough, whole and complete."

All went silent for a while. Not only was the crowd reflecting on the words spoken, they were actually feeling them as if an unknown vibration had trickled into their body.

"So this Beingness has it all?" wondered Sven. "It sounds a bit weird, doesn't it? I've been trying to ask about this ever since we were in the rowing boats. Then it's boundless Love. Then it's limitless Gratitude. Then it's Acceptance or endless Peace. It felt a bit like you were sweet-talking us there."

"But," said Kalle, "it's actually like the candy in Wonka's chocolate factory. Just one can have all tastes possible."

"Good that you noticed that, Sven and Kalle. Remember how we spoke of the white light? Beingness is that white light. It has it all bundled together. It's when you live from the self again that this light crystallizes in the colour you need in the moment. It can be gratitude; it can be surrender. To some, it can be all at once, even in the self."

There was silence again.

"I can't stop feeling this tower is going to collapse," said Olivia out of the blue. "I'd feel a lot more whole ánd complete ánd enough if we'd be a way lot closer to the ground."

"Then way lot closer to the ground it is!"

And so it was that all were guided back to the elevators.

"Just go along," signalled the One with the raven. "I need to find a new cloak. This darned raven."

Follow your heart

With Olivia safely in the middle, they all went down again. By the way, the fact that the whole bunch could fit in the three elevators was courtesy of the One who is writing all this.

Kevin couldn't help but muse while he looked outside. "From all that's been said, I take it we shouldn't be following our heart, now should we?"

The Surrealistic Shamans of Infinite Zero all had a coughing fit while the elevators seemed to slow down on their way down.

"What?" coughed the One who lost his soft brome. "Follow your heart? Who are you, anyway?"

"I'm... Kevin," replied Kevin, overwhelmed with the sudden attention.

"I run a yoga studio in Rome, but I'm actually from-"

"Kevin from Rome?" repeated the One with the Viking horns. "And you are following your heart, now, Kevin? I mean, really!"

"I'm so so sorry, I-"

"They're just messing with ya, dude," chuckled the glowing One. "It's actually good that you bring this up just before this part ends."

"Right," said the One with the dice. "Thought we managed to avoid the topic, but here goes. Follow your heart it is. Well, no, duh, it isn't."

The glowing One patted Kevin reassuringly on the shoulder. "And don't mind him either. It's just his CSDC allergy playing up again."

"What's the fuss about following your heart?" wondered Marwa.

"Well, for one thing, it slows down elevators," scoffed the One with the wrinkled soft brome.

"Look, don't get us wrong," said the One with Vanessa. "The heart is a very powerful concept. It reaches straight to the core essence of your capacity to love, be it others, life itself or what you do with it."

"Unfortunately," remarked the One with the wrinkled soft brome, "it's also prone to confusion and abuse. If it were to have a Nutri-Score, it would certainly get an F for all the sugar it contains."

"Then again," beamed the glowing One, "there might still be a healthy apple underneath the glazed sugar. After all, one could say the same about Beingness. If you'd only talk about it without the actual experience, it would be nothing but sweetness for sure."

"When the heart is mentioned, it basically refers to our deepest inner longings and feelings. And mostly in a very vulnerable context, too."

"Not just vulnerable. The heart can also find itself suppressed or imprisoned in many ways."

"Yes, that too. And somehow, in order to be able to express itself in these conditions, we need an opponent to challenge. Something to rise up to."

"So you are given foes, like the mind, the head or the ego. You know, all those same-same things that ponder, fear and overthink, so nothing good ever happens. They keep you back. They restrain you. They hold you down. Insecurity. Resistance. Blocks. You get the picture."

"And the heart is this knight in shining armour, gifted with this intuitive wisdom which ever knows what is right. When you follow your heart, your actions can be taken with trust and confidence. And so, this reinstated and re-empowered knight eradicates all self-paralyzing doubts which lead nowhere but an alley of missed opportunities."

"Trouble is, it's not true."

"What do you mean, it's not true?" Marwa inquired.

"The longings of the heart are nothing but the longings of the self. They are honest, yes. Authentic, maybe. But the heart is far from being a reliable or steadfast thingy. It can act rather whimsically and isn't overly concerned with practicalities."

"Just married and then meeting this other beautiful person? Wanting to run a bookstore and then, when you have it, you see this wonderful opportunity on another continent? Starting a new book while you haven't finished the other four on your bedside table?"

"It's all nice, but by following the heart while dropping the annoying mind, you may easily find yourself on a bumpy ride. There'll be a lot of valuable lessons and opportunities along the way, sure, yet following your heart can also come with unbearable pain and plenty of trouble."

"So we should listen more to the mind?" dared Kevin. "Is that your advice?"

"No no, we wouldn't dare to give you any advice of the sort. Choosing the way of the mind, the way of the heart or some path in the middle is a difficult exercise. You'll have to figure it out yourselves. But remain vigilant; there will be plenty of CSDCs offering assistance for a price."

"There's one thing we cán say, can't we?"

"I bet you we are going into space again," smirked Jimmy.

The Surrealistic Shamans of Infinite Zero all laughed. "You are a smartass, aren't you? But you are correct. Space happens to be our leitmotif."

"Listen. Basically, we have provided you already with all the parameters required to truly live from the Heart. We have given you space, like an infinite amount of it. We have given you self-awareness, silence, peace and contentment…

"…love and freedom…"

"…acceptance, surrender and trust…"

"…gratitude and abundance."

"We have come a long way," said the One with the magician's staff while proudly admiring her staff. "We have given you experiential knowledge of who you really are and why you are here. You have learned when and how to let go and how to be present in the only possible moment there is: the here and now."

"And so you know," assured the glowing One, "you don't need to chase your heart around in order to reach a goal, meet someone or accomplish something. Your Heart is right there, within you, overwhelmingly present. It has no objectives, it has no needs, it doesn't need to be opened and it can't be hurt."

"When you fall into the Heart," concluded the One with the dice, "you cease to exist as a person. Nothing but Beingness remains. Actually, nothingness ánd Beingness remain – both are simultaneously true. And from this unimaginable, almost impossible position, paradoxically as ever, you can be the most gracious human being there is."

For a moment there was nothing but silence in the elevators.

Ol' Cormac peered up at the people standing around his wheelchair. "Well, that's all nice," he grumbled. "Very nice. I think I need a drink."

The elevators seemed to agree with the grumpy ol' bastard. With a small jerk and Olivia on hands and knees, the way down commenced at top speed once more.

Não sou nada.
Nunca serei nada.
Não posso querer ser nada.
À parte isso, tenho em mim todos os sonhos do mundo.

– Álvaro de Campos –

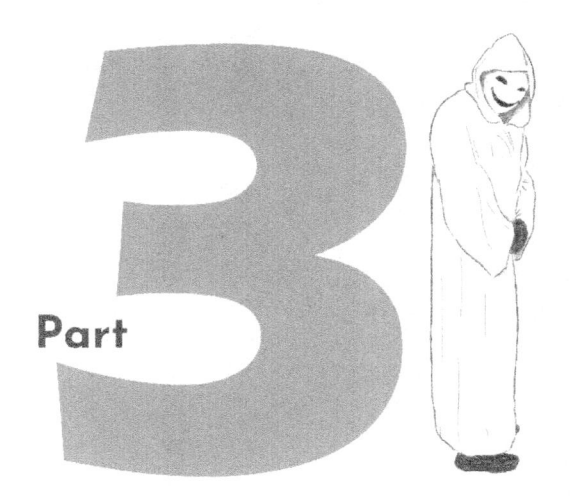

Part 3

Interlude   **God**

The One with the raven pensively strolled through the ruins of an ancient monastery. It was a sunny day. Cloud streets high above revealed a secret message in Morse code if only one would look up and care to read them. The One with the raven rather looked down at the ground. He seemed depressed and mumbled words; one could swear they were swearing.

And so it happened that he stumbled upon a priest who was sitting on a large stone which once was part of a tall pillar. He wore black, with the typical white collar. When he saw the One with the raven approaching, he promptly broke his silent contemplation.

"What's troubling you, my son."

"Oh, Father, I didn't notice you there. Lost in thought, I guess. You see, I just came from Dubai to put on a new cloak. Then, on my journey to my friends, I came across some witnesses of Yod Heh Vau Heh. Got myself lured in a conversation lasting hours."

"Oh, I understand," smiled the priest gently. "And now you come across one of the same batch, don't you? Well, don't be afraid, my son. I will not trouble you with the divine or try to convince you of anything." Then he chuckled. "Of course, you do know, the end of days is nigh. Just a few more billion years, and the sun will explode. Just warning you, that's all."

The One with the raven lightened up. "Thanks, Father. Hope I'm not disturbing your prayers."

"Not at all, my son. Not at all. My prayers are beyond words anyways."

"Should I take that bait?"

The priest smiled. The One with the raven decided to stay a while and sat down on another part of the once-tall pillar (Actually, we can't be sure if it's the same pillar as the whole thing tumbled down over each other).

"So, my son, tell me, do you believe in the Lord?"

"Can't say that I do," admitted the One with the raven. "But do tell me, Father, do you believe in Him?"

"Why yes, I surely do. Why would you ask such a question to a man who dons himself in black?"

"Just wondering. How does one come to believe in such a thing without ever having seen it? I mean, the two young men I spoke to earlier clearly have no experience whatsoever. Still, they are firm believers. No argument can bring even the slightest crack in their steadfastness. All they have is a passionately told story which they passionately pass along. But a passionately told story doesn't make it a true one, does it? The only truth to be found in it, is the emotion it carries across."

"Seems they shook you up pretty well, didn't they? – Anyways, I must say, to be honest, I myself no longer believe in the God from the bible. You see, I once did, indeed. And I confess, I did because I liked the story. And, well, I also was in pain at the time. And in doubt. And the story, well, it gave hope, you see. Something to hold on to. Only years later, I came to realize what you just said yourself. How can I believe something I have never seen or witnessed myself, right? But then… Well, then, I came to experience God. Truly experience Him. And all my doubts vanished. They just did. Not because the stories became true somehow, not at all. It rather was like they lost their relevance. Hard to believe, isn't it?"

"Not at all, Father, not at all. But do tell me, how was that, this experience of God?"

"Hard to say. It felt like I disappeared. Like I no longer existed. There was only God. I felt the purest Love. The purest Gratitude. It was boundless. It was timeless. And after that, somehow, I got put back together again as me. But this time, I felt stronger. More vital. More real. Happy. Content. Like, I am. But also, I am not. I can't really explain it, my son, but I felt like I no longer existed, and at the same time, I was existence itself. As if God came through me – as if he entered me or something. Perhaps, well, most probably, I simply realized He was there all along."

"It seems to me, Father, you have found Truth in your heart. It's the mind which has trouble wrapping itself around it and starts clinging to holy words instead."

"Yes, my son, I like to see it that way too. And, indeed, here's the frustrating part. I have difficulty sharing this experience with my parish. I only have the words of the bible. And my superiors stress me to share these words the best I can. I do. And when I share these words, I honestly see people light up. But I also see the light on their faces is not God's light. It's only mine. And as soon as they go home, that light is gone again. Some of them come to speak to me. They share this frustration. They tell me how they devote themselves to the word of God. Abide by the rules and commandments. But they fail to experience God. In their looking up to Him, they utterly fail to become Him."

'Perhaps, Father, you might give them a different book? There's one called 'A Paradoxical Existence'. Seems rather good. It's less about rules than it is about the discovery of the actual experience."

"Oh, interesting. Did it sell as well as the Bible?"

'Well… Let's just say we are working on that. Anyways, it's not my place to impose things on you. Perhaps, Father, it offers some comfort to know all the people in your parish are just as much part of God as you yourself are, whether they realize it or not. You see, here's the thing. When Eve took a bite from the apple, some like to think she doomed the entirety of mankind. But fact is, it's each and every one of us biting the apple, over and over again. We just can't help it."

"We all do?"

"Precisely. At some point, at a very young age, we all take a bite from the apple, Father. It's simply part of our process. Now, some come to 'unbite' it later on. Most don't.

But please excuse me, Father. Could you tell me if there's a toilet nearby?"

"Ah, of course. Follow me, please. There is one next to the church. It's just a minute's walk from here. Urgent call of nature?"

"Not really. I just need to be in Paris."

"Paris?" wondered the priest while he guided the One with the raven to the toilet. "I'm afraid you'll be visiting a lot more toilets before you get there, my son."

Only after the One with the raven closed the door of the toilet did the priest start to become suspicious.

"Paris? – Now, wait a minute. Was this man wearing a mask with a smile on it? – And did he have a real raven sitting on his shoulder?"

The priest knocked on the door, but there was no response. When he eventually opened the door – it wasn't locked – there was only the toilet. He never saw the One with the raven again (Not in real life anyway. But he did search on Instagram for 'a_paradoxical_existence' and found many posts with the One with the raven depicted in them).

Chapter 1   **Spiritual hodge-podge or existential poverty? Are these the choices we have?**

The three elevators simultaneously arrived at what all thought to be the ground floor. However, when they stepped out, Olivia instinctively fell back down on her hands and knees.

"This is not better!" she shouted.

The rest of the crowd dared to step right up to the railing where they packed up and looked over the skyline of Paris. At an altitude of 57 metres, they were considerably lower than the Burj Khalifa. Olivia, however, for some reason, did not agree.

The Unperturbed Knowers of Unlimited Zilch guided the crowd in separate groups from each of the three pillars of the Eiffel Tower to the south terrace. On their way to their destination on the 4200m^2 platform, they came across multiple little stalls filled with numerous religious and spiritual items. Each stall and all of its items came along with religious and spiritual-looking people. There were amulets, stones, crosses, cards, books, statues, pendants and many different kinds of incense, all whirling around in chaotic harmony. The people behind the stalls wore multiple colours in wide pants or revealing dresses (except for the more pious devotees who rather chose to dress in single colours like black, grey, orange, purple, white or blue, which, when they all huddled together, still made them a very colourful lot). All seemed cheerful and excited as if the incense carried particles of happiness in its ghostly patterns.

"Thrust in the Lord." – "This amulet will protect you from…" – "Free palm reading here!" – "Activate your Kundalini!" – "Ice tub here – You name it, ice tub is good for it!" – "Learn to communicate with angelic entities." – "Quantum Touch – Free healing!" – "Jezus Fucking Christ!!!"

Mind you, that last one did not come from one of the stalls. It came from an unnamed person in the crowd who bumped her toe into an object which best shouldn't be bumped into.

Olivia cautiously followed on hands and knees. But then she totally freaked out when she crawled over the transparent floor, looking directly down at the esplanade below. Mykhailo gently lifted her up in his arms and asked her to close her eyes for a moment. Then he carried her towards a comfortable chair, looking over the Champ de Mars. With a gentle kick of his foot, he gave it a 180° spin so it faced inwards. Here, Olivia finally managed to relax a bit after he gently put her down.

The rest of the crowd huddled together on the cosy terrace. Some looked over the railing. Others gazed upwards at the iron construction towering above them. Only Bram was still behind, standing in line for the toilet. Just when it was his turn, the One with the raven stepped out of the cabinet. "Oh, hi Bram. Make it quick, will you."

Bram just stared for a couple of seconds. Then he shook his head, went inside and made it quick.

The Unperturbed Knowers of Unlimited Zilch had either taken up position behind the counter of two adjacent bars or were walking around, handing out refreshments to the crowd. Needless to say, they started with ol' Cormac, twice.

"Have you seen all these weirdo's around here?" started Bram when he rejoined the crowd.

"Now just you hang on there for a moment, mister!" reacted Marwa. "These are all good people you are referring to! I see no need to call them weird. For all I know, at least they are not blowing up things or shooting others. If there'd be anything weird, then it'd be that."

Bram turned all red and looked down. If the whole thing weren't made of iron, he'd dig a hole on the spot and crawl into it.

"I agree with Marwa," said Paul. "I-

"Hey, now I remember you," Marwa interrupted. "Aren't you that guy chasing that Husky near le Mont-Saint-Michel?"

"Ah, yes. The darn dog tends to escape me all the time. I'm afraid he's a bit notorious for that."

"You were about to say?" intervened Bram a bit jealous.

Paul took a deep breath. "Well, you can say whatever you want about these folks here. You can laugh with them, ridicule them or simply shake your head in disapproval. All fine by me. We can even go global on that. You can mock the believers still frequenting cathedrals while tourists pour in and out around them. You can judge the pious who strictly follow 600-plus rules. You can slap yourself in the face when a president of 52 highly evolved states, capable of building the best and most expensive weapons on earth, asks a non-existing entity to protect them at the end of every single speech. But..." Paul ran out of air.

"I just wonder..." Paul was still out of air. "Aren't we overlooking something here?"

"Like what?" wondered Sven while accepting a long drink from the One with the Viking horns.

"Simple. The fact that they do."

"What do you mean, Paul?" asked Marwa. "Do what?"

"Do all this stuff. Believe it. Work with it. Practice it. Share it. Spread it. I mean, there's a multitude of faiths and religions. Sometimes, they sort of agree; sometimes, one contradicts or overrules the other. However, the simple fact remains: people tend to pick one and consider theirs to be true. The question is: why?"

"Why would that be, Paul?" asked the One with Vanessa while pouring drinks to Marwa and Bram.

All eyes turned to Paul now. "Err, I don't know," he faltered. "I..."

"Come on, Paul," shouted ol' Cormac. "Give us yer best, lad!"

"Well, I think we all share a need for mystery. For... for transcendence. For contemplation, if you prefer that. I just mean... a kind of wonder which goes deeper than, you know, the average kind of awe we usually have for something which all can see in plain sight. I mean, something unknown. Something which can only be touched intuitively... and still... this touch itself, it can be shared with kindred spirits... Don't know if I'm making sense here?"

'I think I can relate to that," confirmed Marwa. "I'm a data scientist. My world is so mental. And if it isn't that, I worry practically all the time about my mother, who is ill, not to mention my brothers, who have a knack for constantly turning up in the wrong place at the wrong time."

Sven whispered to Kalle: "If they're at the wrong place at the wrong time, I guess there's nothing to worry about, no?"

"What I'm saying is, I can use a bit of a counterbalance for all this mental and logic stuff, you know?"

"I totally agree," nodded Charles. "I myself have the same issues with science always being right. Sometimes, I think their attitude borders at the verge of the pretentious. They seem to have figured it all out, while there's so much we still don't know."

"Fair enough," said Oliver. "Certainly when it comes to our inner well-being or a sense of wholeness, I think we all intuitively sense our mental understanding of things often fails us. So yes, a bit of sobriety and casualness might fit us at times. And don't get me wrong, despite being a scientist, I can feel this pull towards a bit of mystery as well."

"Not just that," added Marwa. "Like Paul said, transcendence too. I mean, if it were just about mystery or contemplation, I'd head to the Louvre or paint something myself. Hug a tree and then go back to my laptop. But transcendence is different. It goes beyond our normal experiences. It's unalike to all of us, but somehow also the same."

"And that's the thing," added Andrea. "It's about us too, all together. About who and what we truly are in life and death and how we share this amongst one another. It's where we deeply connect, beyond our little selves, and surely, despite our little selves."

"Yes, something like that," said Paul, unable to agree or disagree with all being said. "It's pretty hard to express. Like yes, a painting can induce wonder and awe. But that can't compete with the wonder and awe we experience in life itself, right? I mean, look around! All this, just because something – well, nothing actually – exploded or imploded like 14 billion years ago. How can we fathom all that? It's pretty normal that we try to grasp this by resorting to all that spiritual hodgepodge, right?"

"Or even try to control it," added Andrea while a young man passed them, marvelling at his newly bought prayer cards. "I mean, we pray for this, we pray for that. Even more, there's like countless techniques and rituals to make something happen out of the blue, like magical healing or gaining fortune and glory. I could tell you all about it."

The One with the raven smiled from behind his bar (Of course he smiled. The mask, remember.) "Perhaps," he suggested, "from what we all here know and have experienced, we can agree on this: **on the one hand**, it is pretty normal you all have questions about existence, and specifically yours in it. Moreover, even if there'd be an answer to all that, you'd still need some means to come to terms with it. Fit it in, so to speak, into this great, primal mystery of being conscious, self-aware human beings."

The One with the catsears raised a finger. Now, before we go into the reason he raised his finger, please don't mistake this One for a hooded One with protruding ears of a cat, like the One with the Viking horns. Catsears, also known as hypochaeris radicata, is a genus of plants in the family Asteraceae. Simply said, it's a pretty yellow flower. While catsears are usually found in the wild or unexpectedly in your garden, they can sometimes be found in a small vase, used as decoration for a pop-up bar on the first floor of the Eiffel Tower.

So… "The good news is," started the One with the catsears, "you lot do already know the answer to all that. You know the Truth. The thing is, well, Truth is Truth, and strictly mentally, that little fact doesn't seem to offer much. Reason can't persuade feelings."

"One could say," said One, "you all know the Truth, but you may not Know it yet."

"Yes," nodded the One with the raven, "but still, **on the other hand,** you all have learned by now how you have this innate capacity to fall into this mysterious, incomprehensible, yet ever present Beingness. It literally is the build-in modus operandi for you to grasp this mystery, which lies beyond the realm of the rational. It's not outside of you. It's not even inside of you. It simply is you. You are It."

"Now, here's the thing," said the One with Vanessa. "While the usual experiences we all have always been about an object and a subject, this particular experience, the experience of Beingness, is void of such a relationship. The seer's eye turns towards itself, and as such, the seeing collapses into something quite unfamiliar to our daily experience. This could be called transcendental indeed, Paul. And this transcendental experience reaches beyond any mental knowledge. It is a Knowing without the typical knowledge which can be learned. It rather is inexpressible. Hence, it is mysterious. Yet it is also more real than anything else."

"So you don't need something 'outside' to clarify, quantify, ratify or explain this experience. It's all in the experience itself."

"Yes, I understand all that," dismissed Andrea. "But we still lack the means to integrate it. To truly live it. You said it yourself before: we can't be in Beingness all the time. Eat, drink and then the toilet, remember?"

"And that's exactly the problem we have," said Marwa. "It seems you have taken this means – which we so desperately need – you've taken it away from us. I mean, honestly, none of you masked lot are fans of CSDCs and what they sell. And obviously, neither are you fans of spirituality or anything of the kind. So-"

The One with the raven raised his hand. "Please forgive us, Marwa, Andrea and all of you. But this is surely not the message we wanted to convey. On the contrary, look at yourself and all around you. You all have this innate tendency to seek for ways to dive back into the experience you lost. And why? Because you have the capacity to do it. So why on earth would we deny that?"

"And although you may not know how, you can. Yes, at first, just like Eve, you will bite the apple and suffer the consequences. Overwhelmed with your identity, you will fail to be whole. You will experience division. You will feel incomplete. You will have this longing for a 'something' which ever seems beyond your grasp, like this word that's at the tip of your tongue but refuses to be uttered."

"But, not to worry," cheered the glowing One, "unlike what is written in the Bible, there is an antidote! You have the ability to disappear into your core, your $\overline{S}$elf, where there is pure presence and wholeness, where everything is connected without the slightest division."

"Exactly," explained the One with Vanessa. "You could say it is built into your hardware. And despite what many may think, it's not even that hard to access. Denying this capacity would be like denying your very nature. And that would lead to existential poverty, now, wouldn't it?"

"Moreover," said the One with the catsears, "I'd say that part of humanity – you know, that lot which has constant access to TV-screens on a wall, in their lap or in their hands – is now more than ever in a desperate need of this transcendental reality. They, you, all suffer a constant superficialness with ever-new bursts of information. Your experiences simply have no time to ripen in the back of your heads or in the depths of your hearts. Every new little thing simply gets overwritten by the next, and the next, and the next. And the Truth you all discovered will suffer the same fate."

Suddenly, there were a lot of ooooh's' and aaaah's coming from the centre part of the tower. A Sufi, neatly dressed up in a white, woollen robe and a red hat, glided on a dead ride towards a platform in the centre of the iron structure. The platform was a perfect metal disc barely 1 metre wide, solidly suspended by four steel cables. When the Sufi landed on the platform, he started to whirl his whirl, proving both his perfection and his faith.

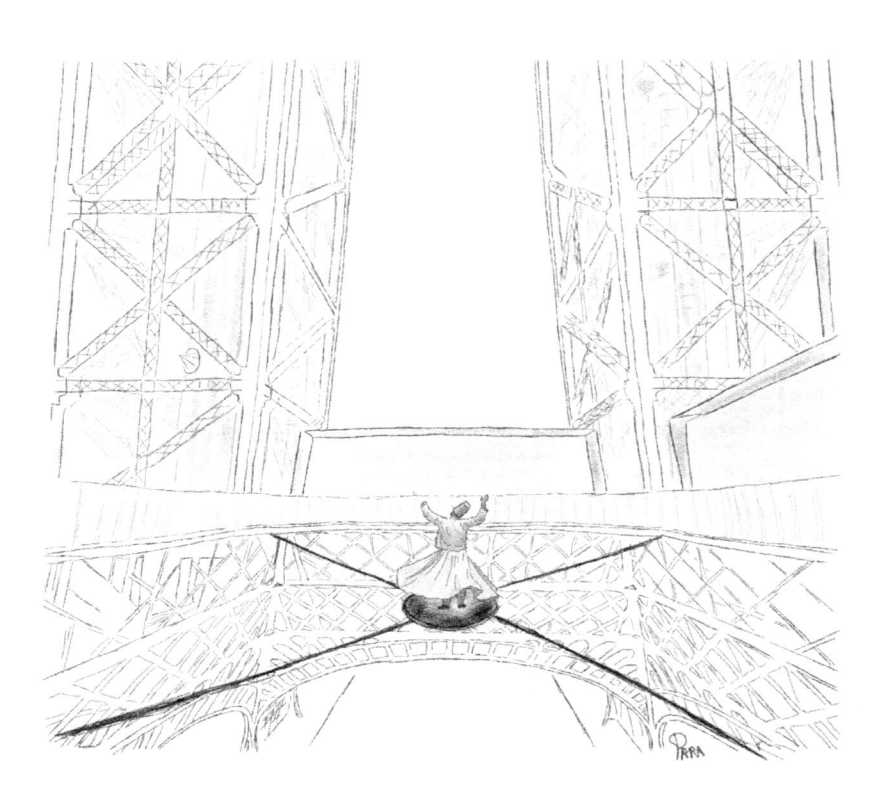

Chapter 2   A genuine spirituality, fair, honest and not ridiculed (impossible, no?)

It took the crowd no more than 30 seconds to get bored by the astounding, gravity-defying, whirling Sufi who'd face imminent death at the slightest loss of balance. And so, the questions rose once more.

"But we are beyond that, aren't we?" queried Charles. "I mean, we 'know' the Truth now. So we are no longer in need of any silly stuff like spirituality, no?"

"Not up to us, agree or disagree," said the One with no characteristics mimicking Master Yoda. "Still, disagree we must."

"Why's that," probed Charles. "I thought-"

"Page 118," replied the One with the catsears. "I quote: 'Truth even tends to get lost within a single lifespan.' And if I may add to that, I'd say it usually is lost by the next day already. So, that's why."

"You see, that's the thing," said the One with the magician's staff. "When you look at mankind from a scientific or technological angle, the growth in those fields is ever progressive in nature. We gain more and more knowledge and wisdom with every single generation."

"And that's also because of us being able to pass it on to the next," added the One previously conducting the green tram. "That is, if we are not burning down our libraries of Alexandria, of course."

"But knowledge of the $\overline{\text{S}}$elf," continued the One with the magician's staff, "that's an entirely different matter. It can't be passed on by parents to their children. It can't be taught at school. Somehow, you all need to rediscover the $\overline{\text{S}}$elf by yourselves. And so, as well, you all need to discover the oneness in the unfolding of the universe and how this unfolding inevitably includes you as well."

"That's if the need for these discoveries happens to rise at all," shrugged the One with the catsears.

Since his robe was still clean, the One with the raven dared to pace up and down with his arms on his back. "Any which way, the rediscovery of the Self requires a frequent, experiential perceiving of Beingness. And even then, this achieved state of boundless and timeless Beingness is often rather short in nature. It collapses soon enough, when the practical, day-to-day-stuff inevitably resurfaces."

"To remedy this, my friends – that is, if you are indeed in need of a remedy – a means to reconnect and rediscover is required. You could call this by many names, like contemplation, meditation, mindfulness, or whatever you prefer."

As far as we're concerned, 'spirituality' is not a bad word at all."

"But the word stinks," protested Jimmy. "It's filled with superstition, and cults, and gurus. I can't return to my homeland and proclaim I've become a spiritual person. They'll block my access to the pub in no time."

Then Jimmy mimicked his friends: "Look, there's Jimmy. He's into mumbo jumbo and whoohoo at the same time. Better hand him a full bottle of whiskey to sober up."

"Well, Jimmy has a point there," remarked the One with the catsears while all laughed. "Spir-it-u-al-i-ty, the word does carry a heavy legacy. Got itself influenced by cultural aspects. Found itself shaped and polluted by fantasy-prone views of countless cults, sects and religious factions of all kinds. Still... Perhaps we need to revisit it a bit so we can come to a renewed understanding?"

"Yes, yes, yes," cheered the glowing One excited. "Let's run over it, shall we? But let's also keep it short. No need for a book in a book, right?"

"Right," started the One with the raven. "If we are to talk about genuine spirituality, we need to rule out some stuff. We need to be precise and crystal clear."

"Well, then here we go," started the glowing One. "Genuine spirituality can't be about ancient or new revelations you need to take for granted. Truth allows a discovery by each and every single one of you, by yourselves, again and again. Truth can ever be touched in the moment, here and now."

"Genuine spirituality can't be about what one prefers to believe," noted the One with the catsears. "Whatever personal reasons one may have, Truth will not yield a single bit to any of your opinions. A dislike for gravity, however persistent and resolute as can be, will not turn you weightless, now will it?"

"Not about attaining powers, genuine spirituality is," added the One with no characteristics in his Yoda voice. "Predicting future, healing hands, reading minds, powerful distractions, these all are."

"Genuine spirituality can't be about rules and dogma," said the One with the bow and arrow. "It can't be about forcing children into a path and dressing them up in the most peculiar ways. From a cultural perspective, this can all be nice in some occasions, but Truth will never be in need of these kinds of enforcement."

The One with the Viking horns felt like adding to this as well: "Genuine spirituality can't be about Valhalla or sacrifice. It can't be about pleasing gods in particular ways. And neither can it be about constantly drinking and feasting after you die, now can it? Anyways, can you imagine how long an eternal feast lasts? You'd be so fat by the first aeon that you'll turn into a black hole."

Then all got silent, especially the One with the Viking horns, who was about to have an epiphany. "Hey! That explains black holes!"

"That's the thing," said the One who never spoke before (he's the silent type). "Genuine spirituality shouldn't be about giving answers to common questions and problems. Spirituality tends to be so practical nowadays. 'What should I eat?' – 'How many times should I go to the toilet?' – 'Should I choose left or right?' – 'Should I divorce my husband?' – 'What school should I send my son to?' - You can't imagine what questions those spiritual leaders on their pedestals get. And the craziest thing of all is that they also tend to give answers to all these questions. It's plain silly."

"Genuine spirituality," sighed the One with the dice, "really folks, genuine spirituality can't be about attaining higher vibrations, paradigmatic shifts, mystical transitions, new eras of consciousness, and all the like where one group attains a higher state than others."

"Neither can it be about some enlightened person who is way ahead of you and is able to magically transmit stuff or initiate you in some lineage of energetic super-entities."

"Nor is genuine spirituality about uplifting others, being a lighthouse, guiding others on the way and all that stuff." The One with the nón lá shook his head while speaking. "I mean, really, help others, yes, please, but this urge to guide others towards some light you just happen to believe in, all because you had a genuine touch with Beingness but couldn't place it and then decided to convince yourself into your own fabricated story where the amount of followers you gather serves as the only evidence of how right you are and-"

"Youshouldbecomearapper,youalmosttalkasfastasIdo," machinegunned 방찬.

"Give the guy some space to breathe," pleaded Olivia concerned.

"I think," dared Bram. "I think genuine spirituality neither can be about leaders and followers, about gurus on a stage or in a podcast, with followers hanging on every word they say like bees on honey."

"Bees don't hang on honey, Bram, they make it."

Bram ignored Marwa's remark and simply went on. "Yeh, but when push comes to shove, it almost always ends up with people abusing their role or them abusing others in the most terrible ways. Just look around; it's ever the same. Some guru is big and hot, and then it turns out he raped women, he had orgies, or he nothing but aspired to become filthy rich and powerful. And if I may say so, it's not always a 'he' in this picture. A 'she' can be pretty mean and devious as well."

This time, Bram had Marwa's full attention. "One could wonder why we fall for all that? Even when they are exposed, many people still follow and defend their cult leader."

"I think it's simple," said Bram. "It's because we get a high on all that stuff. And we want to keep that high to ourselves, no matter what. I mean, it's all one big rave, with people getting euphoric on each other and the cult-music being played for them. The abusive guru or organization is nothing but a conduit for all that. It's like our masked friends have repeatedly told us before: we trick ourselves. And the funny thing is we use tricksters to trick ourselves. Works better, I guess, no?"

It was the One with the magician's staff who answered first. "Very good, Bram! Perhaps now you can understand our appearance better. You see, no sane person would ever start worshipping a bunch of weirdos with silly names, dressed up in a ridiculous outfit and wearing a burlesque mask. If you're on the path of Truth, it's Truth itself that takes centre stage, with nothing and no one else in the spotlight."

"Precisely," affirmed the One with the raven. "Those who try to dress up like us will crash and burn in ridicule, be it on a stage or in front of it. It may work on paper and in the backs of your heads, but it doesn't work in reality unless as a cartoon. Especially that goddamn raven!"

"For crying out loud, man!" growled ol' Cormac from his wheelchair. "What a bunch of negatives yer all are. Could ya not be a wee bit positive and share some good points about that ge-nu-ine spirituality of yours?"

"There, there, mister O'NoOne, " hushed Erin, "let the nice people have a nice conversation." Then her voice got a little firmer while she addressed the Unperturbed Knowers of Unlimited Zilch. "Perhaps you can indulge us and share something positive?"

"Touché, Erin," laughed the glowing One. "Touché."

"Something positive?" repeated the One with the nón lá. This time his tone was more serene and relaxed. "About genuine spirituality, you mean? Well, for one thing, a true and honest form of spirituality needs to address your core being, doesn't it? I mean, you all have this deeper, pressing need to slow down, to rejuvenate and to gain perspective. And I am not referring to eating an energy bar while lying around on a couch, pondering how to tackle the next to-do. It's more profound than that, like more of an existential nature."

"Of course, a basic premise is that a true form of spirituality would be about you being able to freely live and express this deep, inner feeling which is genuine and real, without having to hide it or suppress it. Without it being dismissed or ridiculed by others or by your own inner doubts."

"From that perspective, you really could say this most vulnerable expression should be possible in a safe place because your need for spirituality will also come forth from hurt or loss instead of merely existential reasons. Or simply when you feel totally lost, like when circumstances push you into this tiny spot where you innerly feel all boxed in. When things no longer make sense, and you can't think up a mental or rational way out. In those moments, you need something, something that brings you home, in a place where you feel connected and whole."

"Indeed, you all have realized you are not mere rational beings. Yet still, rationality is a big part of you. So genuine spirituality can only be attained when reason can agree. When it can sit back and relax, having assessed this is safe, and the Heart is allowed to expand with all the love and joy it finds in the reconnection with Truth and life's longing."

"Only a genuine form of spirituality can offer this safe place. It is absent of deceit, absent of abuse, absent of judgemental scrutiny by others. It's this place where you can truly surrender and be. Not just on your own, which is totally fine, but together with others as well. Share silence and peace, sing and dance and express joy, find comfort or a listening ear. And also, take things not too seriously, be a bit breezy and easy-going, while still being affectionate, considerate and present."

"A genuine spiritual practice is basically about being able to live this paradoxical existence of being and not-being at the same time. It's about reconciling this apparently aimless Beingness with the more purposeful, goal-driven identity-self. It's about this gracious state of reconnection with the fundamental Truth while maintaining a serene and meaningful balance between Doingness and Beingness."

"Mind you, genuine spirituality is not just about transcendence. You know, like you all have experienced already when you fall into the boundless and timeless, when you fall into this mysterious amalgam of peace, joy, serenity, love and all. That's all nice, yes, but it's also about coping with yourself and your humanity. You must understand, with your brainstem, your limbic system, your amygdala, hypothalamus, cortex, etcetera etcetera, you are at the pinnacle of evolution. But there's a catch, too. This complex orchestra has a high potential to get out of tune in no time. It can cause a lot of trouble, too. Emotion and reason can clash. Needs can spiral into devastating addictions. Will humanity solve this only by evolving further and becoming strictly rational, logical beings void from emotions? I don't think so."

"I am inclined to disagree," said the One without characteristics mimicking Mister Spock (the Leonard Nimoy one). "I experience no trouble living a strictly logical existence."

All laughed for a moment. Then, the One with the dice continued. "I'd rather say we need a conductor for this symphony instead of less instruments. This conductor is holistic in nature, present in our whole body and absent at the same time. It's this consciousness, this awareness, when it turns towards itself. Genuine spirituality would be about willingly falling into the conductor and realising there's nothing to conduct. The whole symphony plays itself. It wasn't out of tune with the symphony of totality. It was in tune all the time. It only appeared to be not."

"Hey," shouted the One with the Viking horns. "Where did the Sufi master go?"

All jumped up and went to the inner railing to look down. But then they saw the Sufi was still on his platform, whirling as ever, completely in balance… as ever.

"Fooled ya!"

Chapter 3   **Okay, good, spirituality approved! But… How?**

Ol' Cormac looked up at his nurse. "Look at them," he grumbled as usual. "Normally, I'd be the first to judge the whole lot. But now, I don't know. Bit weird, really. I just see this movement, with me being part of it, while me no longer… being at all. Yet I still am. And it's not even confusing!"

Erin looked down on her patient with a softness in her eyes. Still, she couldn't resist. "Oh dear, I think I filled your IV with the wrong dose."

"Ye evil wench!"

They both smiled. Then, the crowd returned and took their comfy seats again.

"I wonder," Erin started, "you just described a genuine form of spirituality. Or you at least laid out some guidelines, I guess. But it's all a bit theoretical if you ask me. Doesn't any kind of spirituality, by definition, come with a way of practice?"

The One with the Viking horns scratched his horn while he tilted his head a bit. "Feels like a trick question. I don't recall us having a 'spiritual practice'. Yet we do seem to have approved spirituality, providing it is genuine. Hm. A paradox. Or a catch-22? You got me by the horns there."

"It's definitely a confusing issue," admitted the One with the magician's staff. "Most spiritual practices aim at something to do or to accomplish. We often assume such things are standard as if they've always been that way. But do they have to be?"

"That's the thing," said the One with Vanessa. "From the perspective of the self, we are pulled in so deep in this paradigm of growth, like more or better, stronger, smarter, more agile, more effective, more experienced and so on. So by nature, we project this line of thinking upon the spiritual: wiser, more tranquil, more connected, more real, more humble, more devout, more enlightened, with a raised consciousness or a higher vibration, etcetera."

"We tend to think the spiritual side of life is equally achieved in steps or stages, requiring effort, practice, commitment and zeal."

"And then we're right back at the doorstep of the many guides and teachers willing to help us progress on the many possible paths."

"I understand this better now," agreed Erin. "But still. I mean, I'm pushing Mr Ol' Grumpy's wheelchair all day. Do I really just wait for a moment of grace where I fall into this Beingness all of a sudden?"

"Now wait a minute," protested ol' Cormac.

"I see what you mean," intervened the One with the magician's staff. "Thing is, in the realization of Truth, any practice – if that even applies – will spontaneously come to you."

"Spontané? Vraiment? Oh, excuse my French, I mean, really? How?"

"Georges," chuckled the glowing One. "If I tell you how, it wouldn't be spontaneous, now would it?"

"I may have something," dared Andrea while raising her hand. With all eyes on her now, she blushed. But unlike earlier in her life, she didn't mind. "Well, ever since that weird episode in that white construct, I've secretly been doing this. It's silly, I know. It takes less than a minute. I softly rub the palms of my hands over each other. Somehow, it increases my sensitivity when I do that. And then I bring them together, flat against each other. I know, it's that stuff yogis do when they meet and say 'Hey, I'm a yogi just like you'. Anyway, I gently raise my arms and bring my thumbs against my forehead while, well, I bow my head a little. And then I bring them back against my sternum, you know, against my heart centre. To end, I put one hand flat on my heart centre, and the other over it. Of course, I'm consciously breathing when I do that. And I allow my chest to expand. And with that, I somehow reconnect with the boundlessness and timelessness of the $\overline{\text{S}}$elf. Yeh, that's it, basically."

"Sounds like it's also an expression of gratitude, no?" asked the One with Vanessa.

Andrea's eyes grew big. "Hey, yes, I didn't even think about that. It's exactly that. But when it allows me to fall into Beingness, it becomes all the other stuff too."

"Very nice, Andrea," complimented the One with the raven. "There you have it, Georges. Andrea's story is a nice example of intuitively and spontaneously expressing deep gratitude for no particular reason. It simply rises. And through it, both the self and the Self share an experience, each in their own dimension, without one outshining the other."

"All seems a bit of a fuss to me," whispered Charles to Georges. "I simply close my eyes, and bang, I'm there."

"Beautiful," glowed the glowing One. "You see, it can be different for everybody. Some may simply whisper 'Thank you'. Others may go 'Om Namah Shivaya' while doing what Andrea does. There's those that burst into song or dance. There's those who climb a mountain and look at the horizon until tears blur their eyes. Each and every single one of you can find your own personal expression for the blissfulness you discovered in the recognition of Truth. And when it comes, it comes natural. You will recognize it by the authenticity it is filled with."

"You will notice soon enough," concluded the One with the magician's staff, "all these expressions have a certain simplicity to them. There's no system or rules. There's no need to publicly prostrate. There's no need to brag about your realization or put on a grand display of how spiritual you are. And in the end, when you are truly immersed in this Truth, with every fibre of your being, your whole existence becomes a practice. Every moment will be permeated with this undefinable Knowingness."

Jimmy wasn't impressed. "Well, that's all nice lads. But that's all talk for when you already know that Truth and all. So what if you are a wee bit like, 'Yeeeees, possible', or 'Nooooo, I don't know yet', about this Truth? Do we need to overcome that on our own, or can we find support in a group?"

"Good point," agreed Erin. "Also, like you, Ancients-of-I-just-can't-keep-track have said like a kazillion times, the realization of Truth can go lost before me Cormac here can blink his eyes."

"Oi!"

"I just mean I follow Jimmy. When we have 'lost' It, do we need to rediscover It on our own, or can we revive It in the company of people who haven't... 'lost' it?"

"A fair question," nodded the One with the raven. "And as we already said on page 272, a genuine form of spirituality does allow a place of sharing and connecting. Even more, it's an absolute requirement, for it is simply in people's nature to affirm such a profound discovery, both to ourselves and others, to live and celebrate it with others, and to give support to others. And surely the power of a group can assist in rekindling the fire that was nearly extinguished."

"However, when it comes to Truth, it can become a bit awkward. I mean, how will you exercise your realization of Truth in a group? Will you come together and call yourself 'Truthies'? Or 'the Followers of Beingness'? Or 'Those that Know'? Will you start displaying some agreed behaviour to state you are like of minds? Like saying 'In Truth'. Or 'It's the way as it is, and it can't be any other way.' Will some dressed-up leader stand on some dressed-up stage and say, 'Let us all fall into bliss now'?"

"You see, it all quickly can become a bit silly. Might even call it tricky, because before you know it, you have a bunch of people engaging in all these activities without truly realizing the Truth. Not to mention how some may be swayed from their doubts by the collective energy rather than reaching true understanding. They'll trade genuine confusion for dubious wisdom. And then it becomes a cult. And a cult comes with leaders. And you all know what happens between leaders and followers."

The One with the catsears took his catsears in his hand and pointed it to the crowd. "That's the very reason we are continuously known as something different, one sillier than the other. There's no cult-ificating us. It'd be ridiculous. But the Truth, it remains firm as it is, and that's what matters."

"Still, as you said Jimmy and Erin, a spiritual practice, individually or in group, can be called for. It can be needed, and it can be useful. Besides, we have taught you some stuff already. See, when it comes to doing some form of practice in order to touch Truth, and experience it in sheer

Beingness, there's these few simply things. First of all, you have our secret exercises. That's already that."

"And next to that," added the One with the magician's staff, "you have this mental contemplation where you innerly look at all your aspects while you are unable to identify any of them as the real You. The sticky notes, remember?"

"Aaaaand," said the glowing One, "you also have a similar kind of contemplation where you try to pinpoint yourself, up to the smallest square millimetre. Pretty good one, if you ask me."

"The other thing you can do anytime, anywhere? Observe. See how things unfold as they do. As they couldn't any other way. No cows falling out of the sky unless you're watching Twister."

"Or Monty Python and the Quest for the Holy Grail. Think there was a flying cow in that one, too."

"Point is," sighed the One with the raven while the raven shook its head, "as we repeatedly said before, each and every single one of you, even if you were the last person on earth, without any guides or leaders to be found, you'd still be able to find Truth on your own, and, keep this discovery alive."

Olivia's eyes seemed to go each in a different direction. "I think I'm getting a bit drunk here. But I love your mocktails, Viking One. Best I ever had."

"Hang on," whispered the One with the Viking horns against the One with the raven. "What's a mocktail? I thought it was a cocktail that came with a joke. So I told her the one about-"

The One with the raven slapped himself against the head while the raven flew off.

Chapter 4   Three important stages for the genuine spiritual ones (this could become a book on its own)

Márcia offered Olivia a glass of water. Erin was still puzzled. "But how would you know for sure?"

"Err, I guess we could ask her to do an alcohol test?" suggested Kalle.

"Not that, ya bampot ," came ol' Cormac to Erin's defence. "She means how can ya be sure you're on to Truth and not some concocted, self-delusional thingy you take for Truth?"

"My point exactly!" pressed Jimmy.

"Hear hear!" motioned Charles.

It seemed all in the crowd somehow were in agreement on this one.

The One without the raven took the floor. But before he spoke, he looked at the sky for a moment. It seemed he already missed the bird on his shoulder.

"Am not!" objected the One without the raven to the One who is writing all this.

Promptly the raven returned. "Oh well," sighed the One with the raven.

"It's a fair point you all make. And you are right; as virtuous as our intentions can be, we should never discard the possibility of being lured once again into some path that leads us astray, be it by others or even ourselves. The thing is…"

"The thing is," continued the One with the magician's staff, "we tend to go all in, purely on emotion, at the risk of being sucked into the next cult."

"While others pick the purely mental approach, ending up in a strictly atheistic, YOLO-attitude, fully reigned by the ego, aiming for mere pleasure or a chapter in future history books."

"So genuine spirituality should be accompanied with a proper balance between mind and heart at all times," emphasized the One with the catsears.

"And in order to establish this," spoke the One with Vanessa, "any genuine form of spirituality should come in three distinctive stages."

"Where all three are not successive in nature but rather kind of circular," added the glowing One while doing a pirouette.

"**First**," spoke the One with the dice, "there is the recognition of that what appears to you as Truth. It's a realization by personal experience, not just a story or a contagious hype."

"It's an honest discovery. Not induced by opioids, mass hysteria, charismatic personalities or anything of the sorts."

"It's gentle, it's serene, it's simple, yet it is profound. It touches you in your very essence. It touches your heart; it touches reason. Both can be in agreement while you yourself disappear."

The One with the nón lá lifted his hand with two fingers pointing up. "**Then**, after the realization, there is this need to hold on to it. It emerges as a longing for repetition. You lost it. You know you had it. So, you seek to experience it again. But it somehow eludes you…"

"…because it is fragile," finished the One with the catsears. "It's a penetrating experience, and still, it's fickle. It's elusive. Like a spark in the dark. Mind-blowing. Unforgettable. And still… gone."

"This second stage is where your desire for a practice pops up. You need a way to remember, to reconnect, to re-experience and to share. And you know it cannot be accomplished by mere rational means. The lines of reason need to be crossed."

"And since it's about existence itself, you automatically seek for something in the realm of spirituality. Something which transcends the mundane."

"And as we said already, there is nothing wrong with a spiritual practice. It's a means to remember. As long as the means don't become the objective, it's ok. Just don't forget, the best practices excel in simplicity."

"And that brings you back to stage one," glowed the glowing One. Then she faltered. "Oh. Hang on. What happened to stage three?"

The One with Vanessa came to the rescue. "Well, **somewhere in between all this**, there is this important third stage, which we would call something like a contemplative evaluation. However high you are on your realization of Truth, some humility is never out of place. What if it's not the Truth? What if you're wrong?"

"Precisely. You all may have witnessed before how others can be wrong while having the feeling they are right. Why would you be different?"

"Hence, an honest evaluation is never a bad thing. Can you find loopholes in this epiphany you stumbled upon? Are there other views? Other opinions? Can you expose flaws or deceptions? Or does your poking around rather affirm your recognition even more?"

"You don't need to become a critic or even a cynic. Not at all. Try to have some fun with it. See it as a game. Can you crack it or not? The outcome is always a win. If you prove it to be a false path, you have gained the opportunity to look for another one. At least you didn't stay stuck in lies. If you can't prove it to be false, well, then you can keep diving in."

"Only Truth can keep you in an infinite loop in these three stages. One, experience. Two, reconnect. Three, challenge."

"Any other system or view will fail the test of scrutiny in the end. Whenever it requires to accept something, or following someone, or to bow down to an idea or a person, it will most definitely fail and break this loop of three."

"And that's a wrap," clapped the glowing One in her hands. "We ran out of drinks anyways."

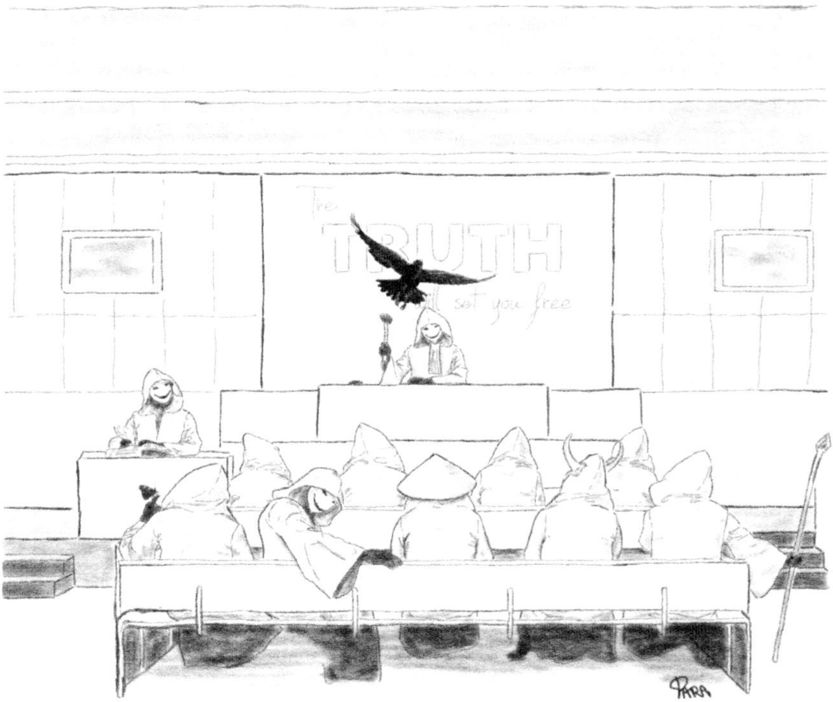
The
TRUTH
set you free

Chapter 5   **Objection, your Honour!**

The crowd decided to descend the awe-inspiring tower on foot. Since each of the four pillars had stairs going down, they spread out evenly over three of them. The Justified Ancients of Infinite Zero decided to go down via the fourth. But once the crowd was out of sight, they faltered. Whispering and muttering rose amongst the masked and hooded figures while they huddled in a circle.

"She told them about stage 3. What do we do now?" – "Stage 3? We're at DEFCON 3, you mean!" – "She just had to mention three stages, hadn't she. Why could she not keep it to two?" – "Up until now they were all meek and docile. I'm telling you, this is about to change. We're in trouble!" – – "I am so sorry!"

And this went on and on in circles. Eventually, as they were falling behind on the crowd, the One with the raven urged them to finally start the descent.

It was quite a long descent, with nothing in particular to mention. Actually, you could call it fairly boring. Well, apart from that moment where a young boy ascending the stairs stuck out his tongue to ol' Cormac – who was as usual carried, wheelchair and all, by Mykhailo – and his parents reprimanded their son, and ol' Cormac grunted with a big smile: "Ah, that's alright. His putting his tongue out like that was decided like 14 billion years ago. And likewise, I'm sure he'll bite it soon enough, and y'all'll remember this ol' mug when he does." And then he stuck out his tongue, Albert Einstein style.

Both parents looked at the old man with wide eyes and open mouths. Then they urged their son to follow them upwards while shaking their heads.

"You ol' bodach," reprimanded Erin her patient. "You're using a pretty plausible event to come for your revenge. Poor kid. Can't unhear what you said there. Destined to become a victim of the CSDCs."

Where were we? Oh, yes, the boring descent. As they reached ground level, the wrought iron surroundings gradually gave way to limestone walls, guiding them deeper underground. And so, they continued downwards on gently illuminated, limestone stairs, fashioned in a sleek architecture which looked pretty modern to the untrained eye. All three groups arrived at an equally modern door in white oak veneer. Men and women in formal attire, wearing neat white gloves, opened the door for them.

They all stepped into a large courtroom. The walls were panelled in light-coloured wood, with sections of milky, translucent glass allowing natural light to enter the room. A blueish floor and silvery ceiling gave the place an ultramodern appearance. The whole architecture exuded a hospitable, friendly and timeless environment (honestly, the sleek design makes it easier to draw the accompanying cartoons in this book and on social media).

When each group saw the other entering from a different corner in the courtroom, they all looked surprised and could do nothing better than greet each other with a disoriented 'Hi'.

"What the freakydifrak!" ol' Cormac exclaimed. "Are they going to put me on trial now for sticking out me tongue?"

"Karma, dude," whispered Jimmy in his ear.

Since standing around quickly became a bit silly, they all took seat on the wooden benches. As soon as they sat down, the Justified Ancients of Infinite Zero entered the room from the remaining corner.

"All rise!" boomed a voice which seemed to come from nowhere.

While the Justified Ancients of Infinite Zero all gathered in the dock of defendants, the One with the raven, wearing a white jabot for the occasion, took place at the bench. When the raven gave a small nod, indicating all could take a seat, all took a seat. That's the power of a small nod, even when coming from a raven.

It was the One who was writing all this who took the position of the court clerk. "Court is now in session," he solemnly said. "Please be seate... Oh, you all already are. So, what do we have? Ah, yes, the crowd versus the

Justified Ancients of Infinite Zero."

"Good afternoon, everyone. My name is... errr, well, I guess it's the Judge with the raven, and I will be preceding this trial. Very well, Mister Clerk, could you please arraign the defendants?"

"Justified Ancients of Infinite Zero, it is charged that you have told the Truth and nothing but the Truth! How do you plead to this charge?"

The answer was unanimous: "Guilty, your Honour!"

"Oh," replied the Court Clerk. "Didn't see that one coming. Could the crowd start their opening statement, please?"

"This is my moment, this is my moment," whispered Paul. "Always wanted to say this. Objection, your Honour!" he shouted. "You can't be the judge while you are part of the accused at the same time!"

"Overruled!" decided the Judge with the raven firmly.

"On what grounds?"

"On the grounds of this silly raven making it impossible for me to sit with my back to you all! So this position as judge is about the only one I can take in this room."

"Fair enough."

"God!" started one person in the crowd of complaining plaintiffs. "How about that for an opening statement!"

"Well, yes, how about that?"

"Well, you took God away from us! But that's just nonsense. I often talk to God. It brings me comfort. And also, how could the universe exist without a creator? There simply has to be a God, despite all you have told us."

The One with Vanessa rose up and greeted the room of plaintiffs. "Ladies and gentlemen, if I may. See, here's the thing. It is perfectly understandable to be baffled about existence, certainly when it seems to have popped up like it did. We all need a beginning, don't we? But God has the same problem. Where did God come from? And here's the strange thing, isn't there, Vanessa? What we can't accept for existence, we can for

God. For some reason we can live with the fact that God's origin will ever remain a mystery."

"While in fact," shared the One with the purpletop vervain (he traded it at one of the stalls near the staircase), "there are a lot of plausible ideas about how the universe as we know it now came into existence. Bottom line of about all of them is this: there's something weird about nothingness. It seems that sheer nothingness is actually bursting with energy. Even a tiny little nothingness seems to radiate particles in and out of existence. Imagine what absolute nothingness could do. Basically, nothingness has no other choice but to give rise to existence."

"But when it comes to speaking to God," said the One with the nón lá respectfully in his hands, "I see no need to avoid talking to Him, or Her. Why would you? I mean, the entire existence is the creator of itself. It's non-sentient, without plan or purpose, yet its path is clear. And along its self-propelled, unrelenting expansion, it reveals a majestic design, radiating beauty, chaos and order, ranging from an unfathomable pulsar in distant space to…"

"… a tiny, little butterfly on my finger here."

"You could call it existence. You could name it God. Once you realize its true nature, it's the same thing. You could even call its irrepressible unfolding 'God's will'. Truth doesn't take this away from you. It rather allows you to recognize you are part of it, to such an extent you cease to exist and become it. You and God are one. Every one of your actions, it's God's will. Every decision to take, every hesitation, it's God's will. Every thought you have, every doubt or clarity of mind, it's all God's will."

"And when you forget, when you collapse into the self, you can use this humble conversation as a reminder so you can remember the $\overline{\text{Self}}$ and be at peace."

"So I can still talk and pray to God?" asked the plaintiff, who was still a bit in doubt.

"You are a human being, my friend," smiled the glowing One. "And as a human being, you are capable and in very need of conversation. With others, with yourself, with the trees and the wind and all. Why not with existence in its entirety?"

"And why would a prayer need to be rational when you are in recognition of Truth?" remarked the One with Vanessa. "A prayer is allowed to be beyond reason. This duality is allowed for the sake of poetry. Like Rumi wrote: *'In the existence of your love, I have become non-existent. This non-existence linked to you is better than all existence.'* He speaks Truth while still talking in I and You. It is the prayer of the s̲elf to the S̄elf, to nothingness, to allness."

"Doesn't work for me," commented Charles. "I'd rather avoid such stuff. It's all too confusing."

"That's fine too, Charles. Abiding in presence, in Beingness, can be your prayer. Perhaps it's the final prayer, where all spoken prayers eventually merge in the silence evoked by the recognition of Truth."

"So basically," concluded the Judge with the raven, "not only do you have a rational reason to refer to the entire existence as God, but also, in your deepest experience of Beingness, at that moment when awareness collapses into itself and gives rise to a state of boundless expansion and timeless presence, a state of pure love, pure joy, yes, pure divinity even, you also have an irrational incentive to stick to God."

"Damned law-gibberish," muttered ol' Cormac between clenched teeth. "Will need to reread that paragraph a couple of times before I get it."

"Sustained and overruled!" concluded the Judge with the raven, while he slammed his hammer on the wooden gavel. ("Hey, this is fun," popped up in his masked mind.)

One person in the crowd objected. "You can't simultaneously sustain and over…"

"Hang on, hang on!" raised an impatient person in the crowd while raising himself. "All this unfolding-of-the-universe stuff, it's… Well, I mean, it's pushing us to… Well, on one hand, there's basically no point, as whatever we do, we couldn't do it any other way, right? But on the other hand, it also feels like I can do anything, any which way. I could decide to completely colour outside of all possible lines. There'd be no limit. I could enjoy things like whatever way I want. I could stuff myself with food, get drunk or have sex. I could switch jobs at a whim, swear in front of my mother, decide to marry, decide to divorce, switch items in the supermarket, knock on doors and run away. I mean, I could do the most chaotic things, seek out nothing but pleasure for my own gain, and not have a care, because it's all determined anyways."

"That's correct," concluded the Judge with the raven while he was about to slam the hammer once more. "Sustai-"

"Hang on, hang on!" interrupted the impatient person persistently. "What do you mean, 'That is correct'?"

"Well, basically, what you are saying is correct," explained the One with the purpletop vervain. "You could do all that. And you'd not be the first trying to either break the causalistic patterns or exploit them. But, I will not bore you with the consequences of such endeavours. You can find that out yourself easily enough. I can tell you, not much good will come of it."

"You see, such an approach is not coming from a real recognition of Truth. It rather is a revolt against a vague idea you 'think' you have about Truth."

"Precisely," said the One with the magician's staff. "We said this before. Without a solid realization of Truth, coming from a real experience, you will only be able to touch it mentally, as if it's only a theory in need to be proven or discarded. It'll lead you to interesting speculations and thought experiments, sure. It can even be a lot of fun too, as long as you don't take it overly serious and can back it up with the experience."

The Judge with the raven addressed the active plaintiffs and the rest of the crowd. "You have all had this profound experience of Beingness. You have all been immersed in the $\overline{\text{S}}$elf. When you recall this experience, how would you relate that to your sort of hedonistic objection?"

"I somehow found myself in agreement with how everything unfolds," answered Márcia. "It is all good. And still, when it feels like it is not good,

I will act upon that. It happens. Why should I resist that, right? But overall, there is this ever-active contentment which erases any need to seek out such stuff which would stretch way beyond my normal flow."

"I tried that already myself," shared the random tourist who skipped Part II in its entirety. "I mean, that colouring outside of the lines stuff. You know, just to see what would happen. I mean, like, would it blow up the universe or something? When it didn't, I even tried some more absurd stuff I'd never would have done otherwise. See if it would benefit me, you know. But as it turned out, I rarely ended up less miserable. Made me realize I do have a set of unexplored options laid out for me in life, but, some are simply beyond me."

"When people seek out peaks," said Andrea, "ravines are bound to be next. But living a flat life isn't much fun either. So we should seek out nice hills, shouldn't we? And occasionally, a holiday to the mountains can still be an option."

She said it in such a funny way all laughed. Then the laughing switched to chattering all around. Everybody suddenly started to relate their story to their neighbour.

"Order, order!" spoke the Judge with the raven with raised voice. Slam with the hammer. "Overruled and sustained."

"Really, you just can't sus-"

"I don't know," said Olivia while shaking her head in doubt. "I just don't know."

"Could you please stand, dear," beckoned the Judge with the raven gently. "I'm sure it's alright."

Olivia stood up and addressed all in the courtroom. "See, ever since I have come to know Truth – and mind you, I accept it – but ever since, my life has only become harder. It's not that I have the feeling that I have no choice any longer. It's quite the opposite. It's like literally everything has become a choice now. 'Should I really be sad about this?' – 'Should I feel guilty?' – 'Should I control my anger?' – "Should I even care about this important choice I'm about to make?' – I understand the Truth, but still, at times it is unbearable."

"I don't understand," said Bram.

"I do," said Marwa. "This Knowing which you have bestowed upon us, just like Olivia, it has brought me as well in a constant state of introspection. I feel like I should be this enlightened person now, radiating peace and joy, and doing everything right, with people looking up to me in amazement and all."

"Well…" started the One with the dice.

"It's like, when I'm sad, immediately this question pops up: 'Why would I be sad?' Because everything unfolds as it does, doesn't it?"

"Well…" started the One with the dice again.

"Or, when I'm angry! Oh my, that one. I can really be angry with myself when I'm angry about something. Why would I be angry in the first place, right? And then, with all this Truth-stuff, I turn out twice as angry as before."

The One with the dice looked at Marwa. Then he looked at the Judge with the raven. Then he looked at Marwa again.

"Well, aren't you gonna say something?" pressed Marwa.

The One with the dice was momentarily lost for words. Then he regained himself. "Look, I hate to repeat ourselves, and I totally understand, but… When you approach Truth with reason alone, most people will never be able to grasp it. It's just a concept, merely an idea, a theory or a hypothesis. It can seem plausible, it can be found to be reasonable, or, it can get classified as utterly ridiculous."

Many plaintiffs boo'd the repetitive argument away. So Soren, who'd been quiet since now, decided to help out. With a warm voice and an open heart he addressed all in the room. "Listen, I understand our misunderstanding, but here's the thing, the mystery of Truth isn't a problem to solve. It's a reality to experience."

"Exactly," added Frank. "This process cannot be understood by stopping it and taking it apart. Our understanding must move with the flow of the process. It must join it and flow with it."

"So, yes, Marwa. Yes, Olivia. Yes, all of you," said the One with the magician's staff, "this is the thing. We may 'think' we understand Truth, because we also shared an experience to a certain degree. But you're more at the point where you stand under it instead, looking up to this Truth in awe and even praise, yet you haven't completely integrated it. You're still processing it. It's like a lot of gears and levers are already put in the right place, but there are still many unaligned too. Getting them all aligned can only happen when you flow with it. When you let go."

"And there's no need to hurry that process," said the One with Vanessa. "To some it comes in a blink of an eye. Others need more time. Some might never reach the end of that process. They'll get bored and hop onto something else. It's important you don't get too practical about it right away. Taking regular moments for a bit of contemplation, for silence or active breathing can be more than enough."

"And hereby I declare overthinking as sustained and overruled," stated the Judge with the raven with a bang of the hammer.

The person objecting to the simultaneous sustain and overrule only grumbled with arms crossed in front of him.

"Objection, your Honour!" shouted one of the plaintiffs. "Leading the witness! I don't agree with overthinking being sustained or overruled!"

"You don't? – I mean: sustained. Please, elaborate."

"To me as well, ever since I know the Truth, things are a bit off. It's not just about overthinking my sadness or my anger. It's the entire mental process as well. It causes inner turmoil and dissension. I mean, the whole thing is one big contradiction. I think thoughts here and now, while you claim they are already thought. I have to make dozens of choices on a daily basis, but you claim they are already made. So, doesn't the knowing of Truth break this chain of causality? Doesn't it allow me some meta-perspective where I can come to a choice which wasn't determined already?"

"You see…" The One with the dice paused, anticipating a new rant. When there didn't came one, the Judge with the raven's fingers went ta-dum ta-dum on his bench. "Oh, sorry. So. You see, the sentences you just spoke had a lot of I's in them. And there's the main culprit. There is no I to decide things. As long as you can't break that paradigm, you will find the recognition of Truth to be as elusive as trying to pluck a piece from a cloud."

"Simply put, Sir, you claim it to be a contradiction, but it's not. It's a genuine paradox, as we have stated numerous times. You really should re-read the cover of this book. You think and you don't. You are and you're not. There's choices and there's not."

"You can choose to abandon Truth and live from the s̲elf as you did before. You can also kid yourself into being pure Beingness and try to be enlightened in a cave on top of a mountain."

"How can there be caves on top of a mountain?" wondered the One with the Viking horns with the typical voice of Terry Jones in Life of Brian.

"At least – when you are enlightened, that is – it won't be dark in there," commented the One with the magician's staff with the voice of Michael Palin in the same movie.

"Order! Order!"

"Or…," continued the One without the bow and arrow (she had to hand her weapons over to the bailiff when she entered), "there's the only other possible alternative: you could live the paradox."

"But I don't choose that! It happens. Or like you lot say: it unfoo'olds."

"I once went into this indoor rollercoaster where everything was pitch black," recalled the One with the Viking horns. "Didn't know what'd come next, but boy, did I have fun."

"Point is, plaintiff, you can be in congruity with existence and enjoy the ride. Or you can scream your lungs out complaining as you try to jump out. Either way, there'll ever be only the ride. Relax a bit. Breathe. Living the paradox isn't that bad. Have some fun."

"Sustained and overruled."

"So it's all an illusion, no?" raised another person in the crowd.

"Oh, that one," whispered the One with the Viking horns to the One without bow and arrow. "If it's not about accountability, then it's the illusion card they play."

"Hush, will ya. Listen."

Who else then the One with the magician's staff raised herself to answer. "An illusion is something that seems to be there, but it's not. Take the typical mirage in a dessert. You see the oasis at the horizon, but it's not there. Still, the mirage is real. You can even capture it on camera. You can point at it, you can talk about it, and everybody knows it when you mention it."

Then she dramatically tapped her staff on the floor. With a poof she was suddenly completely shrouded in white smoke. When the smoke disappeared, she was gone. Then the same smoke appeared a bit further, revealing her once more. (Well, they need to work a bit more on this trick since she wasn't holding her staff any longer. On top of that, she continued with a male voice.)

"And so as well, your thoughts are real. Your you-ness is real. Your feelings are real. Your love for another person is real. There's nothing illusionary about it. And this paradoxical existence allows us to be real, and be not at all, at the same time. There's no picking one over the other. You don't need to collapse the quantum particle. You can remain in superposition and enjoy both ends of it."

"Dangerous it is, talk about quantum," voiced the One with no particular characteristics.

The One with the dice rolled the dice. "A pair of sixes! How about that. Expected to roll two pink elephants there."

"Overruled and sustained!"

For a moment there was silence. The Judge with the raven scanned the courtroom for anyone else raising another accusation. Then his eyes fell upon Ann. She seemed to be sulking.

"What's the matter, Ann?" he asked gently.

Ann was startled for a moment by the sudden attention. Still, she decided to stand. "I don't know really. Somehow your defence seems right, but still, it doesn't seem satisfying. It's a bit of a paradox, isn't it?"

"Here's the thing, Ann," replied the Judge with the raven kindly. "All these objections and their answers, they will never be able to fully satisfy you. They all come from a very intellectual perspective. And while the intellect can be very helpful, it can also start to go in circles, especially when it engages with your more emotional side."

"So how can I get around that and be without doubts?"

"That is a good question, Ann. Keeping faith, trusting our words, none of that would be a good way to go at it, although it is the easiest one. It all is within you, Ann. Remember. Reconnect. The wholeness found in Beingness, together with an unattached observing of everything observable there is, either visible or invisible, are the key ingredients to find this non-mental certainty and wordless knowing."

"It's all you," spoke the One with the purpletop vervain, casually as always. "But also, it's just you. And then again, it never was you."

"Right!" One plaintiff abruptly rose up and addressed both the crowd and the Justified Ancients of Infinite Zero. "I believe extra-terrestrials put us on this planet. There's this scientific fantasy-writer – what's his name? – who is very clear about this."

"Overruled!" decided the One with the raven in a split-second. "That accusation is just another origin story. For all I care, humanity was brought here by extra-terrestrials. Great! And also, so what? Will it make you buy bread instead of sandwiches? It'd be just an extra page in history. But it will not reveal to you where life came from. If it didn't start on this planet, then were did it? Where did your extra-terrestrial ancestors come from? You see, even if humanity was brought here by extra-terrestrials – and that's not even an if, since we perfectly know how humanity evolved here – even if, it would change nothing with regards to Truth."

A young man rose. "How do you explain out of body experiences? And people who can project themselves to different locations?"

"That's just silly," scoffed Charles who was an MI6 Intelligence Officer in his mid-thirties. "If people really could do that astral projection stuff, we wouldn't have to send out agents in the most perilous circumstances. We'd all be sitting safely in our office, like drone pilots, projecting ourselves into the room of world leaders and looking over their shoulders when they read their classified documents."

"Yeh, but you can't do that, now can you?" retorted the young man. "They all have an astral projection shield around them."

Charles could only slap himself in the face at that.

"Overruled and overruled!"

"You can't double overru…"

The bailiff put his index finger at the place where is ear ought to be. The slight inclination of his head indicated he was intensely listening to something. Then his face turned worried. He approached the bench and whispered something inaudible to the Judge with the raven.

"We must keep it brief, ladies and gentlemen. We have a situation."

"Hang on!" shouted a plaintiff. "I mean, objection!"

"Objection who?"

"I apologize. Objection, your Honour! You haven't addressed the out of body experience accusation. Clearly, this is unacceptable. By not touching this subject you indicate to have no answer to that one."

"Fair enough," said the Judge with the raven. "But we do must make haste. So allow me to go all in and tackle out of body experience, past lives, mystical experiences, mind reading, miraculous healings all at once. That is, if you allow me."

"Sustained," answered the plaintiff.

"A plaintiff can't sustain! This whole court case is a mockery of justice."

"Nothing beats a good old mockery," glowed the glowing One.

"Listen," the Judge with the raven began patiently, despite of the bailiff looking more and more concerned by the minute. "All your thoughts and sensations occur in one of the most complex and intricate organs the universe has ever managed to unfold. It is a baffling system. And the most baffling about it is that it usually tends to work pretty well. Nonetheless, it is also prone to tiny faults."

"And small faults," added the One with Vanessa.

"And medium faults." The One with the magician's staff.

"And huge, very huge, humongous faults." The One with the Viking horns.

"Order! – Anyways, we all tend to think ours to be without even the tiniest fault. Unfortunately, this is not always true."

"But such people are put in an asylum," raised Georges. "Or at least, they are in treatment or being medicated."

"That is correct, Georges. Still, it'd be wrong to think it's just one small step from sane to insane. There's a lot in between, sometimes unnoticed, sometimes a little annoying, sometimes utterly weird but still acceptable."

"Some people occasionally here voices. Some people see colours in words and numbers, or they can even hear them."

"Some people mistake their wife for a hat!" shouted Oliver.

"Thing is," continued the Judge with the raven. "A lot of the stuff you raise here, can either be actively stimulated in the brain – like an out of body experience – or there never is any real evidence, apart from dubious claims which never seem to hold up."

"I still have that one million dollars," shouted Mr Randi in the back.

"Order! – The point is, not any of that stuff manages to hit the evening news or the front page of a decent newspaper. It's just thrown around here and there for those to pick up who like to pick it up. It can't be repeated. It can't be witnessed by others. So the main question is, are you willing to put a lot of effort into something which somehow ever remains deeply ingrained in the realms of the ambiguous – to say the least – where people only see what they want to see, believe what they want to believe, without a real chance of ever finding something substantial?"

"You could devote your life to do research on that," spoke the One with the nón lá. "And perhaps you may discover interesting things along the way. But do take into account that you have to be able to present something for 'all' to witness, not just for a group of followers wishing you to be right."

"You can walk this path, Sir," concluded the Judge with the raven. "And I can only wish you Godspeed. But we see no fruit in such endeavours. On the other hand, Truth can be touched for real. It is readily available for you, here and now, and it will remain as such on your path."

"Just see how it feels," said the glowing One. "Will the chasing of questions, for which there might be no answer at all, bring you space? Or will it bring lack? Will it bring comfort? Or will it bring frustration?"

"Hrrrmmm, frustration. To anger it leads." You know who. "Anger leads to hate. Hate leads to suffering."

"Sir," insisted the bailiff. "We really need to go!"

The crow of plaintiffs made a racket when everyone started talking at once. Some shouted similar questions:

"What about euthanasia?" – "What with abortion?" – "How about human rights?" – "Animal rights!" – "Suicide?" – "LBGTQ+ community?" – "Prison sentences?" – "Death sentences?" – "Global warming?" – "Far right?" – "Far left?" – "Far West?" – …

"Order!" A man suddenly shouted from in the back. "Ordeeeeeeeeer! – Orderorderorderorder!! – Oooooorderrr!"

"Thank, you, Mr Bercow," said the Judge with the raven when all turned silent. "Look. All those moral dilemmas will remain unchanged. Truth doesn't push this any which way. At best, Truth allows you peace, comfort and serenity during such debates, or it allows you a refuge of silence, wholeness and rejuvenation at the end of the day. Once you manage to find your peace within this paradoxical existence, you will grow to live it in its entire richness, beauty and craziness."

The main doors slammed wide open with a blast. A team of men and women, all in black suits, white shirts, black ties and sunglasses poured into the room. They were all touching their ear while they evenly spread out. One of them, presumably their leader, approached the bench and addressed the Judge with the raven.

"Sir, CSDCs have been spotted in great numbers. They are descending the stairs while we speak. We must go! Now!"

"This way!" shouted Mr Bercow while pointing the crowd to another door. "Gooooo! – Gogogogogo! – Go'oo!"

And so it was that the crowd and the Justified Ancients of Infinite Zero left the courtroom without a verdict. A lucky twist of fate for sure, as it would have left readers even more divided than perhaps they are now.

Chapter 6   **Chased by the impossible, carrying nothing but possibilities**

Up the limestone stairs they went in an ooooooooordeeeeer-ly fashion.

It was daylight which touched the gasping mouths of all emerging back in the open. The Arc de Triomphe towered majestically above them. Regretfully, there was no time for all to get a stiff neck from looking up. The men and women in black urged them towards two huge, black double-decker busses which were parked in the most inner circle of the Place Charles de Gaulle.

There was a lot of chaos. The 12-lane 'Rotonde' was busier than ever. A bunch of Vespas seemed totally out of sync with the other, mostly jammed traffic. At high speed the buzzing scooters circled the arc while fanatically weaving their way to the centre where the first arrivals of the crowd started to board the buses. A cacophony of angry honks ensued from each car they scratched while passing them without there being proper space to navigate through. At the same time a bearded guy in a black suit, apparently all beaten up, was driving like a madman in the opposite direction. The 1971 (great year!) Plymouth Barracuda, a doorless version so it seemed, deliberately prevented the Vespas from reaching the inner circle. Likewise, on the other half of the immense roundabout, a guy on a BMW motorcycle – without wearing a helmet! – also seemed to be keeping the Vespas from reaching the centre.

While the last persons of the crowd were still coming up from the staircase, a crazy man flew his Nieuport 27 sesquiplane right through the arc while shouting "Go! Go! Goooooo!" (Georges' accent and Doppler effect included). John, in the 1971 car, urged them to get in the bus. Ethan, on the motorcycle, shouted similar instructions. Everybody jumped into the busses. The crowd and the Persistent Pursuers of Infinite Zero all got mixed together.

The One with the driver's license departed with screeching tyres. All in the bus went flat into their seats. Behind them the One without the driver's license tried the same thing. The bus immediately span out of control, hitting the Plymouth Barracuda and tossing John out of his car (should have had doors to begin with). Luckily, the One without the driver's license quickly regained control and managed to team up with the first bus.

Behind them, John was being thrown around in an inhuman fashion by cars and Vespas. His stamina was totally wicked. Ethan hunted him down and urged John to hop on the motorcycle. The two black double-decker buses increased speed and went round and round the 'Rotonde' until everything got blurry.

EXT. ARC DE TRIOMPHE – DAY

Everything suddenly goes dark. Then light returns. Traffic is back to normal. Two men are standing in the middle of the Rotonde.

JOHN

You are in the wrong movie, my friend.

ETHAN

No, you are in the wrong movie.

JOHN

No, you...

MR BEAN

Ullo

Everything goes dark again.

The two black double-decker buses hit the road with a big thud as if they came falling out of the air. They landed in the midst of a much smaller roundabout. The amount of traffic however seemed about the same. It was filled with black-and-yellow cabs, scooters, tuk-tuks, bicycles, trucks-the-size-of-a-regular-car, people, motorcycles and a cow.

The cow was a problem.

The One without a driver's license somehow had overtaken the first bus and found herself in the lead. She yanked her steering wheel hard to the right and barely managed to evade the cow. That's the good news. The fruit vendor's cart next to the roundabout was an altogether other issue. A direct hit! Bananas, mangoes, the food vendor and a lot of unknown fruit flew up in the air. Luckily, most of the fruit was saved by the fruit vendor in midair. The black double-decker bus, however, crashed into a bush behind the cart (a bus crashing into a bush?) and came to a complete stop.

The second bus, even though it was driven by the One with a driver's license, smashed straight into a soft drinks booth. It was a bit ironic because one of the soft drinks hit Sajeev straight in the face. It didn't feel soft at all to him. The poor man is currently still in the hospital.

"Quickly!" shouted Hrithik from the chopper above all that stepped uninjured out of the busses. "Get to the tuk-tuks! They are coming!" (Somehow, there was this cloud of infernal fire behind him – a misplaced CGI for sure – our apologies).

All of a sudden, the Vespas appeared on the other side of the roundabout. The crowd momentarily looked startled when they heard the roaring engines. It seemed as if a swarm of killer wasps was heading their way. Everybody ran as fast as they could to the tuk-tuks.

As the Persistent Pursuers of Infinite Zero didn't feel targeted by the incoming CSDSs, they went at it more slowly. They were pleased to see how everybody got spread out in the available tuk-tuks in just a few seconds time. It was the sound of the 2-stroke engines that almost managed to wipe the smiles off their masks. With heavy spluttering, accompanied by metal clangs as if the engines were about to explode, the tuk-tuks managed to roll into traffic just in front of the Vespas. As they accelerated, so did the rattling sound of the worn diesel engines.

It was Erin who took the lead. Ol' Cormac held on with all his might as his wheelchair flanked the tuk-tuk like a sidecar to a motorcycle. Erin drove straight into the heavy traffic surrounding them. Four other ex-plaintiffs sat in the back, holding on to each other as if their life depended on it. It did.

"Out of ur way, ye boggin bampots!" ol' Cormac yelled. "Honk yer horn, Erin. Honk for yer life."

Erin's frantic honking was to no avail as it went lost in the habitual honking of the local drivers. She saw no choice but to wildly manoeuvre left and right to get through without slowing down.

"They're all nuts!" yelped Bram who was steering the tuk-tuk in the tail of the train they all formed.

"Just stay focused!" shouted Marwa next to him. "Or better, let me drive!"

"OhmyGod," gasped Bram as a young child suddenly appeared in front of their tuk-tuk. In a reflex, Marwa pulled the steering wheel from Bram's hands. The tuk-tuk bounced over a curve. All the passengers in the back bumped their heads into the ceiling of the tuk-tuk. At that moment one of the Vespas came up next to their right flank. With in front of them nothing but a steep ramp, which was supposed to be used for loading a cart, Bram found himself in an impossible position.

"Bram?" was all Marwa was able to scream.

"Hold on!"

About higher vibrations and confused poles

Bram's tuk-tuk went flying high up in the air. One of the Vespas followed and got alongside them. Then... time... seemed... to...   slow...

down... for... both... vehicles... In the background stood a giant statue of Shiva, all tranquil and meditative, as if it was he who froze time. Somehow, the occupants of the tuk-tuk and the Vespa weren't afflicted by this divine weirdness.

"There's no need to resist," spoke a charming fellow on the Vespa while they were in midair. "Don't you see you are clinging to old patterns blocking you from making this crucial shift in consciousness?"

"What do you mean?" asked Bram politely.

"Don't you feel it? The whole planet is shifting to a new frequency. We are on the verge of entering a new dimension. It's evolution. And it's science, too. There's the wobbling of precession – or something like that. The poles are going to invert any time now..."

"You just had to ask, didn't you?" whispered Marwa to Bram.

"...the time of lower vibrations is about to end. If you don't raise your own, you will remain stuck in three dimensional space. There will only be fear, lack and violence. People in the old paradigm are all into polarization and division for their own gain, forcing us to choose sides. But humanity is transitioning, for sure. Will you be amongst those that step into the next level, or will you stick to greed, control, scarcity, lack (did I mention that one already?), shame,... Anyways, there is an urgency, my friends, and it is relentless in its calling. You surely hear it, too. And I'm sure you are unsure how to respond. But we have these empowering tools. It will be the largest leap in the evolution of humanity to date, I'm telling you."

"Thank you," replied Bram once more politely. "But I'm afraid this particular leap we are in now is all the leap I can take in one go."

Marwa was less cordial. "Funny you accuse the world of polarization and then start talking about those who will make the shift and those who are too blind to see. Could you please fly somewhere else?"

Time took its regular pace. The tuk-tuk landed hard, bounced up, landed hard again, bounced up one more time and then continued its course. The Vespa landed in a trench which was waiting to be filled by something which was eventually forgotten.

Any chance of a coincidence?

Up in the front Erin was still honking her way through the crowded streets. Then, ol' Cormac signalled her to make a hard right towards an enormous building with a small gate. All the others followed with screeching tyres and rattling engines. One of the pursuing Vespas couldn't make the turn in time and crashed into a stall of colourful fabrics.

When they drove through the narrow gate, a serene and symmetric landscape revealed itself. "Hey," shouted Ann excitedly from the back of the tuk-tuk which was piloted by Paul, "that's the Taj Mahal! Awesome! Always wanted to visit it."

Erin bounced down the stairs and landed on the neatly cut grass. The Vespas followed them pertinaciously, pulling curvy lines in the pristine landscape. Erin tried to shake them off by zigzagging between the trees next to the long water tank which led straight towards the Taj Mahal.

One of the Vespas overtook Paul's tuk-tuk. In a final attempt to shake off his pursuer, he hopped his tuk-tuk straight over the water tank towards the other side. The Vespas driver was not deterred and succeeded in the very same manoeuvre. Then... time... froze...

"What a coincidence!" said an extremely charming woman on the Vespa alongside them. "I was just thinking about the Taj Mahal the other day, and see, now we are here."

"Remarkable indeed," answered Paul. "Does this also explain why you are hovering next to our tuk-tuk?"

"Well, maybe, who knows?" answered the charming woman. "It all makes you feel like there is more to it, no? Bottom line is, my friend, there's no such thing as coincidences. You must have noticed this numerous times. You think, 'Hey, that's a strange coincidence'. But at the same time, you feel it in your gut that there's something hidden in plain sight."

"I had that feeling, too," added the charming man sitting behind the charming woman. "Couldn't make sense of it. But then I learned how there are very precise patterns occurring in our lives, with a very specific meaning for each and every one of us. It's called synchronicity. It's not coincidence. It's a message!"

"And the beauty of it is that they help us make the necessary decisions in life. You know, when you feel stuck and wander aimlessly around, the universe will lead you in the right direction."

"Or the universe can also tell you you are exactly on the right track. You see, there is a certain 'order' in the universe and…"

"I'm happy to hear that," said Mr Bercow from the back of the tuk-tuk. "Makes my job so much easier."

"… and it brings peace and abundance into our lives. I can offer you this great program which has ten steps to cultivate synchronicity."

"And when you've completed that track, I can offer four simple steps to connect with your path. And all that we offer at a temporary discount. It's a once-in-a-lifetime opportunity."

"My dear friends," began Ann. "Have you ever heard of the butterfly effect? You know, the silly little butterfly flaps it wings and causes a thunderstorm on the other side of the planet? Okay, that's silly, of course, right? But still, can you imagine the impact if 'the universe' intervened in daily causality just to pass me this particular message? Like repetitively sending me the same sequence of numbers all over the place, like on a medicine vial, an airplane banner ad, the license plate of a car, a TV show… Can you imagine what had to be set in motion to pull that off? Things that needed to be brought in place. People's lives would need to be affected, like even years upfront. It would unavoidably result in an endless stream of changed patterns. And I'm sure not all would have a positive outcome."

Paul looked at Ann in amazement. "Gosh, hadn't looked at it like that." Then he felt like addressing the charming folk on the Vespa. "Look, I admit, these coincidences are real and present in our lives. I will not argue with that. Yet here's the thing, and this will sound very boring to you guys, but for one, we like to filter these things out. Like me. I often think about my mother-in-law. And then I try to unthink that. And then, after 3000 times of thinking about her, I suddenly receive a phone call from her. And I say, 'Hi, what an amazing coincidence! I was just thinking about you.' And she cynically goes, 'And why were you thinking about me?' And I go 'Errrr…'

Anyways, these coincidences also happen to be nothing but a statistical probability. You see, it's pretty normal that there are patterns to be found in existence. Otherwise, it'd be all pure chaos. The real beauty is our capacity to see connections between apparently unrelated things. Sometimes this will lead to new discoveries or insights, but more often than not, there's simply no real connection at all. Our mind just connected two dots which in reality will always remain separated."

Mr Klein, who sat right next to Mr Bercow, leaned forward to participate in the conversation. "Yes, Paul, that sounds really boring indeed. If you ask me, coincidences are a beauty on their own. In a way, it's like art. Sometimes, it just occurs out of the blue, and it can simply amaze me or make me smile. Sometimes, I unconsciously tend to provoke it when my radar seeks for confirmation."

"Exactly," said Paul. "Like when you are thinking about buying a tuk-tuk and all of a sudden you see tuk-tuks everywhere, you know, while you never noticed their presence before."

"Errr," went Mr Klein. "That may not be the best example, Paul. But fair enough, it's a fact that we tend to look for guidance or direction when we are frozen by doubt. There are so many important decisions we need to make in life. And sometimes we simply do not have enough information to make that decision. That makes us very uncertain. Now, a sudden coincidence will not necessarily guide us into making the right decision, but it may still help us make one and come to terms with it. Feel more confident about it. Make the best of it, you know."

"That's why I love coincidences," bellowed Mr Bercow. "It's not so much like I have the feeling they are guiding me, but they do tell me the rational and irrational parts of me are in sync, if you get what I mean."

"Like your mind is set on something," said Ann, "and in your heart, you are set on it as well. And when mind and heart are in agreement, our looking and listening, conscious and unconscious, tune in with those specific bits of our surrounding reality. We are able to grasp more elements, more details, and solve the creative puzzle that got our intention in the first place."

"I like to see coincidences as little jokes of the universe," smiled Paul. "You can cease them in the moment, for something useful, maybe; for a small deviation of the worn path, possibly. But mostly simply for putting a smile on our often all-too-serious faces. Like when I walk the dog in the evening, and the streetlight goes out at the very moment I walk under it. And when I'm just a few steps further, it pops back on again. I don't seek a message in these oddities. I just smile."

"Bollocks," grunted the charming man on the Vespa. "We are wasting our time here. Let's find some other people."

And so it happened that time took its normal pace once more. Paul managed to land the tuk-tuk smoothly on the grass on the other side of the water tank. There he paused for a moment to find those bearings which had already been lost in a previous chapter.

"You know what saddens me sometimes?" mused Mr Bercow.

"What's that?" wondered Ann.

"Well, people are always in a hurry nowadays. They run from A to C, from home to work and back again. On the highway. In the supermarket. Always frustrated to see how the other lane is ever the faster one. Until they switch, cause disorder – boy, I hate that – and still end up in the slower one. They see other people around them as nothing but obstacles in their way. We practically dehumanize all of humanity during that ride from A to D."

"Oh, I see," whispered Ann a bit ashamed, realizing she now and then matched the description.

"Yeh. All we want is to get to places where we need to do things. And the funny thing, the really funny thing is, we complain nothing beautiful ever happens to us. No opportunities. No chances. While so many might have passed by on our way, we just didn't care to notice them. A to E. Forgot about B and D.

And then, when we happen to find a moment to contemplate this, we decide to seek out these folks on Vespas, hoping they will lead us to opportunity. I mean, really! If only people would look around a bit more. In between all this humdrum and occasional silly coincidences, there actually lies beauty and opportunity to grab. Just open your eyes and ears a bit instead of wearing these horse blinkers all the time. If only people would slow down a-"

"Out of ur wey ye dossinit bamsticks ye!"

Erin came honking like a frantic in their direction. On her tail followed the other tuk-tuks, swarmed by Vespas all around them.

"There's no way out of this place," shouted Erin. "We need to go out by the main gate again."

Paul brought the clutch in and switched to first gear. Then his right wrist went all the way down while he slowly released the clutch and steered to the left. The tuk-tuk span at its axis while digging a nicely curved trench in the freshly trimmed lawn. When the tuk-tuk lined up with the others, he went full throttle and managed to catch up. All went through the main gate while tourists in front of it hurled themselves left and right to safety.

Time-out for a little divination

The Spasskaya Bashnya spat out a lively procession of tuk-tuks and Vespas. While fast and furiously speeding away, the Cathedral of the Intercession of the Most Holy Theotokos on the Moat (!) rose at their right side. There was no time, however, to bask in its glory.

Tourists on the Red Square were running in panic in all possible directions at the same time. At first Ayush thought it was because of the flame-like domes on top of the Cathedral of the Intercession of the Most Holy

Theotokos on the Moat (!!). Then he wobbled his head and thought 'You silly, that's not it,' while he figured it was simply because of them being chased by the CSDCs.

Still he was wrong. The real reason why people were running and screaming appeared to be a Cessna 172 which was about to land in front of the Kremlin.

"What the freaky-di-frack!" exclaimed ol' Cormac while being jostled about in his wheelchair-sidecar. "What is it with these planes today?"

The Cessna landed right between the tuk-tuks and the chasing Vespas. Two of the Vespas smartly cut the arc of the tuk-tuks and sided left and right with the one of Jimmy. Jimmy steered straight to the sidewalk next to a large shopping centre ahead. Despite there being trees on the left and terraces on the right, the Vespas kept flanking the tuk-tuk with barely an inch of space between them. When one Vespa was about to crash into a tree, and the other was about to crash into a nicely set table for two, time... froze... once... more...

"Hi, good sir," greeted a charming fellow, Jimmy and his passengers. "I have these most beautiful tarot-decks with me. I can sell you one on the spot. Or even better, I can do you a reading. It will most definitely give you answers to all your questions, whether it is about love, your career or health."

"Hi there," said a charming girl on the other Vespa. "Could you tell me your birthday and place of birth?" she asked Mykhailo. "I can draw you an astrological chart which can guide you in the days and years to come. This really is must-have-need-to-know information."

"Sod off, will ya!" was Jimmy's direct reply.

"Mind your language, will you," chided Oliver. "There's children in the back here."

"Besides, Jimmy," said Márcia while suckling her twins. "It's pretty rude to give such a reply. It's typically a way to condemn something without having the slightest idea what it is about. People are so biased nowadays, really."

Jimmy blushed and grumbled.

"Thank you, mam," said the charmingly smiling, charming man on the Vespa. "A little divination for you perhaps?"

"Now hang on there," answered Márcia. "Let's not get ahead of ourselves here. When it comes to divination, I must, in all politeness, agree with Jimmy here. Astrology or the Tarot are not to be used for divination. Mind you, they can be fun and even useful, but not in the way you charming lot are overselling them."

"That sounds interesting," said Oliver. "What do you mean, Márcia?"

"Well, see," started Márcia. "The beauty about Tarot, numerology, astrology, I Ching or I Chang and all, is that they cover a wide and sometimes pretty complete range of the human psyche. And that makes these 'tools' interesting, see, because what we mostly do, running about in our daily existence with its habitual patterns, is that we cover a lot of our psyche up in the dark. Or we simply overly focus on one aspect, while in reality, there is so much more to us. Astrology or Tarot is based on nothing but smartly covered randomness. But still, this randomness allows you to meet other aspects of yourself which you didn't know about."

"So it isn't that bad to have one?" blushed Mykhailo, feeling guilty about having a Rider-Waite deck on his bedside table at home.

"To be honest, I happen to have a tarot deck myself," admitted Márcia. "And I surely do not use it for divination. But it can be capable of giving me new insights, you know, things I'd otherwise never have thought about. Sometimes it's just crap; sometimes, it's fun. And sometimes it is really helpful. It's just a matter of using this stuff in a sensible way instead of abusing it for personal gain."

Time unfroze. Jimmy reacted instantly. He braked hard, revved up and veered left, out of the small pathway between trees and terraces. You can imagine how the two Vespas ended up. (Now, before you go overly imaginative about that, nobody got harmed, and all damages were compensated.)

The whole group crossed the Red Square once more. They would have been apprehended for sure if it weren't for the German pilot who found himself surrounded by dozens of policemen. Nonetheless, with no other obstacles available, the Vespas quickly overtook the tuk-tuks. The tuk-tuk drivers, synced up as a team by now, simultaneously decided to brake hard in an attempt to scatter the Vespas in all directions but theirs. But from the moment they hit the brakes, all started to slip away and skid. Some went full 360. Some 245. Others 108. When they eventually came to a full stop, they all found themselves on a large field of ice.

One can't channel across the channel; that's a fact

In the open sea to their left, they saw a polar bear clinging to her cub on a small raft of ice. 'Can you please, please take this seriously and do something about this?' the mother bear seemed to speak with just the look of her eyes. 'I mean, really, you lot may think all this can only unfold as it is doing right now, and yes, you may be right about that. But still, you can't claim this Truth of yours prevents you from taking the big and necessary actions, now does it?' (Stuff polar bears can think, incredible, right?)

"Hit the throttle!" screamed Kalle to Sven. "They are coming!"

"I am!" shouted Sven. "The wheels keep spinning on this ice!"

When one of the Vespas sided with their tuk-tuk, both vehicles started an elegant spin that required no freezing of time (it was too cold for that, anyway).

"Hey there!" A smiling, very charming and sweet-sounding gentleman addressed 방찬 in the back. "Hello, my friend. Have you ever heard about Angelic Channeling? Did you know we are surrounded by intelligent beings? They are invisible to most of us, I know. But that doesn't mean you can't communicate with them."

"Iwouldn'tknowwhattotellthem," replied 방찬 in all honesty.

"Oh, but you don't need to tell them anything, my friend. They will speak to you. They might provide you with guidance and wisdom. They might even dictate to you books that are guaranteed to become bestsellers."

"Ohyoumeaninspiration?Ihavetonsofthatandit'scomingtomeatspeedsyou can'timangesonothankyouverymuch."

"I'd be careful with that stuff, mister," advised Andrea from in the back of the tuk-tuk. "All this channelling stuff is nothing but an imaginative mind connecting with the subconscious. From there, you start to project a different personality towards yourself. This can be very tricky. Even if you'd be mentally a full hundred per cent alright – and honestly, who is? – still, this may change quickly if you dive too deep into this stuff."

"That sounds scary," remarked Kalle.

"It is," emphasized Andrea. "You see, it allows creative thoughts to flow, yes, and it also allows one to be more confident about these thoughts. But this confidence can quickly result in a person becoming overconfident. You start to take it for really real. Any honest criticism becomes a potential threat that needs to be taken care of. All because you simply can't allow the slightest possibility of that what is being channelled to be wrong. After all, that would take the main drive away: the confidence in the fact that there's 'something' communicating with you. The House of Cards would collapse in its entirety. So you persist, no matter facts or reason."

"Errr." The charming fellow couldn't look more charming while looking confused. "Perhaps I could bring you in contact with a deceased relative? That will open your eyes. Besides, I'm sure there is a message you'd like to hear from them, no?"

"Nope, all good," was Sven's short reply.

"We all have the ability to communicate with our deceased loved ones, my 'friend'," said Andrea. "The more we loved them, or the more time we had spent with them, the more they are embedded in our own psyche. Their way of talking, their way of thinking, their way of reacting. It's inside of us. And we are able to touch that."

"Exactly," exclaimed Sven. "That's what I always say: 'What would grandpa do?' And then I can make a pretty good guess at that. It may at times be false, but still, it brings me comfort."

"Beautiful," said Andrea. "See, as long as you don't start thinking there really is some form of channelling going on, I'd call it a pretty neat feature in our human design."

"Just promise me one thing," laughed Kalle. "When I go, please let me be in peace. Don't start buzzing me phone up there because I will toss it straight out of heaven."

"What makes you think you're going to heaven," asked Sven sarcastically.

The Vespa suddenly span out of control. At the same time, Sven managed to bring his tuk-tuk out of the spin and regrouped with the others. For a small moment, it seemed that the Arctic was untouched by human folly. The sky was all blue without the slightest cloud lingering around. All were mesmerized by the white sun above them.

I don't want to come back!

When they looked down again, they first only saw the sun a kazillion times. The rattling of the engines was noisier than ever. A giant structure started to unravel slowly before their eyes. A few blinks of the eyes later all realized they were about to collide straight into the Great Pyramid of Giza (which should teach them not to stare into the sun while chasing tuk-tuks or being chased by Vespas). Without any of the drivers needing to think about it, they all spontaneously hit the brakes. Vespas and tuk-tuks all slid, whirled and span in a hodgepodge of… Ves-tuks and tuk-pas.

When all went full throttle in first gear, they caused a mini-sandstorm that lasted for minutes. The Vespas were the first to jump out of the sandstorm. Then the tuk-tuks followed.

"Out of ur wey ye doaty dobbers ye!" Only then did good ol' Cormac realize how the situation had turned around. "Brakes, Erin, and hard left!"

Erin saw what her patient was aiming for. There were like a hundred buses parked near the pyramids. Cormac was aiming to take cover behind them. The plan sounded good. But due to a lack of telepathic connection, the other tuk-tuk pilots didn't have a clue what to do. Some took a hard left; some took a hard right, and with new buses arriving on the scene, it all became a pretty big tuk-tuk-mess.

Meanwhile the charming people on the Vespas realized they were chasing nobody and came to a stop. In no time, they turned around and continued their pursuit. This time, they had their eyes set on the tuk-tuk of Georges.

"Georges!" screamed Paul while passing him from the opposite direction. "Watch out! You've got two bogeys at your six!"

"Je comprend rien qu'il dit!" mumbled Georges. "Two boobies on my sex? A quoi pense ce type?"

When the Vespas managed to encircle the tuk-tuk, it dawned on him. With no way out, all Georges could do was come to a full stop.

"Now we are going to get it," shivered Ayush.

They were greeted by a charming couple on their left. On their right, a charming fella with a long, grey beard lifted his vintage aviator goggles. "Hello, good people. Fear not. We only have the best intentions."

"In fact, we want to save you. You may not realize this, but you are all lost souls."

"Well, that's fair," answered Charles. "We actually have no clue where we are going, now have we?"

The charming husband's face beamed when he met agreement. "Exactly! You see, you are all trapped in this cycle of reincarnation."

"Err," tried Charles, "I don't think-"

"And there's a good reason for this," continued the spouse. "You are in this cycle simply because you need to progress as a soul. See, your soul chose this incarnation for exactly this reason. You need to heal many wounds and resolve many issues that you have collected in previous lives. Only then can you advance on the spiritual path."

"But not to fear," spoke the charming bearded guy. "We can help."

"Issues of past lives?" fumed Georges. "Monsieur, you can't imagine the issues I'm already dealing with in this one. My plate is full if you see what I mean."

"I know, I know, I totally get you," said the charming husband. "But here's the thing. Once you succeed, you will progress into more advanced incarnations, right until you are ready to guide others."

"After that," spoke the charming spouse with the sweetest tone possible, "you will step into a higher existence. There, you will continue to evolve even more until, eventually, you merge into the light."

"And then what?" asked Georges.

"Err, well… well then you basically are no more. You are one with the light, one with the divine source. There's no you any longer."

"What?" exclaimed Georges. "So, instead of dying right away and being done with it, you are telling me I first have to live, I don't know how many lives, go back to school in each and every one of them, and in the end, I disappear all the same as well?"

"Well, err… That's not wh-"

"Really, fellas, what's with this higher existence, higher realms and higher vibrations anyway? I mean, like, what if you are suffering from vertigo? That'd be an extremely unpleasant situation, wouldn't it?"

"Why does it always need to be such a big effort?" asked Ayush. "Why can't it be easy? Why can't we simply find bliss and fulfilment here and now instead of this promise in another lifetime? I mean, you are not even promising me a nice pension when I retire, like politicians do. You are promising me something in a far, far future. Might take thousands of years before I can retire. Wonder what my union would say about that? They'd be charging the capital before you can blink with your eyes."

"Who are these people?" asked the spouse while her charming face contracted for a moment into a far less charming wrinkle.

"No idea," answered the bearded fellow. "I'm fed up with this. Need to go home and check my social media. See if I've caught something there."

The power of a gem

Erin decided to take the north road downwards. All seemed to follow her lead. Just a few hundred metres further, the road started to descend more than anticipated.

"Hoo, there, Erin," cautioned ol' Cormac. "We're picking up speed here."

From behind them sounded shouting: "Out of our way, you idiots!"

Ol' Cormac looked over his left and right shoulder. "Now, who can be so rude?"

Then his eyes went wide open. In a reflex, he let go of the tuk-tuk. A man wearing a yellow jersey on a bicycle flashed in between them. Ol' Cormac clutched the armrests of his wheelchairs so hard his fingers went white.

"Whoooooooooooooooooo!!" The wheelchair went swaying across the street. At one moment, he got next to Erin again. "What are you doing?" she shouted. "Cut it out, will ya!"

"Out of our way!"

A man in a green jersey whooshed by on their right. When Cormac swayed to the right, a man in a white jersey, tailed by a man in a red polka dot jersey, speeded down between the wheelchair and the tuk-tuk. "Conard!" one shouted. It was immediately followed by excessive honking of a motorcycle that passed them as well. The cameraman perched on the motorcycle's rear unleashed a barrage of indiscreet gestures aimed at those in the tuk-tuks.

"Mon Dieu!" gasped Georges behind them. "We're on the Col de Sarenne in L'Alpe d'Huez."

Charles couldn't believe it. "What? That means we are about to get caught by-"

"Le peleton!" finished Georges in fear. "They will crush us."

Meanwhile, Bram managed to close in on the leading tuk-tuk. "We need to get in there," he informed Marwa. "Ol' Cormac is about to fly out at the next curve." With full throttle, Bram sided on Cormac's right flank. Everybody in the tuk-tuk was holding on to everybody.

"Hang on there, Cormac! I'll give you a little pushback to Erin."

"Just a little more!" groaned ol' Cormac while reaching out for the tuk-tuk. "Almost got it!"

"Yes!"

Bram let out a sigh of relief. "Phew. That was close."

When he looked to his right, he saw something new in Marwa's eyes. When she added a smile to it, there was no doubt. This was Bram's best day of his life. Then, a Vespa managed to get by him on his left. It swayed further leftwards and lined up with the tuk-tuk of Erin.

"Good day to you, miss," started the charming Vespa-driver. "Excuse me for troubling you on this fine day. May I just borrow a brief moment of your time?"

Erin kept her face looking straight forward, focused on the bendy road they were ascending at a speed which could be called ludicrous in tuk-tuk terms. Her eyes, however, couldn't resist peeking to the left. The lady on the back of the Vespa held out a curawood display case. Underneath the clear acrylic lid was a variety of neatly arranged gemstones and crystals.

Ol' Cormac leaned forward from the other side. "They look pretty," he judged.

"Indeed, Sir, indeed," answered the lady pleased. "But there's much more to them than just what meets the eye. For example, here we have this beautiful green emerald. It is known to improve your eyesight. It even gives the wearer psychic powers. It can lift depression and relieve insomnia."

"All that in just one stone?" answered ol' Cormac, amazed. "Do you know how many pills I have to take for that!"

"Forget about pills, Sir. Or take this protective stone here. It's called agate. It attracts strength and can awaken your talents. Or this one, amethyst. It brings calmness and clarity. It attunes you with intuition and eases obsessive-compulsive behaviour."

"How about that one?" wondered ol' Cormac while pointing out. "The green one with the red specks."

"Ah, that's a bloodstone, Sir. It improves blood circulation and assists in purifying the blood. It helps lessen feelings of anger or impatience."

"That one might be good for you," remarked Erin while focusing on the road ahead. They were approaching the first village. The street ahead was filled with extremely enthusiastic people on the left and right.

"This one is my favourite," continued the lady in the colourful, hippy garments. "Aventurine. It attracts prosperity and-"

Erin got a bit annoyed. She interrupted the nice, charming lady mid-sentence. "Could you please find another moment to sell us these rocks? We have a situation here!"

Ol' Cormac looked over his shoulder to see what Erin was fretting about. Then his mouth fell open. 'Le peleton' was closing in on all of them. They were about to be overrun by millions of cyclists (at least, it seemed like that many).

"Besides," shrugged Erin. "I already carry amazonite on me. It gives a soothing and calming effect. It dispels negative energy and allows me to let go of sadness and grief."

"You believe in that stuff, Erin?" asked Olivia from in the back. "Didn't see that one coming."

"No, lass, I don't believe in that stuff in the way you mean it. Of course, these stones have no powers at all. They're just pretty stones, that's it. But, on the other hand, there's the power of the mind, the power of the subconsciousness. Like that amethyst, you wear around your neck. Did you know it also aids in the reduction of arthritis? Of course, the stone does nothing of the kind. But that small, tiny little thought has a very strange power on its own. It can penetrate your psyche, where it can offer some form of relief. Just like mindfulness, it can also offer relief from pain. You see, Olivia, the stones have nothing to do with it by themselves. It's all you. The stones are just an aid. See, you can will yourself mentally out of your pains as much as you want; the effect will most probably be that you feel them even more. But the idea of a stone being able to do it can just do that trick your rational thinking could never accomplish."

"Oh, miss, you should come and work with us," exclaimed the lady on the Vespa. "While I would sell stones to the gullible, you could take on the sceptics. Imagine our revenue!"

From the back of them, there came shouting and screaming in all kinds of languages. 'Le peleton' was just a few metres away from the tuk-tuk in the rear end.

"Allez! Allez! Allez!" shouted Georges, unable to resist himself. Then he realized this wasn't the moment to encourage the cyclists. "Mon Dieu, qu'est ce que je fais maintenant."

"This is getting out of hand here," decided the charming Vespa driver, who appeared to be the leader of the lot. "I told you guys we should stick to the internet! Let's get out of here."

"See you in another life, folks!" shouted the lady while the Vespas managed to steer into smaller streets to the left and right.

It was just the tuk-tuk's now. When they exited the small town, the road made a curve to the left. On the right side of it, way down, was a large field of grass. Just when 'le peleton' was about to smash into them all, Bram made a bold decision. "On meeeee!" he shouted and steered right into the field.

A remedy for every single ailment

All careened down the steep hill. To make things worse, the tuk-tuks had to jump a trench to make it to the other side of the meadow. When they touched the ground rather hard, all started to bounce out of control. Some turned on their side, others toppled over. Wheels went flying into the air, together with all sorts of other tuk-tuk-parts. There were even humans flying around, which seemed to be fun, that is, as long as the flying part lasted.

As if, by a miracle, Jimmy's tuk-tuk was the only one that remained upright and undamaged. Márcia and Oliver, both carrying one of the twins, thanked and praised him for his driving skills. A bit further, Marwa helped Bram to his feet.

"On me?" she intoned. "Really?"

Bram blushed. The best-day-of-his-life feeling went straight down the drain. Then she kissed him on the cheek. "You silly. You were amazing!"

The ups and downs a man can meet in a single day.

While most were still coming back to their senses, two charming looking men entered the centre of the field, where they all lay scattered around. In no time, they set up a tent-like construction. Except it wasn't a tent. The tent poles solidly clicked into the ferrules, but remained naked.

Jimmy was the first to approach. "Neat pyramid you made there. I guess you're waiting with the canvas until the sun's down, right?"

"Not at all, my friend. This is as it is."

"Oh, okay. Wow, didn't know they made tentpoles out of gold."

"It's copper, my friend, plated with gold. They are placed precisely at 51 degrees."

"It's a healing pyramid," explained the other charming fellow. "We guessed you lot could use some healing after that little adventure."

"I can also do you a light-healing or heal you with my hands. Whatever you choose. It's extremely effective, and on top of that, we will charge you only a small fee."

Meanwhile, Georges, who fell into a pretzel after whooshing out the tuk-tuk, had unpretzeled himself and came to join Jimmy. "C'est vraiment exceptionnel, ca. How does it work?"

"Oh, that's simple. You see, the pyramid deflects cosmic radiations by letting them fall on its apex downwards. Then, at the bottom, a bio-energy field is created with the help of the gravitational force of Earth's magnetic field. Or something like that."

"The pyramid also has a strong ionization effect on the person lying inside of it. You'll get radiated by negative ions. Now, don't you worry, this is a very positive thing! It enhances the oxygen intake and stimulates healing."

"Vous vous moquez de moi!" gasped Georges.

"We wouldn't dare! It's all science. Well, not the light healing. No idea how that works. Still, it does. So it doesn't really matter, does it?"

"What do you think, Andrea?" asked Jimmy.

"I think the human body is perfectly capable of healing itself. To a certain extent, of course. Still, the time it takes to heal via this pyramid will be about the same as it takes for normal processes to do their thing. The difference will be the amount of money in your pocket."

"Oh. So you are against it?"

"Against these frauds, yes, of course. But I wouldn't throw it all away, you know. Our mind really can have a certain influence on our healing capacities. Regrettably, it's often of a blocking kind. We are tense. We are tight up. We push a lot of hormones into our bloodstream, which aren't really productive in terms of the healing process. Problem is we can't push the healing process by using our mind. You can't will yourself to heal. Only when we manage to relax can our natural healing take its optimal course."

"Oh, but you can relax in our pyramid," cheered the charming men. "We only charge you one hundred euros for a 15 minute session."

Andrea rolled her eyes. "Georges. You can find your own tools to ease up. Be it gentle breathing or the caring touch of a genuine person. The best angle to approach this is not 51 degrees but an attitude of acceptance. Accept what is happening to you. This will create the needed ease in your unease. From there, the healing process can properly begin, either through conventional methods or by means that help you relax. It all depends on the ailment, but a little breathing, a little mindfulness, visualization or vibrating sounds, it can all help."

The charming men spit on the ground. "Conventional methods! Yuk."

"Yuk yourselves, gentlemen," scolded Andrea. "Here's the thing I learned: We tend to blame conventional methods when they fail us, true. But when we turn to unconventional methods, like yours, we almost always blame ourselves when they don't work. Outrageous if you ask me."

"Indeed," concluded Georges. "Gentlemen, could you please remove yourselves and this pyramid. It somehow doesn't fit the scene. Although I don't know why yet."

"I agree with you, Andrea," said Erin when the two men walked away in a very ill mood. "Gemstones, pendants, special water, or whatever can all assist in normalizing the healing process of our body. But I have come to experience now how simply Knowing the Truth is enough for me. In the realization of Truth I have come to this most relaxing acceptance. There's even gratitude in it, isn't that odd? And the thing is, even if I'd be beyond treatment, I know I will still be content. I still would feel this acceptance and gratitude until the moment of my very last breath."

"You're not going to euthanize me, are ye?" feared ol' Cormac.

"Don't be silly. Of course, we'd fight for every chance and every moment there is. But none of us are immortal either. At a certain point, I would rather accept that and choose peace and contentment over dying disgruntled or in fear. I know in my heart when my day comes, be it sudden or after illness, I will be happy and grateful. My body might allow me a smile no longer, but my Heart will wear it to the very end for sure."

"Hmm," mused Mr Bercow while he watched how the two men disappeared at the horizon. "It all makes one wonder what happened to humanity when the listening ear of a person who genuinely cares has become in need of payment. Or a gentle tap on the back, a hug, or a minute of shared silence comes by the euro."

"I see your point, Sir," agreed Bram. "We've become a greedy lot, no?"

"Hmm, no, Bram," disagreed Mr Bercow. "I don't think it's that. See, many of us truly have a warm heart and this genuine motivation to help others. And while doing so, we also reach out to kindred spirits, be it on a walk in nature, at an annual convention, or on the bloody internet. It usually is the latter which lures us with attractive and glamorized posts in a different direction. We think we are spot-on on our destined path, but in reality we find ourselves stuck in these expensive trainings, all having their specific, intricate techniques and stories. The worst of all is they also lure us into a narrative where we are supposed to make a business out of this, if not to make money, then at least to regain the costs it took to complete their training. But it's all a trap. It turns us from a warm and compassionate human being into a spiritual business model."

"But how do you explain their success?" asked Marwa.

"Well, first of all, success is a pretty big word here. There is the factual success and there's the success they mostly sell with what is called 'anecdotal evidence'. But when it comes to actual success, it's pretty simple. All those methods and ever new techniques they concoct ..."

Andrea felt like finishing that. "...in truth, of course, all have this very simple, underlying principle in common: what they effectively do is allow us to ease up. Relax. And in doing so, our inner healing processes are allowed to take their natural course, without the obstructions of our negative or overly tight attitude."

"Exactly, Andrea. So basically, the good people lured into this healing scheme are doing nothing but what once was the simplest expression of humanity amongst people in a community. We all intrinsically are healers by caring for each other, with kindness and compassion, by listening, by being there and offering attention and a little understanding. You don't need a business card and a website for all that."

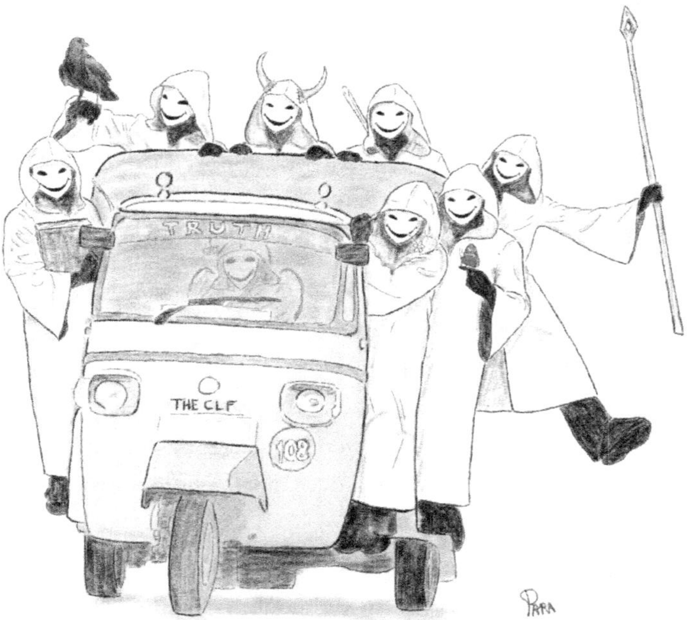
TRUTH
THE CLF
108
PARA

Chapter 7   The Last Temptation (now, doesn't that sound gloomy?)

Suddenly, they all heard shouting from a distance: "Hey!" – "What's up!" – "What kept you so long?"

The Bygone Magi of Infinite Zero appeared to be standing in front of the Stonehenge monument. With their hooded cloaks and robes silhouetted against the ancient stones, they beckoned the weary group to come and join them.

The faces of all in the crowd cheered up while they walked towards the ever-awkward-looking figures. Except one.

"What kept us?" cursed ol' Cormac. "What kept us! And where were you lot? Could've used a bit of help with those CSDC-eejits."

"Well," answered the One with the magician's staff. "First of all, it was pretty hard to keep up with you. There was only one tuk-tuk left, you know. So we all had to fit in."

Sven couldn't believe his ears. "You all could fit in one tuk-tuk!"

"Sure," answered the One with the bow and arrow. "Even my bow and arrow got in there. I think the record is about 27 people in one tuk-tuk (fact-check: it's true). So we were doing just fine."

"Secondly," continued the One with Vanessa. "We kinda lost track of time at the Taj Mahal. Such a magnificent structure! Took pictures and selfies all over the place."

"And last but not least," finished the glowing One in an encouraging tone. "You all did such a great job without us."

"You really did," agreed the One with the raven. "But we must hurry now. The sun is about to set and we need to go to Glastonbury."

"But our tuk-tuks are nearly all destroyed," objected Kalle. "How-"

"Stonehenge," explained the One with the raven. "It's a portal to the Tor. You only need to know how to get through. Follow us in precisely the same way."

The Bygone Magi of Infinite Zero, followed by the crowd, passed through the eastern trilithon, came back through the one facing Glastonbury, passed through the eastern trilithon again, and repeated this pattern for a specific amount of times (we omitted some vital trilithon-passages just so that you wouldn't go give it a try yourself).

At a certain point, they suddenly walked out of St Michael's Tower on top of Glastonbury Tor. A slight breeze met them while their gazes got lost in the landscape around them.

"Beautiful," marvelled Erin. "Always wanted to come to this place."

"Yes, let's take a rest here and enjoy the scenery," suggested the One with the raven.

Only then did it strike them that they all really could use a break. The Bygone Magi of Infinite Zero and the crowd haphazardly mixed around on the soft grass of the Tor.

"So what about the mess we made at Stonehenge?" wondered Kalle.

"Not to worry", answered the One who is writing all this. "All cleaned up as we speak."

And so, they sat on the Tor. The sun was still a bit above the horizon. Its golden rays turned distant waters gold as well. It was a magical, once in a lifetime view: the golden dusk of Avalon.

A man in a kilt ascended the Tor and started blowing his bagpipe. As if she was waiting for him, a girl with a djembé joined in. Bagpipe and djembé actually went along quite well.

"I am still waiting for a catch," pondered Ann out loud. "Like this big reveal or something."

"What big reveal are you aiming for?" queried the One with the dice.

"Like this twist at the end that you didn't see coming, while of course, you secretly hoped for it. You see, the non-dualists-"

"AUCH!" The glowing One reached for her heart in pain.

"Ew," cringed the One with the magician's staff.

"Don't wanna hear it, don't wanna hear it," squeaked the One with the

Viking horns while holding his hands where his ears were supposed to be.

"What did I say wrong?" bleated Ann.

"You mentioned 'them'," explained the One with the hedgerow cranesbill.

"Who?"

"The non-dualists!"

"AUCH!" – "Ew!" – "Not hearing it!"

"What about the non-dualists?"

"AUCH!" – "Ew!" – "Still not hearing it!"

"Stop that! What about them?"

"Well," explained the One with Vanessa. "First of all, there is no such thing as 'non-dualists'."

"There's not?"

"Well, there is. But they are probably divided into as many factions as you can find in the monotheistic religion of the god of Abraham. And just as much, they all have their own views and interpretations. And also just as much, obviously, each one of them has it right. They might not kill each other over their differences as much as the 'monotheistics' have done-"

"…and still do…"

"… but they can be pretty annoying amongst each other in thinking one to be right over the other."

"Bickering about what 'real' non-dualism is," said the glowing One.

"Outwitting each other about whether it is pronounced 'advaita' or 'adwaita'", shared the One with the bow and arrow.

"Outdo each other with who has the oldest text to refer to," added the One with the dice. "Or debate about how a particular line should be interpreted. Or call each other names, like 'neo'…"

"…while each of them claiming to be anything but 'neo'."

"I didn't realize 'neo' is a swear word," wondered Kalle. "I thought it was that guy in the movie?"

"I think it's plain silly," scoffed Sven. "Just think about it. Neo is the One, which is exactly what this not-two lot is constantly talking about. Should be a compliment, no?"

"Enough, enough," tempered the One with the raven. "Tell us, Ann, what twist were you hoping for?"

"Well, the non-dualists…"

"AUCH!" – "Ew" – "Cutting my ears of!"

"Stop that!! All of you! So, what I heard them say is, well they say consciousness is eternal. And also, consciousness is everywhere. The whole universe is conscious. As a matter of fact, consciousness is able to exist independently of the body. So when the body dies, we still go on in the form of this Beingness, this awareness, no?"

"The One with Viking horns, the One with the magician's staff and the glowing One smacked themselves against the forehead. That sounded like 'Smack!' (because they did it perfectly synchronized).

"What' their problem?"

"Well," spoke the One with the raven gently. "**On the one hand**, it's once again semantics leading us a bit astray. See, the experience of Beingness is rather timeless in nature. And when one is a bit overly enthusiastic, 'timeless' can easily become 'eternal'. But of course, there is an essential difference between the two."

"We never said the timeless experience of Beingness is everlasting."

"Also, as every observation occurs in the one who is looking," added the One with the dice, "one could say the observed universe is pervaded with consciousness. But that is all your personal perspective. The universe 'appears' in your awareness. Or, your awareness is coloured by existence. Same thing. Hence, strictly subjectively speaking, consciousness and the universe are one and the same."

"Don't get it." – Sven.

"It goes back to Plato in the cave. We can never objectively know existence. We only have the appearance of it in our awareness."

"In a way, this promotes a bit of a solipsistic view on things. Luckily, existence tends to appear to all of us in a pretty consistent way, thus arguing against the idea of me being this single super-entity dreaming this all up."

Oliver turned himself to the crowd. "Also," he started, "in a solipsistic universe, there'd be only you. But you would never have come across someone or something else. Hence, the concept of 'I' or 'You' could never come about. There would always be only you." That led to many puzzled expressions on many puzzled looking faces (as talks about solipsism often do).

"Thank you, Oliver," said One, whose smiling mask nearly turned into a puzzled frown. "So, from a strictly subjective perspective, you could truly state that all is consciousness, but that doesn't mean the entire universe is pervaded with consciousness, let alone it being conscious itself."

"Or intelligent in the shape of our own intelligence."

"So these not-two-folks have got it all wrong?"

"Well, it's more like they are stuck in ancient words and interpretations."

"And their hopes." The One with Vanessa brought her thumb and index finger so close together that the gap between them was nearly invisible. "Even when they are this close to Truth, they still can't let go of this final temptation: the idea that consciousness is a lasting thing, stretching beyond the temporal body we all have."

"That brings us to **our other hand**. Besides the semantics, there's folk that actually believe the universe is made of consciousness."

"Say what?" – Kalle.

"Oh, I know what you're saying. You're talking about the 'haaaard problem', aren't you?" – Andrea.

"What's the bloody haaaard problem?" – Jimmy.

"Well, some people can't handle the idea of consciousness simply being an emergent phenomenon in the human brain. They choose to believe a quality, like a colour, or a smell, is an experience which is not occurring in neurons and dendrites and axons and all. As such they create a problem that cannot be solved, unless... you conclude the entire universe has to be made of consciousness."

"Yeh," said Anil who happened to pass by. "But that doesn't really explain anything. Nor does it lead to testable hypotheses. It's nothing more than an easy get-out to a non-existing mystery. The hard problem doesn't allow any scrutiny, nor does it provide evidence. It's nothing but a philosophical exercise which keeps you running in circles and..."

"... is picked up by those who use it to cling to an everlasting life," added Rebecca. "Just like they abuse quantum mechanics for that purpose."

The One with the dice rolled his dice and mused at the outcome. "A conscious universe? Or a materialistic one? It's an interesting discussion, indeed. Whichever one eventually wins, it will still not affect the outcome of my roll. Observe, my friends. Look deeper than the eyes can see and witness Truth here and now while playing this game of philosophy."

"Come to think of it," said the One with the bow and arrow, "there's also those who persist in keeping this idea alive that consciousness can be improved, like 'higher' consciousness and stuff. But that is nothing but a quest of vanity in vain. See, consciousness rather is like an unchanging light. It only 'appears' to shine more brightly, when the obstacles which obscure it are gently removed. It's in no need of elevation."

"Sometimes, Ann," concluded the One with the raven, "it's good to ask yourself this: do you really need ancient poetry from a faraway land and a long forgotten past to teach you Truth? There's so many different translations for each text. There's so many interpretations of each translation. And ever again a new person pops up who claims to have the best and most precise translation of all."

"Don't get us wrong, Ann. These studies can be fun. Yet the bottom line remains, you can simply find Truth within, all by yourself. No need for these distractions and the gentle, soft-speaking people on the stage."

"Hey, it's actually pretty weird," expressed Andrea, who clearly had spent a lot of time on YouTube, "when you closely look at their modus operandi. They serenely and wisely sit in front of their audience, with a glass of water, the finest bouquet and all. And somehow they believe they can pass on the experience by their mere presence. Or at least, that's what their followers are hoping for. And when that's not working, they start filling the silence with an endless string of words. It is absolutely incredible how they can go on and on and on."

Olivia understood completely what Andrea was saying. "And everybody is nodding. And all are agreeing. But in the end, their devotees still don't have the experience, apart – perhaps – from this priceless moment of peace which they all lacked in their inner sea of thoughts. – Spend years myself doing just that. Best I got from it is was the peacefulness that pervaded the atmosphere there."

Andrea nodded. "But that doesn't mean we really understood and turned their wisdom into a wordless Knowing, does it? So the words become the experience instead. And the person next to the flowers once more ends up as a prophet who is praised and worshipped by all – worldwide birthday parties included."

Ann was confused. "There's still one thing left that troubles me. Don't they also say consciousness is pure? It's always there, even when we sleep. It cannot be damaged or anything. How does that work?"

"I think those non-dualists," dared Oliver, "and a lot of other people too, should spend some time in the centres where we threat people with severe brain damage. Face them straight on with how consciousness can get corrupted or erased all together."

"Basically," decided the One with the magician's staff, "there's something very non-non-dualistic about their stories. They either patronize or appease their followers. And while they speak and quote about the eternal and limitless nature of consciousness, with attributes like pure, unborn and all, they forget one important thing."

Ta-daa! The final cliffhanger! And you were just about to go to sleep. Darn!

Chapter 8   The final leap

"Wait," reacted Kalle worried. "What do you mean? What important thing?"

"Right," said the One with the raven while throwing a quick glance at an imaginary watch on his wrist. "Let's all huddle together a bit more. Don't want other people to hear this."

"Let's all cuddle?" understood to glowing One. "Great idea!"

And so, they collectively gave each other a hug. Although the One with the raven impatiently glanced once more at his wrist, he also seemed pleased with the relaxed atmosphere which came about with 'The Great Cuddle'.

"So," started the One with the magician's staff once all were done, "you have all learned about the nature of the self and how it inescapably merges in its totality with the unfolding of the entire existence."

"You also have experienced the nature of the S̄elf, and how it somehow seems to escape causality. And while nothing ever seems to happen in Beingness, its radiating presence somehow has a profound effect on how we navigate existence as a person. We feel pervaded by joy and peace, by love and acceptance, by serenity and clarity, by a Knowing which no longer needs to pick a fight with that which undeniably is the Truth."

"You have come to live the paradox of being a person, and, of not being at all. You live this day to day life, with all its challenges and obstructions, as well its simple moments of joy and happiness. And simultaneously you experience yourself to be void of personhood, pervaded by simple presence, timeless and boundless, free and untainted."

"But, just like all paradoxes eventually collapse, so does this one."

"What do you mean, raven-dude?"

"There is no you," explained the One with the raven softly. "That you already knew. But in Truth, my dear friends, consciousness itself, Beingness itself, the S̄elf, it is just as absent as the 'you' you thought you were. It is just as much part of the great unfolding as anything else. It doesn't exist 'outside' or 'next to' reality."

"You see, the final leap into Truth is not merely the realization of self, $\overline{S}$elf and existence, but the fullest recognition that the $\overline{S}$elf as well is as much a part of it as everything else. It is all this single Oneness playing itself out."

"So, placing the $\overline{S}$elf upon a pedestal, high above the identity-self and the whole of existence, would be the final and biggest mistake one could make."

"The metaphorical wave we see ourselves to be, is caused by the Ocean. The longing of the wave to return, is inspired by the Ocean. The collapse of the wave into the Ocean, is the doing of the Ocean. The wave never was… it all ever was the Ocean."

"Those who recognize Truth to the fullest will realize this recognition was never their accomplishment to begin with. There is nothing and no one to accomplish. It all is ever accomplished. It all is ever perfect as it is."

"When the empty cup itself is recognized to be fictional as well, the delimiter between the space in the cup, and the space outside of the cup, finally dissolves into the oneness which was ever present all along."

"So, life after death, you ask? There's not even life before death. There is no life; there is no death. It's all this unfolding. It's all 'that'."

Ann just couldn't grasp what was being said. "So when I die, it really is the end?"

"No, Ann," said Erin. "You were never here to begin with. Not you, not your ego, not your self or the $\overline{S}$elf. You see, everybody, as long as you can't let go of your self, you will remain stuck in this pattern of thinking there is something more or something everlasting. You will only experience Truth, the $\overline{S}$elf, as a concept within the self. Once you have really experienced the $\overline{S}$elf, and mind you, we all already did; you will intuitively know this. Not with words. Not even with feelings. But really Know. And then you will see straight through the paradox. And you will still live it. And you will laugh. Because, in the end, we're not even like the smallest grain of sand. We are nothing at all. – I have felt this for quite a while now. And it's not a depressing or nihilistic thought at all. I have never felt so good in my entire life, really. I'm no longer afraid to die. And at the same time, my immanent death is like this constant guide in the now. I cherish every moment. I've never felt this alive, like ever."

Moved by her story, ol' Cormac couldn't refrain himself from shedding a tear. "Well, lass, ye may be nothing as much as I am, but I tell ya this, ye'r not just me nurse, ye'r me teacher! And I'll follow ya everywhere… Well, practically, it'd be you following me, ye know, pushing me wheelchair and all. Still…" Ol' Cormac faltered and started to blush. Erin couldn't resist passing him a loving smile. "Aaarggh, you silly, smiling wench, you know perfectly well what this ol' bugger is trying to tell ya!"

"We are really getting late," pressed the One with the raven. "It has already started."

"Oh no," worried the glowing One. "We need to run!"

"Wait," decided the One with the raven. "We'll never make it by running. But I recently learned a trick with toilets. Follow me!"

"A trick with toilets?"

The One with the raven didn't listen and decisively walked straight into St Michael's Tower. All followed…

… and all disappeared.

Chapter 9 A joyous festival of cheerful presence and aliveness

Something was amiss at the backstage toilets. Despite people coming out, the lights above each of their doors remained red. When all doors finally only had red lights, and people in long queues where pressing knees against each other or pinching their privates, the doors all opened.

Robed and hooded figures where the first to exit. Then followed the members of the crowd. Bystanders couldn't believe their eyes and all forgot about their urgent calls of nature.

The members of the crowd felt a bit awkward and could say nothing but "Hi" – "Hello" – "Hi" – "Good day to you" – "Ullo" – while they followed the Ancient Mystics of Infinite Zero with their mouths dropped open in amazement by the scenery they'd landed in.

They found themselves amidst a kazillion people, of all colours, all ages, dressed up in all possible clothing, and most of all, all radiantly cheerful. It was like humanity's best had decided to join up at one single spot on the planet.

"Love this place!" beamed the glowing One.

"Let's head for the The Park," suggested the One with the raven.

At first there was no possibility for the crowd to navigate through the masses. Luckily, the One who is writing all this managed to clear a line straight to their destination. The Park was a vibrant place of eclectic fabulousness. Moving a bit uphill, they could set their eyes on both the iconic Ribbon Tower and the main stage. By now it had become totally dark. Glastonbury Festival was about to kick off with the main act.

"Fricky-di-frack!" exclaimed ol' Cormac. "Will ya look at that! Their main stage is built in the shape of a pyramid!"

"Probably hoping the ion-thingies will improve their singing," chuckled Sven.

For the record, it is important to mention that the Pyramid Stage was renamed to the Truth Stage for this special occasion (and the actual Truth Stage was renamed to the Peace Stage).

"Oomyyygooooodd!" screamed Olivia with a pitch high enough to lure all the dogs in the area. "It's Sylvia. And Marsali and Willem! No, I mean Hans."

All looked into the direction she pointed. There they also spotted Martha, Javier, Ella, Frodo, Inessa, Tegan, István and a lot of others. They were accompanied by Mow Jee, the Sad Guru, Desert Tulip, Dr. Gregg T. and some other CSDC-folk.

Everybody in the crowd seemed to know somebody of the ones who had left the group during part I. There was hugging and embracing. There was chitter and there was chatter. Then tears rolled down Sylvia's cheeks.

"What's the matter, Sylvia?" asked Andrea.

"It's Yvonne. She passed away about a week ago. She would have been so happy to see you all again. But she wanted all of you to know she was totally content and at peace when she died."

"How is that possible?" asked Andrea. "You all ran away into these fabricated stories. I felt so sad when you did, you know. We found the Truth, Sylvia. We really did."

"I know you did," laughed Sylvia while tears kept rolling down her happy smile. "So did we!"

Bram shook his head in disbelieve. "Wait, what?"

Then all were distracted by laughter and warm conversations. The noises came from the Ancient Mystics of Infinite Zero and the CSDCs. It appeared they were all well acquainted and even intimate, shaking hands and patting each other on the back.

"What the frack's going on?" demanded ol' Cormac.

"Hello there, ol' chum," smiled Mow Jee while he approached.

"Hello yerself, ye sneaky wee bastard. About to sell me trickery again, are ya?"

"There there," hushed the One with the raven. "It's alright. These are our friends. They were all in on our little scheme. You see, they're not really CSDCs. We just hired them to trick you, that's all."

"What?" exclaimed Kalle. "Why would you do such a thing?"

"I think I get it," raised Frank. "How could we attempt seeing Truth without knowing Falsehood? It'd be like trying to see Light without knowing Darkness."

"Ye sneaky little devils!"

The phony CSDCs all laughed. "You need not worry about us no longer," laughed the Sad Guru. "But still, best remain wary of our look-alikes."

"And don't forget the most devious ones," said Dr. T. "The ones that pop up in your mirrors. Remember, we all trick and fool ourselves, constantly. You will surely not see the last of that."

"But tell us," pleaded Andrea when her attention returned to Sylvia. "How did they make you come to our recognition of the Truth?"

"Easy," replied Sylvia. "After they admitted it all was nothing but a little prank by our Ancient-lot, they simply handed us the book. We were there with you on every page."

"I must tell you," confided Martha, "we never could have imagined how not-being could be an acceptable thing. You know, when you say it like this, it utterly sounds ridiculous. And still, we Know it is true now. We accept it to be true. And somehow, we are more present than ever before."

"I feel the same thing!" emphasized Roger. "I could never have imagined being in agreement with an idea that radically wipes me away from existence. The realization of being nothing at all was like an epiphany which literally blew me away – which is, I know, paradoxical, because there's nothing to be blown away, right? Anyhow, there was only emptiness after that. Not emptiness in the sense of lack, mind you, it was more an emptiness in which my presence itself felt limitless. Well, I really can't call it 'my' presence. It was simply Presence."

"Can I share something too?" asked Hee-Young politely.

"Of course you can."

"I felt liberated." Then Hee-Young paused. But the crowd allowed him the floor. "I can't even describe what I felt liberated from. It was like, well, like liberation itself, regardless of what thing, person, or idea I'd be liberated from. Perhaps, simply of everything, everywhere, all at once. Funny thing is, after that, it didn't feel like there was nothing left to do. I felt filled with purpose. Not purpose in the sense of a particular goal or wh-whatever. I was simply imbued with purpose, no matter what I'd do. I do, I do, I do, but simultaneously, I do nothing, no-thing at all. Some people make it an effort to do nothing, or to be nothing. They don't understand. It requires no effort. It is already so."

"I experience it like this," started Inessa. "Every little moment I reconnect with this recognition, by merely briefly contemplating upon it, I instantaneously feel radiant and exuberant. I feel alive, like I've never felt alive before. It's no more or less than that. I mean, not an aliveness I would cling to and want to persist forever, or an aliveness I'd like to spread to all of humanity. No, just alive, here and now, or better, nowhere never."

István nodded. "I never felt this complete before. I mean, I am okay as I am. I am alright, even when I am not. It makes no sense at all, and still, somehow, it does. It's weird shit, you know. I still tend to pinch myself in the arm to come out of this trip or dream."

"That's all nice folks," said Mischa, "but none of you have mentioned the serenity that comes about with this realization. Now, make no mistake here, it's not like I now all of a sudden am capable of always making the best decisions. It's more like, like it is all okay, even if it turns out not to be a good decision. Even if I didn't find the right words or the best timing. Mistakes are still there, but they no longer undermine me, if you know what I am saying."

Andrea took it all in. But Yvonne was still lingering in the back of her mind. "It seems we all have another thing in common," she said. "It seems we are all prepared and ready to die. Here and now. No regrets. No bucket list. No last meal. Because once you realize this Truth, you Know, there is no life or death. It's all this one big unfolding. Yet still, simultaneously, we all share this lust for life, as if this inner, ebullient force acts up as an answer to life's longing for us."

"To be and not to be," mused Sir William. "It's not even a question."

"You know what," said a depressed looking, little dog, "I'm happy too."

"Hey!" shouted Javier from high up on the Ribbon Tower with his arms spread out. "It feels like this! The Truth is no longer a destination far up ahead, at the end of a long, steep path. It rather is a vantage point from where every step can be set firmly in the presence of deep trust, clarity, serenity and bliss."

"Ye better get your arse down here straight away, ye misfit, or yer next step will be yer last!"

"So?" wondered Georges. "What's next? Are we about to hand out flyers and reach out to others to share our insights? Start a new organization? Create a website? Facebook? Instagram? YouTube? X? Tiktok?"

There was a silence like no one had ever experienced before. The Ancient Mystics of Infinite Zero still had their smiles on their masks, but somehow it felt like the curve of their smiles went the opposite way.

Charles immediately sensed Georges asked the wrong question. But he also understood what Georges was trying to say. "I don't think Georges means he wants to convert people into a new kind of faith or something. It's just, well, we are still human beings, aren't we? Can't kindred spirits like us not come together? Would that turn us into just another cult?"

Sound's back!

"You can, Charles," spoke the One with the raven. "Sure. But before you do, you may ask yourself if there really is a need to set something up like that. Look around. Every day, everywhere, you can come across kindred spirits in those simple, day-to-day situations where there is an exchange of love and joy, honesty, innocence and authenticity. Seems to me that's more important than opposing a group of those who know the Truth against those who don't. It's all perfect as it is, remember?"

"It's starting!" yelled the glowing One excitedly. "Let's dance!!!"

It was Annie on the Pyramid, no, the Truth Stage, who kicked off with one of the most memorable synth riffs ever. The crowd went absolutely crazy when Dave joined in with his guitar and the both of them gave their best performance of 'Sweet Dreams' ever.

Cat Stevens represented all Seekers with 'On the Road to Find Out'. The Who brought early laughter with the typical, misleading 'Who are you?'-question. And Jem threw in some sweet irony with 'Just a ride'.

Next came The Levellers. They were greeted with deafening applause when they started with 'Together all the way' and finished their set with 'What a beautiful day'.

Then came Pearl Jam, singing about Dancing Clairvoyants, followed by an intimate version of 'Present Tense'. It was Queen who obliterated the space of intimacy with a fantastic spectacle while bringing 'One Vision' and 'Innuendo' (during which Freddy emphasized the $\overline{\text{S}}$elf by drawing a horizontal line at the level of his eyebrow while passing his legendary wink to the Ancient Mystics of Infinite Zero). After that there was intimacy once more with 'Who wants to live forever', followed by the Fleet Foxes with 'Helplessness Blues'. Peter Gabriel was allowed three songs. 'Four kinds of horses' came first. Then 'i/o'. He finished with the rather bouncy and buoyant 'The Road to Joy'.

Many, many more passed by on the stage. Joan Osborne changed her lyrics for the occasion to 'What if God was all of us'. Donovan got everybody laughing and dancing with 'There is a mountain'. The Beatles tried to hit the spot with 'Let it Be'. Coldplay came close in describing the transientness of Truth with 'O'. Peter Gabriel popped up again, dressed as a stagehand and sang 'Love can heal', which got the crowd in the right mood for The Wanderer with 'We're all going home'. Then it was on to Kevin James who serenely joined in with 'Into the Beauty'.

With all lights out, except for a few white spots, a bunch of children appeared on the stage, chanting 'What's the meaning of life?'. Then the lights suddenly went crazy when Soul II Soul jumped in with 'Get a Life'.

The music played from 3 am for seemingly all eternal. It was only then that the crowd, sweaty and exhausted, yet full of bliss, decided to leave on the Last Train to Trancentral.

"I'm glad to go home now," said Andrea. "I really need some time to contemplate all this."

"Absolutely," agreed Ann. "I'm exhausted too. And I have yet a very long way to travel. Luckily I can do these secret exercises to keep me going and stay connected."

Charles stared out the window into the darkness. "I think I'm going to write a book with little bits and pieces about Truth and Beingness, emptiness and nothingness." Then he immediately took his pen and notebook and started to write: *Knowing what we know, we nonetheless remain as we are. For not even the deepest realization of Truth can quieten the expressions rising naturally within our identity-selves. They can be of profound beauty, to be enjoyed and to be cherished. We ever remain relationship-beings, begifted with the capacity to live the paradox of being and not-being at the same time. We are still allowed to simultaneously have a relationship with the divine, and be one with it.*

Oliver's head went left and right while he peeked over Charles's shoulder. His mouth was wrinkled, but his eyebrows rose in appreciation. "Not bad," he nodded. "Could use some tweaking here and there, but not bad."

"I think I'll pick up my pretzel-posture again," shared Georges. "While it has been all effort before, now I can just take a frequent moment to abide in Beingness. With nothing more to gain or to attain, I can finally relax into it."

"I'm going to make some effort being a bit more nice to me nurse. That's not odd, isn't it?"

Nurse Erin smiled. "I'll simply continue to be whoever I was before. I was good. I am good. It's all good. Anyways, who else would want to take care of this old tosser?"

"What! – Ye evil…"

"When I return home," said Tom, "I will frequent our church a bit more. You can say whatever you like about those who built it, but they did manage to create a safe haven which allows me to really let go of myself and be God. Besides, the art in there is just beautiful."

"I think I'll work a bit on my vertigo issues," said Olivia. "You know, it did complicate stuff at times, and who knows, there might be a sequel. Better be prepared, right?"

"I will finally inscribe for that druid training," declared Leni. "Been wanting to do this for ages. Knowing what I know now, I'm ready for it. I want to be more connected with nature – and with the deep, ancient wisdom the Elder have always drawn from it."

"Imightbetheonewhoisgoingtorevealthesecretexercises," machinegunned 방찬.

"Iwillputitinasongwhichtheywillallsingalongwithoutrealisingthesecretishiddenwithinit."

"And I think I'm going to marry an accountant of another country," said Kalle. "And our business will flourish."

"Hey, I'm an accountant of another country." You should have seen his eyebrows.

"Hmm, this may sound silly," hesitated Hans, "but I think I've never been happier and more content than I am now in this moment."

"Why's that silly?" asked several people at the same time.

"Well, because, ever since I've really integrated Truth, I happen to say this frequently, even more than once a day. A little bit absurd, isn't it? If I'd tell this to my wife, she'd be searching for white powder all around the house for sure."

"Shoot!"

"What is it, Bram?"

"We forgot to say goodbye to our masked friends."

"Fricky-di-frack, the infant is right! How could we forget?"

"I'm sure they can handle it," chuckled Marwa while she gave Bram a hug. "Won't they, infant?"

The Ancient Mystics of Infinite Zero hadn't noticed a thing. They kept dancing long after the last note faded. They simply were inexhaustible.

Epilogue

The next morning, there was silence. The brightly shining and colourful people, young and old, were all written back to their homes. The garbage got neatly sorted, and the field's grass was as pristine as ever before. Only the skylark broke the silence with its morning song.

Pristine?

The Ancient Mystics of Infinite Zero were staring at the rising sun.

"Oh," said the One who is writing all this. "I remember now."

"Remember what?"

"Ann! She's from the Cook Islands! Didn't see that one coming, did ya? Well, neither did she. But there happened to be a boat and…"

They all gave the One who is writing all this a playful jab on the shoulder. Then they merrily laughed one last time.

"It is time, my friends," declared the One with the raven.

And so it was that they started to walk towards the sunrise. They all dropped their masks. They all dropped their hooded cloaks. There was a magician's staff lying in the grass. A deck of cards. Viking horns. A bow and an arrow and a nón lá. A hedgerow cranesbill, a book and a pair of dice.

While a raven disappeared at the horizon, a little butterfly kept flying about at the spot where traces of footsteps seemed to appear in the grass. Until even the footsteps ceased to be.

Hang on! Wait a minute! Skylarks and vanessa atalanta's, they get along just fine, don't they?

Another epilogue (the last one, I swear)

When Adebowale finally returned home, he immediately went to see his sister.

He found the young woman lying in bed. "Ayofemi," he softly said while his eyes turned wet. She clearly only had a few breaths left. "Ayofemi, I failed you. I am so sorry. I found the Truth. I really did. But it's useless. I cannot use it to heal you. I am so, so terribly sorry."

Tears rolled down his eyes. But Ayofemi managed to smile.

"You silly, sweet brother of mine," she whispered. "The truth, dearest Adebo, is that you love me, and I love you. I couldn't long for anything else. I am content, brother. I am at peace with that."

Her eyes no longer blinked. Adebowale closed them for his sister. He smiled and wept at the same time. She was right. And despite his grief and the heartbreaking scream he unleashed into the universe, he was content and at peace as well. For he knew the Truth, and he realized no Truth would ever be able to take away the love he felt in his heart.

Rumour has it that some people spotted an odd-looking raven during Ayufemi's memorial service. One person even believed it had a butterfly on its shoulder. But this was honed away by everyone else.

방찬's Song

Lorem ipsum dolor sit amet, consectetur adipiscing elit, sed do eiusmod tempor incididunt ut labore et dolore magna aliqua. Totam rem aperiam eaque ipsa, quae ab illo inventore veritatis et quasi architecto beatae vitae dicta sunt, explicabo. The secret to the secret exercises is the wavelike pulse. In the presence of a pulsation, either by physical, vocal or mental exercises, Beingness rises naturally in the silence that follows. The pulsation can be produced by repetition. Physically, one can perform a sequence of simple movements which are to be repeated for a short time. It is good to alternate between quick movements which are linked to the breath, and slow movements when deeper breathing is advised. The key is to not elevate the heart rate too much, because then consciousness will not be able to collapse into itself. Vocally one can create a repetition of sound which creates a wavelike pulsation as well. One can also do the sound mentally. Or one can imagine a dot to turn into a sphere and back again. There are multiple possibilities as long as the underlying principle of the pulsation is kept as the essence. In between the exercises, and certainly also at the end, one can linger in the residue of this pulsation. It is here where the I will collapse into awareness itself. Nam libero tempore, cum soluta nobis est eligendi optio, cumque nihil impedit, quo minus id, quod maxime placeat facere possimus, omnis voluptas assumenda est, omnis dolor repellend[a]us. Temporibus autem quibusdam et aut officiis debitis aut rerum necessitatibus saepe eveniet, ut et voluptates repudiandae sint et molestiae non recusandae. Itaque earum rerum hic tenetur a sapiente delectus, ut aut reiciendis voluptatibus maiores alias consequatur aut perferendis doloribus asperiores repellat. – Ye he yei hei

Printed in Dunstable, United Kingdom